CORE-PLUS MATHEMATICS PROJECT

Course 1
Part B

Contemporary Mathematics in Context

A Unified Approach

Arthur F. Coxford
James T. Fey
Christian R. Hirsch
Harold L. Schoen
Gail Burrill
Eric W. Hart
Ann E. Watkins
with
Mary Jo Messenger
Beth E. Ritsema
Rebecca K. Walker

Glencoe McGraw-Hill

New York, New York   Columbus, Ohio   Chicago, Illinois   Peoria, Illinois   Woodland Hills, California

Glencoe/McGraw-Hill

*A Division of The **McGraw·Hill** Companies*

 This project was supported, in part, by the National Science Foundation.
The opinions expressed are those of the authors and not necessarily those of the Foundation.

Send all inquiries to:
Glencoe/McGraw-Hill
8787 Orion Place
Columbus, OH 43240-4027

ISBN: 0-07-827539-3 (Part A)
ISBN: 0-07-827540-7 (Part B)

Contemporary Mathematics in Context
Course 1 Part B Teacher's Guide

1 2 3 4 5 6 7 8 9 10 004/004 10 09 08 07 06 05 04 03 02

About the Core-Plus Mathematics Project

The **Core-Plus Mathematics Project (CPMP)** is a multi-year project funded by the National Science Foundation to develop student and teacher materials for a complete high school mathematics curriculum. Courses 1–3 comprise a core curriculum appropriate for *all* students. The fourth-year course continues the preparation of students for college mathematics.

Development Team

Project Directors

Christian R. Hirsch
Western Michigan University

Arthur F. Coxford
University of Michigan

James T. Fey
University of Maryland

Harold L. Schoen
University of Iowa

Senior Curriculum Developers

Gail Burrill
University of Wisconsin-Madison

Eric W. Hart
Western Michigan University

Ann E. Watkins
California State University, Northridge

Professional Development Coordinator

Beth E. Ritsema
Western Michigan University

Evaluation Coordinator

Steven W. Ziebarth
Western Michigan University

Advisory Board

Diane Briars
Pittsburgh Public Schools

Jeremy Kilpatrick
University of Georgia

Kenneth Ruthven
University of Cambridge

David A. Smith
Duke University

Edna Vasquez
Detroit Renaissance High School

Curriculum Development Consultants

Alverna Champion
Grand Valley State University

Cherie Cornick
Wayne County Alliance for Mathematics and Science

Edgar Edwards
(Formerly) Virginia State Department of Education

Richard Scheaffer
University of Florida

Martha Siegel
Towson University

Edward Silver
University of Michigan

Lee Stiff
North Carolina State University

Technical Coordinator

Wendy Weaver
Western Michigan University

Collaborating Teachers

Emma Ames
Oakland Mills High School, Maryland

Laurie Eyre
Maharishi School, Iowa

Annette Hagelberg
West Delaware High School, Iowa

Cheryl Bach Hedden
Sitka High School, Alaska

Michael J. Link
Central Academy, Iowa

Mary Jo Messenger
Howard County Public Schools, Maryland

Valerie Mills
Ann Arbor Public Schools, Michigan

Marcia Weinhold
Kalamazoo Area Mathematics and Science Center, Michigan

Graduate Assistants

Diane Bean
University of Iowa

Judy Flowers
University of Michigan

Gina Garza-Kling
Western Michigan University

Robin Marcus
University of Maryland

Chris Rasmussen
University of Maryland

Rebecca Walker
Western Michigan University

Production and Support Staff

Lori Bowden

James Laser

Michelle Magers

Cheryl Peters

Jennifer Rosenboom

Anna Seif

Kathryn Wright

Teresa Ziebarth
Western Michigan University

Software Developers

Jim Flanders
Colorado Springs, Colorado

Eric Kamischke
Interlochen, Michigan

Core-Plus Mathematics Project Field-Test Sites

Special thanks are extended to these teachers and their students who participated in the testing and evaluation of Course 1.

Ann Arbor Huron High School
Ann Arbor, Michigan
  Kevin Behmer
  Ginger Gajar

Ann Arbor Pioneer High School
Ann Arbor, Michigan
  Jim Brink
  Fay Longhofer
  Brad Miller

Arthur Hill High School
Saginaw, Michigan
  Virginia Abbott
  Felix Bosco
  David Kabobel
  Dick Thomas

Battle Creek Central High School
Battle Creek, Michigan
  Teresa Ballard
  Rose Martin
  Steven Ohs

Bedford High School
Temperance, Michigan
  Ellen Bacon
  David DeGrace
  Linda Martin
  Lynn Parachek

Bloomfield Hills Andover High School
Bloomfield Hills, Michigan
  Jane Briskey
  Homer Hassenzahl
  Cathy King
  Ed Okuniewski
  Mike Shelly

Bloomfield Hills Middle School
Bloomfield Hills, Michigan
  Connie Kelly
  Tim Loula

Brookwood High School
Snellville, Georgia
  Ginny Hanley
  Marie Knox

Caledonia High School
Caledonia, Michigan
  Daryl Bronkema
  Jenny Diekevers
  Thomas Oster
  Gerard Wagner

Centaurus High School
Lafayette, Colorado
  Sally Johnson
  Gail Reichert

Clio High School
Clio, Michigan
  Denny Carlson
  Larry Castonia
  Vern Kamp
  Carol Narrin
  David Sherry

Davison High School
Davison, Michigan
  Evelyn Ailing
  John Bale
  Wayne Desjarlais
  Darlene Tomczak
  Scott Toyzan

Dexter High School
Dexter, Michigan
  Kris Chatas
  Widge Proctor
  Tammy Schirmer

Ellet High School
Akron, Ohio
  Marcia Csipke
  Jim Fillmore
  Scott Slusser

Firestone High School
Akron, Ohio
  Barbara Crucs
  Lori Zupke

Flint Northern High School
Flint, Michigan
  John Moliassa
  Al Wojtowicz

Goodrich High School
Goodrich, Michigan
  Mike Coke
  John Doerr

Grand Blanc High School
Grand Blanc, Michigan
  Charles Carmody
  Nancy Elledge
  Tina Hughes
  Steve Karr
  Mike McLaren

Grass Lake Junior/Senior High School
Grass Lake, Michigan
  Larry Poertner
  Amy Potts

Gull Lake High School
Richland, Michigan
  Virgil Archie
  Darlene Kohrman
  Dorothy Louden

Kalamazoo Central High School
Kalamazoo, Michigan
Sarah Baca
Gloria Foster
Bonnie Frye
Amy Schwentor

Kelloggsville Public Schools
Wyoming, Michigan
Jerry Czarnecki
Steve Ramsey
John Ritzler

Knott County Central High School
Hindman, Kentucky
Teresa Combs
P. Denise Gibson
Bennie Hall

Loy Norrix High School
Kalamazoo, Michigan
Mary Elliott
Mike Milka

Midland Valley High School
Langley, South Carolina
Ron Bell
Janice Lee

Murray-Wright High School
Detroit, Michigan
Anna Cannonier
Jack Sada

North Lamar High School
Paris, Texas
Tommy Eads
Barbara Eatherly

Okemos High School
Okemos, Michigan
Lisa Magee
Jacqueline Stewart

Portage Northern High School
Portage, Michigan
Pete Jarrad
Scott Moore

Prairie High School
Cedar Rapids, Iowa
Dave LaGrange
Judy Slezak

San Pasqual High School
Escondido, California
Damon Blackman
Ron Peet

Sitka High School
Sitka, Alaska
Cheryl Bach Hedden
Dan Langbauer
Tom Smirich

Sturgis High School
Sturgis, Michigan
Craig Evans
Kathy Parkhurst
Dale Rauh
JoAnn Roe
Kathy Roy

Sweetwater High School
National City, California
Bill Bokesch
Joe Pistone

Tecumseh High School
Tecumseh, Michigan
Jennifer Keffer
Kathy Kelso
Elizabeth Lentz
Carl Novak
Eric Roberts

Tecumseh Middle School
Tecumseh, Michigan
Jocelyn Menyhart

Traverse City East Junior High School
Traverse City, Michigan
Tamie Rosenburg

Traverse City West Junior High School
Traverse City, Michigan
Ann Post

Vallivue High School
Caldwell, Idaho
Scott Coulter
Kathy Harris

West Hills Middle School
Bloomfield Hills, Michigan
Eileen MacDonald

Ypsilanti High School
Ypsilanti, Michigan
Keith Kellman
Mark McClure
Valerie Mills
Don Peurach

Overview of Course 1
Part A

Unit **1** ▶ Patterns in Data

Patterns in Data develops student ability to make sense out of real-world data through use of graphical displays and summary statistics.

Topics include distributions of data and their shapes, as displayed in number line plots, histograms, box plots, and stem-and-leaf plots; scatterplots and association; plots over time and trends; measures of center including mean, median, mode, and their properties; measures of variation including percentiles, interquartile range, mean absolute deviation, and their properties; transformations of data.

Lesson 1	*Exploring Data*
Lesson 2	*Shapes and Centers*
Lesson 3	*Variability*
Lesson 4	*Relationships and Trends*
Lesson 5	*Looking Back*

Unit **2** ▶ Patterns of Change

Patterns of Change develops student ability to recognize important patterns of change among variables and to represent those patterns using tables of numerical data, coordinate graphs, verbal descriptions, and symbolic rules.

Topics include coordinate graphs, tables, algebraic formulas (rules), relationships between variables, linear functions, nonlinear functions, and *NOW-NEXT* recurrence relations.

Lesson 1	*Related Variables*
Lesson 2	*What's Next?*
Lesson 3	*Variables and Rules*
Lesson 4	*Linear and Nonlinear Patterns*
Lesson 5	*Looking Back*

Unit **3** ▶ Linear Models

Linear Models develops student confidence and skill in using linear functions to model and solve problems in situations that exhibit constant (or nearly constant) rate of change or slope.

Topics include linear functions, slope of a line, rate of change, intercepts, distributive property, linear equations (including $y = a + bx$ and *NOW-NEXT* forms), solving linear equations and inequalities, using linear equations to model given data, and determining best-fit lines for scatterplot data.

Lesson 1	*Predicting from Data*
Lesson 2	*Linear Graphs, Tables, and Rules*
Lesson 3	*Linear Equations and Inequalities*
Lesson 4	*Looking Back*

Unit **4** ▶ Graph Models

Graph Models develops student ability to use vertex-edge graphs to represent and analyze real-world situations involving relationships among a finite number of elements including scheduling, managing conflicts, and finding efficient routes.

Topics include vertex-edge graph models, optimization, algorithmic problem solving, Euler circuits and paths, matrix representation of graphs, graph coloring, chromatic number, digraphs, and critical path analysis.

Lesson 1	*Careful Planning*
Lesson 2	*Managing Conflicts*
Lesson 3	*Scheduling Large Projects*
Lesson 4	*Looking Back*

Overview of Course 1
Part B

Unit 5 ▶ Patterns in Space and Visualization

Patterns in Space and Visualization develops student visualization skills and an understanding of the properties of space-shapes including symmetry, area, and volume.

Topics include two- and three-dimensional shapes, spatial visualization, perimeter, area, surface area, volume, the Pythagorean Theorem, polygons and their properties, symmetry, isometric transformations (reflections, rotations, translations, glide reflections), one-dimensional strip patterns, tilings of the plane, and the regular (Platonic) solids.

Unit 6 ▶ Exponential Models

Exponential Models develops student ability to use exponential functions to model and solve problems in situations that exhibit exponential growth or decay.

Topics include exponential growth, exponential functions, fractals, exponential decay, recursion, half-life, compound growth, finding equations to fit exponential patterns in data, and properties of exponents.

Unit 7 ▶ Simulation Models

Simulation Models develops student confidence and skill in using simulation methods—particularly those involving the use of random numbers—to make sense of real-world situations involving chance.

Topics include simulation, frequency tables and their histograms, random-digit tables and random-number generators, independent events, the Law of Large Numbers, and expected number of successes in a series of binomial trials.

Capstone ▶ Planning a Benefits Carnival

Planning a Benefits Carnival is a thematic, two-week, project-oriented activity that enables students to pull together and apply the important mathematical concepts and methods developed throughout the course.

Contents

Part B

Unit 5 ▶ Patterns in Space and Visualization

Unit 6 ▶ Exponential Models

Correlation of Course 1 to NCTM Standards

The *Contemporary Mathematics in Context* curriculum and the instructional and assessment practices it promotes address the focal points of the National Council of Teachers of Mathematics' *Principles and Standards for School Mathematics*. By design, the **process standards** on Problem Solving, Reasoning and Proof, Communication, Connections, and Representation are an integral part of each lesson of every unit in the curriculum.

The chart below correlates Course 1 units with the **content standards** for grades 9–12 in terms of focus (✓) and connections (+).

Correlation of Course 1 to NCTM Standards					
Course 1 Units / NCTM Grades 9–12 Content Standards	Number and Operations	Algebra	Geometry	Measurement	Data Analysis and Probability
Patterns in Data	+	+		✓	✓
Patterns of Change	+	✓		+	+
Linear Models	+	✓		+	✓
Graph Models		+	✓		
Patterns in Space and Visualization	+	+	✓	✓	+
Exponential Models	✓	✓	+	+	+
Simulation Models		+			✓
Capstone—Planning a Benefits Carnival	+	✓	✓	✓	✓

Curriculum Overview

▶Introduction

Contemporary Mathematics in Context Course 1 is the first year of a four-year integrated mathematics program developed by the **Core-Plus Mathematics Project (CPMP)**. The curriculum builds upon the theme of mathematics as sense-making. Through investigations of real-life contexts, students develop a rich understanding of important mathematics that makes sense to them and, in turn, enables them to make sense out of new situations and problems. The curriculum materials have the following mathematical and instructional features.

■ Unified Content

Each year the curriculum advances students' understanding of mathematics along interwoven strands of algebra and functions, statistics and probability, geometry and trigonometry, and discrete mathematics. These strands are unified by fundamental themes, by common topics, and by mathematical habits of mind such as visual thinking, recursive thinking, and searching for and explaining patterns.

■ Mathematical Modeling

The curriculum emphasizes mathematical modeling, including the processes of data collection, representation, interpretation, prediction, and simulation.

■ Access and Challenge

The curriculum is designed to make more mathematics accessable to more students, while at the same time challenging the most able students. Differences in students' performance and interest can be accommodated by the depth and level of abstraction to which core topics are pursued, by the nature and degree of difficulty of applications, and by providing opportunities for student choice of homework tasks and projects.

■ Technology

Numerical, graphics, and programming/link capabilities such as those found on many graphing calculators are assumed and approprately used throughout the curriculum. This use of technology permits the curriculum and instruction to emphasize multiple representations (verbal, numerical, graphical, and symbolic) and to focus on goals in which mathematical thinking and problem solving are central.

■ Active Learning

Instructional materials promote active learning and teaching centered around collaborative small-group investigations of problem situations, followed by teacher-led whole class summarizing activities that lead to analysis, abstraction, and further application of underlying mathematical ideas. Students are actively engaged in exploring, conjecturing, verifying, generalizing, applying, proving, evaluating, and communicating mathematical ideas.

■ Multi-dimensional Assessment

Comprehensive assessment of student understanding and progress through both curriculum-embedded assessment opportunities and supplementary assessment tasks supports instruction and enables monitoring and evaluation of each student's performance in terms of mathematical processes, content, and dispositions.

This curriculum promises to make mathematics accessible and more meaningful to more students. Developing mathematics along multiple strands nurtures the differing strengths and talents of students and simultaneously helps them to develop diverse mathematical insights. Developing mathematics from a modeling perspective permits students to experience mathematics as a means of making sense of data and problems that arise in diverse contexts within and across cultures. Engaging students in collaborating on tasks in small groups develops their ability to both deal with, and find commonality in, diversity of ideas. Using calculators as a means for learning and doing mathematics enables students to develop versatile ways of dealing with realistic situations and reduces the manipulative skill filter which has prevented large numbers of students from continuing their study of significant mathematics. In addition, calculator graphics offer powerful new ways of visualizing mathematics across each of the strands.

▶Unified Mathematics

Contemporary Mathematics in Context is a unified curriculum that replaces the traditional Algebra-Geometry-Advanced Algebra/Trigonometry-Precalculus sequence. Each course features "strands" of algebra and functions, statistics and probability, geometry and trigonometry, and discrete mathematics. Each of these strands is developed within focused units, connected by fundamental ideas such as symmetry, matrices, functions, and data analysis and curve-fitting. The strands also are connected across units by mathematical habits of mind such as visual thinking, recursive thinking, searching for and explaining patterns, making and checking conjectures, reasoning with multiple representations, inventing mathematics, and providing convincing arguments and proofs. The strands are unified further by the fundamental themes of data, representation, shape, and change. By encountering each strand each year from a more mathematically sophisticated point of view, students' understanding of mathematics and its connections deepens across the four-year curriculum.

Algebra and Functions

The algebra and functions strand develops student ability to recognize, represent, and solve problems involving relations among quantitative variables. Central to the development is the use of functions as mathematical models. The key algebraic models in the curriculum are linear, exponential, power, polynomial, logarithmic, rational, and trigonometric functions. Each algebraic model is investigated in four linked representations—verbal, graphic, numeric, and symbolic—with the aid of technology. Attention is also given to modeling systems of equations, both linear and nonlinear, and to symbolic reasoning and manipulation.

Statistics and Probability

The primary role of the statistics and probability strand is to develop student ability to analyze data intelligently, to recognize and measure variation, and to understand the patterns that underlie probabilistic situations. The ultimate goal is for students to understand how inferences can be made about a population by looking at a sample from that population. Graphical methods of data analysis, simulations, sampling, and experience with the collection and interpretation of real data are featured.

Geometry and Trigonometry

The primary goal of the geometry and trigonometry strand is to develop visual thinking and student ability to construct, reason with, interpret, and apply mathematical models of patterns in the visual world and physical contexts. The focus is on describing patterns with regard to shape, size, and location; representing visual patterns with drawings, coordinates, or vectors; predicting changes and invariants in shape; and organizing geometric facts and relationships through deductive reasoning.

Discrete Mathematics

The discrete mathematics strand develops student ability to model and solve problems involving enumeration, sequential change, decision-making in finite settings, and relationships among a finite number of elements. Topics include matrices, vertex-edge graphs, recursion, voting methods, and systematic counting methods (combinatorics). Key themes are discrete mathematical modeling, existence (*Is there a solution?*), optimization (*What is the best solution?*), and algorithmic problem solving (*Can you efficiently construct a solution?*).

▶ Organization of Course 1

The curriculum for Course 1 consists of seven units and a culminating capstone experience. Each of the units is comprised of four to five multi-day lessons in which major ideas are developed through investigation of rich applied problems. Units vary in length from approximately four to six weeks. The final element of Course 1, the capstone, is a thematic two-week project-oriented activity that enables students to pull together and apply the important modeling concepts and methods developed in the entire course.

In developing Course 1, the Core-Plus Mathematics Project chose mathematical content which the developers believed was the most important mathematics all ninth-grade students should have the opportunity to learn. In particular, the content of the last units in the text are not viewed as optional as is often the case with traditional textbooks. The developers believe that this content is so important and broadly useful that it should be completed by students before they embark on Course 2 of the *Contemporary Mathematics in Context* series. This is the primary reason why the texts for Courses 1-3 are available in a two-volume edition. Schools whose student population does not complete Course 1 in a single year can use Part B of the two-volume edition with these students as tenth graders while new ninth-grade students begin Course 1 with Part A. Schools block-scheduling classes will find flexibility for designing course content with two volumes that is not normally available with single-volume texts.

The organization of the student text differs in several other ways from traditional textbooks. There are no boxed-off definitions, "worked-out" examples, or content summaries. Students learn mathematics by doing mathematics. Concept images are developed as students complete investigations and later concept definitions appear. Mathematical ideas are developed and then shared by groups of students at strategically placed Checkpoints in the lessons. This discussion leads to a class summary of shared understandings.

▶ Instructional Model

The manner in which students encounter mathematical ideas can contribute significantly to the quality of their learning and the depth of their understanding. *Contemporary Mathematics in Context* units are therefore designed around a specific cycle of instructional activities intended primarily for small-group work in the classroom and for individual work outside of the classroom.

In Class The four-phase cycle of classroom activities—*Launch, Explore, Share and Summarize*, and *Apply*—is designed to actively engage students in investigating and making sense of problem situations, in constructing important mathematical concepts and methods, in generalizing and proving mathematical relationships, and in communicating their thinking and the results of their efforts. The summary below describes these phases of classroom instruction.

LAUNCH full-class discussion

Think About This Situation

In-Class Instruction

The lesson begins with a teacher-led discussion of a problem situation and of related questions to **think about**. This discussion sets the context for the student work to follow and helps to gen-

EXPLORE small-group investigation

INVESTIGATION ▶

erate student interest; it also provides an opportunity for the teacher to assess student knowledge and to clarify directions for the group activities. *Teacher is director and moderator.*

Classroom activity then shifts to **investigating** focused problems and questions related to the launching situation by gathering data, looking for patterns, constructing models and meanings, and making and verifying conjectures. As students collaborate in small groups, the teacher circulates from group to group providing guidance and support, clarifying or asking questions, giving hints, providing encouragement, and drawing group members into the dis-

SHARE AND SUMMARIZE full-class discussion

Checkpoint

cussion to help groups work more cooperatively. The unit materials and related questions posed by students drive the learning. *Teacher is facilitator.*

A teacher-led full-class discussion (referred to as a Checkpoint) of concepts and methods developed by different small groups then provides an opportunity to **share** progress and thinking. This discussion leads to a class **summary** of important ideas or to further exploration of

APPLY individual task

▶On Your Own

a topic if competing perspectives remain. Varying points of view and differing conclusions that can be justified should be encouraged. *Teacher is moderator.*

Students are given a task to complete on their own to **reinforce** their initial understanding of concepts and methods. The teacher circulates in the room assessing levels of understanding. *Teacher is intellectual coach.*

Out of Class In addition to the classroom investigations, *Contemporary Mathematics in Context* provides sets of MORE tasks, which are designed to engage students in *Modeling* with, *Organizing*, *Reflecting* on, and *Extending* their mathematical knowledge. MORE tasks are provided for each lesson in the CPMP materials and are central to the learning goals of each lesson. These tasks are intended primarily for individual work outside of class. Selection of

MORE tasks should be based on student performance and the availability of time and technology. Also, students should exercise some choice of tasks to pursue, and at times they should be given the opportunity to pose their own problems and questions to investigate. The chart below describes the types of tasks in a typical MORE set.

MORE: Out-of-Class Activities	
Modeling	*Modeling* tasks are related to or provide new contexts to which students can apply the ideas and methods that they have developed in the lesson.
Organizing	*Organizing* tasks offer opportunities for integrating the formal mathematics underlying the mathematical models developed in the lesson and for making connections with other strands.
Reflecting	*Reflecting* tasks encourage thinking about thinking, about mathematical meanings, and about processes, and promote self-monitoring and evaluation of understanding.
Extending	*Extending* tasks permit further, deeper, or more formal study of the topics under investigation.

Summarizing Activities In the *Contemporary Mathematics in Context* curriculum, students learn mathematics by doing mathematics. However, it is important that students prepare and maintain summaries of important concepts and methods that are developed. To assist in this matter, the "On Your Own" task in the final lesson of each unit asks students to prepare, in outline form, a summary of the important ideas developed in the unit. Templates to guide preparation of these unit summaries can be found in the *Teaching Resources*. In addition, students should create a Math Toolkit that organizes important class-generated ideas and selected Checkpoint responses as they complete investigations. "Constructing a Math Toolkit" prompts are provided in this *Teacher's Guide* to assist in identifying key concepts and methods as they are developed by students. (See the *Teaching Resources* for blackline masters to assist students in organizing their Math Toolkits.)

▶Curriculum-Embedded Assessment

Assessing what students know and are able to do is an integral part of *Contemporary Mathematics in Context* and there are opportunities for assessment in each phase of the instructional cycle. Initially, as students pursue the investigations that make up the curriculum, the teacher is able to informally assess student understanding of mathematical processes, content, and their disposition toward mathematics. Then at the end of each investigation, the Checkpoint and class discussion provide an opportunity for teachers to assess the levels of understanding that various groups of students have reached as they share and summarize their findings. Finally, the "On Your Own" problems and the tasks in the MORE sets provide further opportunities to assess the level of understanding of each individual student.

A more detailed description of the complete CPMP assessment program is given on pages xix–xxiii of this text and in *Implementing the Core-Plus Mathematics Curriculum*, pages 46–58.

Implementing the Curriculum

▶Planning for Instruction

The *Contemporary Mathematics in Context* curriculum is not only changing what mathematics all students have the opportunity to learn, but also changing how that learning occurs and is assessed. Active learning is most effective when accompanied with active teaching. Just as the student text is designed to actively engage students in doing mathematics, the teacher's resource materials are designed to support teachers in planning for instruction; in observing, listening, questioning, and facilitating student work, and orchestrating classroom discussion; and in managing the classroom.

The *Teacher's Guide* provides suggestions, based on the experiences of field-test teachers, for implementing this exciting new curriculum in your classroom. You probably will find new ideas that can at first be overwhelming. The developers highly recommend that teachers who are teaching *Contemporary Mathematics in Context* for the first time do so at least in pairs who share a common planning period.

Each of the items listed below is included in the *Teacher's Guide* for each unit.
- Unit Overview
- Objectives, suggested timeline, and materials needed
- Instructional notes and suggestions
- Suggested assignments for each MORE set
- Solutions for Investigations and MORE tasks
- Unit summary and a look ahead

The *Teaching Resources* include blackline masters for creating transparencies and handouts. *Assessment Resources* include quizzes for individual lessons, end-of-unit exams, take-home assessment tasks, projects, and semester exam tasks. Special calculator software has been developed to support students' investigations and modeling applications in each of the four strands. The software for the TI-82, TI-83, and TI-92 graphing calculators is available on disk for downloading from Macintosh and DOS- or Windows-based (PC) computers.

Each unit of *Contemporary Mathematics in Context* includes either content which may be new to many teachers or new approaches to familiar content. Thus, a first step toward planning the teaching of a unit is to review the scope and sequence of the unit. This review provides an overall feel for the goals of the unit and how it holds together. The *Scope and Sequence* guide shows where specific mathematical topics fit in the complete four-year curriculum. Working through the student investigations, if possible with a colleague, provides help in thinking about and understanding mathematical ideas that may be unfamiliar.

In the *Teacher's Guide* you will find teaching notes for each lesson, including instructional suggestions and sample student responses to investigations and MORE sets. Thinking about the range of possible responses and solutions to problems in a lesson proves to be very helpful in facilitating student work.

Although not stated, it is assumed that students have access to graphing calculators at all times for in-class work and ideally for out-of-class work as well. Downloading and becoming familiar with the specially designed calculator software will require advanced planning, as will acquiring physical materials.

The developers recommend that the homework (MORE) assignment *not* be held off until the end of the lesson or the investigation just preceding the MORE set. Some teachers choose to post the MORE assignment at the beginning of a lesson along with the due date—usually a day or two following planned completion of the lesson. Other teachers prefer to assign particular MORE tasks at appropriate points during the course of the multiday lesson, and then assign the remaining tasks toward the end of the lesson. Note that all recommended assignments include provision for student choice of some tasks. This is but one of many ways in which this curriculum is designed to accommodate and support differences in students' interests and performance levels.

It is strongly recommended that student solutions to Organizing tasks be discussed in class. These tasks help students organize and formalize the mathematics developed in context and connect it to other mathematics they have studied. Structuring the underlying mathematics and building connections are best accomplished by comparing and discussing student work and synthesizing key ideas within the classroom.

▶Orchestrating Lessons

The *Contemporary Mathematics in Context* materials are designed to engage students in a four-phase cycle of classroom activities. The activities often require both students and teachers to assume roles quite different than those in more traditional mathematics classrooms. Becoming accustomed to these new roles usually takes time, perhaps a semester or more, but field-test teachers report that the time and effort required are well worth it in terms of student learning and professional fulfillment. Although realistic problem solving and investigative work by students are the heart of the curriculum, how teachers orchestrate the launching of an activity and the sharing and summarizing of results is critical to successful implementation.

Students enter the classroom with differing backgrounds, experience, and knowledge. These differences can be viewed as assets. Engaging the class in a free-flowing give-and-take discussion of how students think about the launch situations serves to connect lessons with the informal understandings of data, shape, change, and chance that students bring to the classroom. Try to maximize the participation of students in these discussions by emphasizing that their ideas and possible approaches are valued and important and that definitive answers are not necessarily expected at this time.

Once launched, a lesson may involve students working together collaboratively in small groups for a period of days punctuated occasionally by brief, whole-class discussion of questions students have raised. In this setting, the lesson becomes driven primarily by the instructional materials themselves. Rather than orchestrating class discussion, the teacher shifts to circulating among the groups and observing, listening, and interacting with students by asking guiding or probing questions. These small-group investigations lead to (re)invention of important mathematics that makes sense to students. Sharing, and agreeing as a class, on the mathematical ideas that groups are developing is the purpose of the Checkpoints in the instructional materials.

Class discussions at Checkpoints are orchestrated somewhat differently than during the launch of a lesson. At this stage, mathematical ideas and methods still may be under development and may vary for individual groups. So class discussion should involve groups comparing their methods and results, analyzing their work, and arriving at conclusions agreed upon by the class.

The investigations deepen students' understanding of mathematical ideas and extend their mathematical language in contexts. Technical terminology and symbolism are introduced as needed. This sometimes occurs in student materials immediately following a Checkpoint and before the corresponding "On Your Own" task. These connections should be introduced by the teacher as a natural way of closing the class discussion summarizing the Checkpoint.

Managing Classroom Activities

▶ Active Learning and Collaborative Work

The *Contemporary Mathematics in Context* curriculum materials are designed to promote active, collaborative learning and group work for two important reasons. First, a collaborative environment fosters students' ability to make sense of mathematics and develop deep mathematical understandings. Collaborative learning is an effective method for engaging all the students in the learning process, particularly students who have been underrepresented in mathematics classes. Second, practice in collaborative learning in the classroom is practice for real life: students develop and exercise the same skills in the classroom that they need in their lives at home, in the community, and in the workplace.

Value of Individuals

Perhaps the most fundamental belief underlying the use of collaborative learning is that every student is viewed as a valuable resource and contributor. In other words, every student participates in group work and is given the opportunity and time to voice ideas and opinions. Implementing this concept is not easy. It does not happen automatically. In order to set a tone that will promote respect for individuals and their contributions, classroom rules should be established and agreed upon by the learning community. Students should be included in the process of formulating the rules. The teacher should initiate a discussion of group rules and then post them in the classroom. The teacher should model all of the rules correctly to show that "we" begins with "me." Those who do not adhere to the rules must accept the consequences in accordance with classroom or school disciplinary procedures.

Importance of Social Connections

Even in classrooms in which the rules for showing respect have been clearly established, experience has shown that students still cannot talk with one another about mathematics (or social studies, or literature, or any other subject) if they do not first have positive social connections.

One way to develop this kind of common base is through team-building activities. These short activities may be used at the beginning of the year to help students get acquainted with the whole class, and may be used during the year whenever new groups are formed to help groupmates know one another better. Team-building activities help students learn new and positive things about classmates with whom they may have attended classes for years, but have not known in depth. The time taken for these quick team builders pays off later in helping students feel comfortable enough to work with the members of their group.

Need for Teaching Social Skills

Experience also has shown that social skills are critical to the successful functioning of any small group. Because there is no guarantee that students of any particular age will have the social skills necessary for effective group work, it often is necessary to teach these skills to build a collaborative learning environment.

These social skills are specific skills, not general goals. Examples of specific social skills that the teacher can teach in the classroom include responding to ideas respectfully, keeping track of time, disagreeing in an agreeable way, involving everyone, and following directions. Though goals such as cooperating and listening are important, they are too general to teach.

One method of teaching social skills is to begin by selecting a specific skill and then having the class brainstorm to develop a script for practicing that skill. Next, the students practice that skill during their group work. Finally, in what is called the processing, the students discuss within their groups how well they performed the assigned social skill. Effective teaching of social skills requires practicing and processing; merely describing a specific social skill is not enough. Actual practice and processing are necessary for students really to learn the skill and to increase the use of appropriate behaviors during group work and other times during class.

One of the premises of collaborative learning is that by developing the appropriate skills through practice, anyone in the class can learn to work in a group with anyone else. Learning to work in groups is a continuous process, however, and the process can be helped by decisions that the teacher makes. *Implementing the Core-Plus Mathematics Curriculum* provides information and support to help teachers make decisions about group size, composition, method of selection, student reaction to working in groups, and the duration of groups. It also provides advice on dealing effectively with student absences.

The culture created within the classroom is crucial to the success of this curriculum. It is important to inculcate in students a sense of inquiry and responsibility for their own learning. Without this commitment, active, collaborative learning by students cannot be effective. In order for students to work collaboratively, they must be able to understand the value of working together. Some students seem satisfied with the rationale that it is important in the business world. Others may need to understand that the struggle of verbalizing their thinking, listening to others' thinking, questioning themselves and other group members, and coming to an agreement increases their understanding and retention of the mathematics while contributing to the formation of important thinking skills or habits of mind.

Issues of helping students to work collaboratively will become less pressing as both you and your students experience this type of learning. You may find it helpful to refer to *Implementing the Core-Plus Mathematics Curriculum* and discuss effective cooperative groups with colleagues a few weeks into the semester.

▶Assessment

Throughout the *Contemporary Mathematics in Context* curriculum, the term "assessment" is meant to include all instances of gathering information about students' levels of understanding and their disposition toward mathematics for purposes of making decisions about instruction. You may want to consult the extended section on assessment in *Implementing the Core-Plus Mathematics Curriculum.*

The dimensions of student performance that are assessed in this curriculum (see chart below) are consistent with the assessment recommendations of the National Council of Teachers of Mathematics in the *Assessment Standards for School Mathematics* (NCTM, 1995). They are much broader than those of a typical testing program.

Assessment Dimensions

Process	Content	Attitude
Problem Solving	Concepts	Beliefs
Reasoning	Applications	Perseverance
Communication	Representational Strategies	Confidence
Connections	Procedures	Enthusiasm

Sources of Assessment Information

Several kinds of assessment are available to teachers using *Contemporary Mathematics in Context*. Some of these sources reside within the curriculum itself, some of them are student-generated, and some are supplementary materials designed specifically for assessment. Understanding the nature of these sources is a prerequisite for selecting assessment tools, establishing guidelines on how to score assessments, making judgments about what students know and are able to do, and assigning grades.

Curriculum Sources

Two features of the curriculum, questioning and observation by the teacher, provide fundamental and particularly useful ways of gathering assessment information. The student text uses questions to facilitate student understanding of new concepts, of how these concepts fit with earlier ideas and with one another, and of how they can be applied in problem situations. Whether students are working individually or in groups, the teacher is given a window to watch how the students think about and apply mathematics as they attempt to answer the questions posed by the curriculum materials. In fact, by observing how students respond to the curriculum-embedded questions, the teacher can assess student performance across all process, content, and attitude dimensions described in the chart on page xix.

Specific features in the student material that focus on different ways students respond to questions are the Checkpoint, "On Your Own," and MORE (*Modeling*, *Organizing*, *Reflecting*, and *Extending*) sets. Checkpoint features are intended to bring students together, usually after they have been working in small groups, so they may share and discuss the progress each group has made during a sequence of related activities. Each Checkpoint is intended to be a whole-class discussion, so it should provide an opportunity for teachers to assess, informally, the levels of understanding that the various groups of students have reached.

Following each Checkpoint, the "On Your Own" tasks are meant to be completed by students working individually. Student responses to these tasks provide an opportunity for teachers to assess the level of understanding of each student.

The tasks in the MORE sets serve many purposes, including post-investigation assessment. Each type of task in a MORE set has a different instructional purpose. Modeling tasks help students demonstrate how well they understand and can apply the concepts and procedures developed in an investigation. Organizing tasks demonstrate how well students understand connections between the content of an investigation and other mathematical and real-world ideas. In-class discussions based on Organizing tasks are a crucial step in assisting students' development of a full understanding of the mathematical content and connections. Reflecting tasks provide insights into students' beliefs, attitudes, and judgments of their own competence. Extending tasks show how well students are able to extend the present content beyond the level addressed in an investigation. The performance of students or groups of students in each of these types of tasks provides the teacher with further information to help assess applicability, connectedness, and depth of the students' evolving understanding of mathematics.

Finally, an opportunity for group self-assessment is provided in the last element of each unit, the "Looking Back" lesson. These activities help students pull together and demonstrate what they have learned in the unit and at the same time provide helpful review and confidence-building for students.

Student-Generated Sources

Other possible sources of assessment information are writings and materials produced by students in the form of student mathematics toolkits and journals.

Mathematics Toolkits Students should create a Math Toolkit that organizes important class-generated ideas and selected Checkpoint responses as they complete investigations. Constructing a Math Toolkit prompts are provided in the *Teacher's Guide* to assist in identifying key concepts and methods as they are developed by students. (See the *Teaching Resources* for blackline masters to assist students in organizing their Math Toolkits.)

Journals Student journals are notebooks in which students are encouraged to write (briefly, but frequently) their personal reflections concerning the class, the mathematics they are learning, and their progress. These journals are an excellent way for the teacher to gain insights into how individual students are feeling about the class, what they do and do not understand, and what some of their particular learning difficulties are. For many students, the journal is a non-threatening way to communicate with the teacher about matters that may be too difficult or too time-consuming to talk about directly. Journals also encourage students to assess their own understanding of, and feelings about, the mathematics they are studying. The teacher should collect, read, and respond to each journal at least once a month.

The *Contemporary Mathematics in Context* assessment program provides many items that can be placed in students' portfolios, including reports of individual and group projects, Math Toolkit or journal entries, teacher-completed observation checklists, end-of-unit assessments (especially the take-home tasks), and extended cumulative projects. See *Implementing the Core-Plus Mathematics Curriculum* for additional portfolio information.

Assessment Resources

The *Contemporary Mathematics in Context* teacher resource materials include for each unit a third source of assessment information—*Assessment Resources*. Included in the *Assessment Resources* are end-of-lesson quizzes and end-of-unit assessments in the form of an in-class unit exam, take-home assessment tasks, and projects. Calculators are required in most cases and are intended to be available to students. Teacher discretion should be used regarding student access to their textbook and Math Toolkit for assessments. In general, if the goals to be assessed are problem solving and reasoning, while memory of facts and procedural skill are of less interest, resources should be allowed. However, if automaticity of procedures or unaided recall are being assessed, it is appropriate to prohibit resource materials. Since many rich opportunities for assessing students are embedded in the curriculum itself, you may choose not to use all the lesson quizzes for each unit.

End-of-Lesson Quizzes Two forms of a quiz covering the main ideas of each lesson are provided. These quizzes, which are the most traditional of all the assessment methods and instruments included with the *Contemporary Mathematics in Context* materials, are comprised of fairly straightforward problems meant to determine if students have developed understanding of the important concepts and procedures of each lesson.

In-Class Exams Two forms of in-class exams are provided for each unit and are intended to be completed in a 50-minute class period. The two forms of each exam are not necessarily equivalent, although they assess essentially the same mathematical ideas. Teachers should preview the two versions carefully, and feel free to revise or delete items and add new ones, if necessary, using the *Assessment and Maintenance Worksheet Builder* CD-ROM.

Take-Home Assessments Take-home assessment tasks are included for each unit. The students or the teacher should choose one or, at most, two of these tasks. These assessments, some of which are best done by students working in pairs or small groups, provide students with the opportunity to organize the information from the completed unit, to extend the ideas of the unit into other areas of interest to them, to work with another student or group of students, and to avoid the time pressure often generated by in-class exams.

Projects Assessment traditionally has been based on evaluating work that students have completed in a very short time period and under restricted conditions. Some assessment, however, should involve work done over a longer time period with the aid of resources. Thus, assessment projects are included in unit assessments. These projects, which are intended to be completed by small groups of students, provide an opportunity for students to conduct an investigation that extends and applies the main ideas from the unit and to write a summary of their findings.

Midterm and Final Assessment A bank of assessment tasks, from which to construct an exam that fits your particular class needs and emphases, is also provided.

Scoring Assessments

High expectations of the quality of students' written work will encourage students to reach their potential. Assigning scores to open-ended assessments and to observations of students' performance requires more subjective judgment by the teacher than does grading short-answer or multiple-choice tests. It is therefore not possible to provide a complete set of explicit guidelines for scoring open-ended assessment items and written or oral reports. However, some general guidelines may be helpful. When scoring student work on open-ended assessment tasks, the goal is to reward in a fair and consistent way the kinds of thinking and understanding that the task is meant to measure. To score open-ended assessment tasks, teachers should have a general rubric, or scoring scheme, with several response levels in mind; a specific rubric; and anchor items. (See *Implementing the Core-Plus Mathematics Curriculum* for more details.) The general rubric is the foundation for scoring across a wide range of types of open-ended tasks. The following general rubric can be used for most assessment tasks provided with *Contemporary Mathematics in Context*.

General Scoring Rubric

4 points	Contains complete response with clear, coherent, and unambiguous explanation; includes clear and simple diagram, if appropriate; communicates effectively to identified audience; shows understanding of question's mathematical ideas and processes; identifies all important elements of question; includes examples and counterexamples; gives strong supporting arguments
3 points	Contains good solid response with some, but not all, of the characteristics above; explains less completely; may include minor error of execution but not of understanding
2 points	Contains complete response, but explanation is muddled; presents incomplete arguments; includes diagrams that are inappropriate or unclear, or fails to provide a diagram when it would be appropriate; indicates some understanding of mathematical ideas, but in an unclear way; shows clear evidence of understanding some important ideas while also making one or more fundamental, specific errors
1 point	Omits parts of question and response; has major errors; uses inappropriate strategies
0 points	No response; frivolous or irrelevant response

Assigning Grades

Because the *Contemporary Mathematics in Context* approach and materials provide a wide variety of assessment information, the teacher will be in a good position to assign a fair grade for student work. With such a wide choice for assessment, a word of caution is appropriate: *it is easy to overassess students, and care must be taken to avoid doing so*. A quiz need not be given after every lesson, nor an in-class exam after every unit. The developers believe it is best to vary assessment methods from lesson to lesson, and from unit to unit. If information on what students understand and are able to do is available from their homework and in-class work, it may not be necessary to take the time for a formal quiz after each lesson. Similarly, information from project work may replace an in-class exam.

Deciding exactly how to weigh the various kinds of assessment information is a decision that the teacher will need to make and communicate clearly to students.

Maintaining Skills

The developers have identified a set of paper-and-pencil technical competencies that all students should acquire. To provide additional practice with these core competencies, a special maintenance feature is included in blackline master form in the *Teaching Resources* or on the *Assessment and Maintenance Worksheet Builder* CD-ROM. Beginning with Unit 4 of Course 1, "Graph Models," and then continuing with each unit thereafter, a supplementary set of maintenance tasks provides periodic review and additional practice of basic skills. These skills will be continually revisited to ensure mastery by each student at some point in the curriculum.

Use of the maintenance material following the start of Lesson 2 of each unit will allow students time to work simultaneously on skills during the latter part of a unit without interrupting the flow of the unit. You may wish to allow a few minutes at the end of selected class periods to revisit these skills with various groups of students who need assistance while other groups choose an Extending task.

The maintenance material prepared for each unit spans technical competencies across each of the strands. In each case, the first presented task is a contextual problem, but the remaining tasks are not contextualized. Students should *not* use a calculator for these tasks unless so directed.

Reference and Practice Books (RAP Books)

A *Reference and Practice* book is available to accompany Course 1 of the program. The Course 1 RAP book provides students with summaries of concepts and skills from middle school courses; practice sets to review and maintain concepts and skills; and exercise sets that provide test-taking practice for standardized tests. This handbook also contains tips for taking standardized tests. These supplements are intended for student reference and use outside of regularly scheduled class times. Suggested assignments are listed in the Planning Guide for each unit.

Additional Resources

Implementing the Core-Plus Mathematics Curriculum contains expanded information on the scope and sequence of Courses 1–4; on managing classroom activities; and on the assessment program. It also provides a list of colleges and universities to which students from field-test schools have been admitted. A section on communication with parents is also included. You will find it useful to have the implementation guide available for reference throughout the school year.

Unit 5

Patterns in Space and Visualization

UNIT OVERVIEW The four unifying themes of the *Contemporary Mathematics in Context* curriculum are patterns in data, change, chance, and shape. Consideration of shape is important, not only in geometry, but also in the other strands of this curriculum because the shape of a distribution of data gives you information about that distribution; the shape of the graph of an algebraic model of a situation may be used to better understand how the variables are related; and the shape of a probability distribution provides vital information about questions of individual probabilities as well as the range of probabilities.

In the case of geometry, considerations of shape are central. After all, some define geometry as the study of shapes, their properties, and their relations to other shapes. This unit integrates two-dimensional and three-dimensional shapes. Three-dimensional shapes bombard us daily, and we are asked to recognize, work with, manufacture, compare, and represent such space-shapes. Space-shapes, when examined more closely, often appear to be composed of several plane-shapes. The faces of a cardboard box or the top of an oatmeal box are, for example, plane-shapes. Thus, the two kinds of shapes are connected to one another. The fundamental or big idea of this unit is one of shape and properties of shapes. Students should be encouraged to think of shape as fundamental. The relations among shapes and properties of individual shapes are ways to make the fundamental notion of a shape a richer concept.

When investigations take more than one day to complete, it is helpful to begin the class with a summary discussion of the previous day's concepts. Of course, short end-of-period discussions of that day's mathematics will provide some closure to the group work.

Unit 5 Objectives

- To use geometric shapes and their properties to make sense of situations involving data, change, chance, and discrete structures
- To use visualization to interpret and reason about space and plane situations
- To classify, construct, and sketch models of space-shapes
- To use plane- and space-shapes to model real-life situations
- To find appropriate measures (perimeter, area, volume) of plane- and space-shapes
- To classify polygons and analyze their properties
- To identify and explain different kinds of symmetry for plane- and space-shapes

Patterns in Space and Visualization

Unit **5**

Unit 5

325

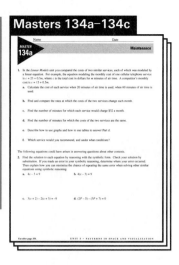

Shapes and Properties

Throughout the curriculum, transformations are used to analyze and describe shapes and their properties. In Course 2, transformations are revisited and given algebraic representations using coordinates. The idea of similarity transformations occurs frequently within the curriculum, leading to congruence as a special case of similarity transformations in Course 3.

This unit begins with a study in which ancient columns are modeled by paper models to determine the shape or shapes that support the greatest weight. The columns are modeled geometrically by prisms and cylinders. The development initially stresses space-shapes as students make models, examine their characteristics, and try to sketch the models in three different ways. A key characteristic of the space-shapes developed is symmetry in a plane.

Among the most useful ideas related to shapes are perimeters, areas, and volumes. These topics are treated next with an emphasis on the common misconceptions that perimeter of a shape determines its area and that the surface area of a space-shape determines its volume. Several activities are included to refocus on the true situation. In order to determine areas and perimeters of some shapes, the Pythagorean Theorem is needed. It is reintroduced and used to find altitudes of isosceles triangles. Having this knowledge, students will be more flexible in finding perimeters, areas, and volumes for a variety of shapes.

The faces and bases of space-shapes are used to introduce polygons and their properties. Much of this material should be familiar to students, but it is important to review and emphasize the symmetry ideas of reflection and rotation. The regular plane-shapes are used to explore patterning that leads (1) to tilings (tessellations) and (2) to fold-up models of the Platonic space-shapes. Symmetry in the plane is extended to strip patterns and to tilings. The symmetry of tilings is used to analyze works of art and to construct Escher-like original works.

You may find that the assumptions in this unit about student geometric understandings are ambitious, and that you need to supplement the materials to help students become competent with fundamental geometric ideas. As more contemporary middle school mathematics programs are implemented, these deficiencies may become less pronounced.

This chart provides an overview of the ideas in this unit and identifies some of the relationships among them.

NOTE: You may wish to use the CMIC *Reference and Practice* book that accompanies Course 1 to help students polish previously learned skills. See page xxiii and the planning guide for more information.

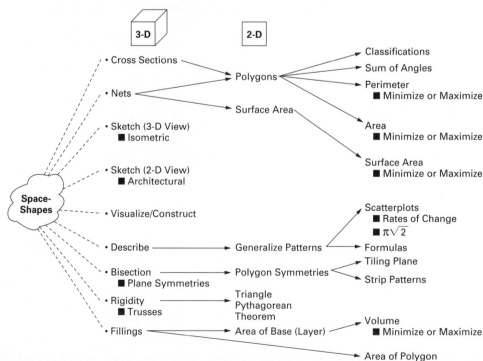

See Masters 134a–134c for Maintenance tasks that students can work on throughout Unit 5.

Unit 5 Planning Guide

Lesson Objectives	MORE Assignments	Suggested Pacing	Materials
Lesson 1 *The Shape of Things* • To use plane- and space-shapes to model real-life situations • To classify, construct, and sketch models of space-shapes • To identify and explain different kinds of symmetry for plane- and space-shapes • To use visualization to interpret and reason about plane and space situations • To develop an understanding of the essential characteristics of a space-shape that make it a prism or a pyramid • To develop an understanding of cross section and reflection (bilateral, plane) symmetry of space-shapes	**after page 329** Students can begin Modeling Task 1 or 2 from page 335 **page 335** **Modeling:** 1 or 2, and 3* **Organizing:** 1, 3, and 4 **Reflecting:** 3 **Extending:** Choose one* **after page 344** Students can begin Modeling Task 1 or 3 or Organizing Task 2 or 5 from page 347 **page 347** **Modeling:** 1 or 3, and 5* **Organizing:** 2 and 5 **Reflecting:** 1 **Extending:** Choose one*	10 days	• Teaching Resources 135–141 • Assessment Resources 171–176 • 8.5 × 11 paper • 6 × 8 index cards or other small cardboard or Styrofoam platforms • Small paperback books or other stackable objects • *Optional*: 5–6 cubes of modeling clay, Play-Doh®, or Styrofoam® • Transparent cubes • Wire cutters if pipe cleaners are not pre-cut • Interlocking cubes, if available • Each group: 1 ruler, 1 roll of scotch tape, 75 10-cm straws, 27 12-cm straws, 6 16-cm straws (these can be made from 75 standard size straws), 150 pre-cut pipe cleaner sections (5–6 cm long), 2 wire cheese cutters (optional) • *Optional*: RAP Book Exercise Set 12, Practice Set 7
Lesson 2 *The Size of Things* • To use geometric shapes and their properties to make sense of situations involving data, change, chance, and discrete structures • To (re)develop and use formulas to find perimeter and area of plane-shapes • To (re)develop and use the Pythagorean Theorem to find lengths • To (re)develop and use formulas to compute surface area and volume of space-shapes	**after page 358** Students can begin Reflecting Task 1 or 3 from page 370 **page 336** **Modeling:** 3 and 4 **Organizing:** 1, and 3 or 4* **Reflecting:** 3 and 4 **Extending:** Choose one* **page 377** **Modeling:** 1, and 3 **Organizing:** 1, and 3 or 4* **Reflecting:** Choose one* **Extending:** Choose one*	10 days	• Teaching Resources 134a–c, 142–146 • Assessment Resources 177–182 • Various size boxes: cereal, Quaker Oats, *etc.* • Centimeter rulers, string, or transparency grids • Models built in Investigation 2 • *Optional*: RAP Book Exercise Set 13
Lesson 3 *The Shapes of Plane Figures* • To classify polygonal plane-shapes, including special quadrilaterals • To recognize line and rotational symmetry in plane-shapes • To identify regular polygons that will tile a plane • To interpret and draw nets for space-shapes • To recognize and create translation and glide reflection symmetries • To use isometric transformations to analyze and create symmetric patterns in the plane	**after page 388** Students can begin Modeling Task 2 or 4; Organizing Task 3; Reflecting Task 3; or Extending Task 5 from page 395 **page 395** **Modeling:** 2 or 4, and 5* **Organizing:** 1 and 3 **Reflecting:** Choose one* **Extending:** Choose one* **after page 404** Students can begin Modeling Task 1, 2, or 3; Organizing Task 2 or 3; Reflecting Task 1, 2, or 3; or Extending Task 1 or 2 from page 408 **page 408** **Modeling:** 4 and choice of 1, 2, or 3* **Organizing:** 2, 3, and 4 **Reflecting:** Choose one* **Extending:** Choose one*	9 days	• Teaching Resources 147–159 • Assessment Resources 183–188 • Scissors • Colored pencils • Plain white paper • Large paper for making class lists • *Optional*: RAP Book Exercise Set 14
Lesson 4 *Looking Back* • To review the major objectives of the unit		3 days (includes testing)	• Teaching Resource 160 • Unit Summary Master • Assessment Resources 189–206 • *Optional*: RAP Book Exercise Set 15

When choice is indicated, it is important to leave the choice to the student.
Note: *It is best if Organizing tasks are discussed as a whole class after they have been assigned as homework.*

Lesson 1 · *The Shape of Things*

The world, the space in which you live, is three-dimensional. Buildings, plants, animals, toys, tools, even molecules are three-dimensional; they are **space-shapes**. Space-shapes develop in nature and are built, observed, and used in all countries and cultures. They can be beautiful, unusual, large, or small. If a space-shape is to serve a purpose, it may need to have special characteristics. For example, it may need to bounce or resist strong wind forces. It also may need to support great weight, use space efficiently, or be hollow or filled.

Think About This Situation

Look at the photo of Biosphere 2 shown above and at objects around your classroom. Identify two or three space-shapes.

a List some characteristics of the space-shapes you see.

b How are two-dimensional shapes (*plane-shapes*) used to make these space-shapes?

c Choose one of the space-shapes in your classroom.

- Draw a sketch of it.

- Explain how you might use numbers to describe its size.

Lesson 1 *The Shape of Things*

Master 135

LESSON OVERVIEW This first geometry lesson from the *Contemporary Mathematics in Context* curriculum introduces students to the major theme of shape, along with the relationship of how an object's shape affects how the object functions. In Investigation 1, students compare the relative strengths of columns that have various shapes. In Investigation 2, students think about rigidity of shapes. Investigation 3 focuses on visualizing and sketching three-dimensional figures, and Investigation 4 on rigidity of space-shapes. The study of shapes and their uses is expanded in the Course 2 unit, "Geometric Form and Its Function." The term "space-shape" is used in these materials to refer to any three-dimensional shape. We will refer to space-shapes in three different ways: as a *solid* object, as a *shell*, or as a *skeleton* or frame. Also, "plane-shape" is used to refer to two-dimensional shapes.

A full-class discussion aimed at helping students become familiar with these new terms and their appropriate uses is an excellent way to introduce this lesson. One way to begin the discussion is to ask students to react to the term "space-shape" and to speculate on its meaning. A variety of responses will arise such as "shapes from space or Star Trek" or "shapes that are spaced out." Relate the term "space-shape" to three-dimensional shapes. Ask for examples of space-shapes and help bring out the distinction between solids and shells, both of which are space-shapes.

Once "space-shape" has some meaning for students, you can keep discussion going by asking groups of students to discuss the statements in the "Think About This Situation" on page 326. They probably will need only about 8–10 minutes to form responses. Reassemble the class and ask groups to share their thoughts. You can use student responses to assess their present knowledge regarding polyhedra and polygons. If it is clear that the class is well-versed in certain aspects of these shapes, you may want to adjust the assignment for the MORE tasks accordingly.

Lesson Objectives

- To use plane- and space-shapes to model real-life situations
- To classify, construct, and sketch models of space-shapes
- To identify and explain different kinds of symmetry for plane- and space-shapes
- To use visualization to interpret and reason about plane and space situations
- To develop an understanding of the essential characteristics of a space-shape that make it a prism or a pyramid
- To develop an understanding of cross section and reflection (bilateral, plane) symmetry of space-shapes

See additional Teaching Notes on page T418C.

EXPLORE small-group investigation

INVESTIGATION ▶ 1 Designing and Testing Columns

During this investigation, students will be working with space-shapes (columns) and exploring some of their characteristics. Students will design an experiment, build several space-shape models, record data, and draw conclusions. You could suggest to students that they might want to predict the weight-bearing capacity of each type of column before they test it. This investigation is designed to help students become comfortable with the language of space-shapes and to focus attention on a few of the many characteristics of space-shapes.

Most students will begin by placing light objects on the cardboard platform or index card. They will see quite soon that the paper columns can support substantial weight. Students may consider using paperback books as weights.

NOTE: Each group should be careful to standardize the sequence of weights (books) used to test each of their columns. "Weight" can be represented as the number of books (or other objects) used. Since the sequence is fixed, the number approximates the weight. Students should use objects heavy enough to collapse the circular column and also light enough to show variation among the columns.

Since students will be comparing the relative strength of the columns, it is important that the columns be made as uniform as possible. The paper should be taped in the same place, and the weights should be placed in the same position. The folds should be crisp and should face away from the center of the column. The folds on the column need to be perpendicular to the table, so before creasing make sure the sides of the paper match exactly. Sharp creases can be made by placing the paper on a desk, pressing down with a thumb or finger, and running along the fold several times.

You might want to prepare one set of columns, neatly folded and taped, to reinforce the verbal directions in Activity 2. Ask students if they foresee any difficulties with the experiment. If no one mentions the words "until the column crumbles" then draw their attention to this, and set up a column with a support which is off center. Ask, "What is likely to happen with this set up?" Even the briefest of discussions helps to avoid the frustration of collecting poor data from columns that slide out from under the weight before they reach the "crumble" point.

To make the triangular columns, students should measure and mark the paper at 0.5 inches, 4.0 inches, and 7.5 inches. It is important that the triangles be as close to equilateral as possible. A scalene or isosceles triangle does not hold as much weight as an equilateral triangle of the same perimeter. (This is another possible investigation.)

See additional Teaching Notes on pages T418C–T418D.

INVESTIGATION ▶ 1 Designing and Testing Columns

Space-shapes come in all shapes and sizes and have many uses. For example, many ancient cultures used filled or solid space-shapes to make columns in their buildings. The Greek Parthenon shown here is made of marble. Thus, the columns had to be designed to support great weights.

The columns the Greeks used were solid marble. You can model the Greek columns with *shells* rather than solids. That is, your columns will be hollow like tin cans (with no top or bottom) rather than filled like hockey pucks. In this investigation, you will seek an answer to the question:

"What type of column supports the most weight?"

1. As a group, brainstorm about a possible answer to this question. What column characteristics do you think support your choice?

2. Now, work in pairs to complete the experiment described below.

   a. Select four sheets of 8.5×11-inch paper such as typing paper, copy machine paper, or computer printer paper.

   b. Make four columns, each 8.5 inches high. The bases of the columns should have the following shapes:

   - triangular with all equal sides;
   - square;
   - eight-sided with all equal sides;
   - circular.

   For consistency, leave a half-inch overlap and tape the columns closed. Be sure to tape near each end.

   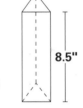

   8.5"

   c. Set up the following weight-supporting situation to collect data.

   - Choose a level surface.
   - Place a small rectangle of cardboard (about 6×8 inches) on top of a column.
   - Choose a sequence of objects to be placed on the cardboard platform. (**Note:** Be sure to use the same sequence for each test.)
   - Carefully add objects until the column collapses. Measure and record the maximum weight supported.
   - Organize and display your data in a table.

3. Make a graph of your data with *number of sides* on the horizontal axis and *maximum weight supported* on the vertical axis.

   a. Where along the horizontal axis did you put "circular column"? Why?

   b. What appears to happen to the maximum weight supported as the number of sides of the column increases?

   c. Use your table or graph to estimate the weight-supporting capacity of a 6-sided column. To check your estimate, make a 6-sided column and find the maximum weight it supports.

Checkpoint

In this investigation, you explored the weight-bearing capacity of differently-designed columns.

a Why do you think the ancient Greeks chose to use cylindrical columns?

b What are some other questions about column design that seem important and which you could answer by experimentation?

Be prepared to share your group's thinking and questions with the class.

On Your Own

Latoya investigated what happened to the amount of weight supported when she increased the number of columns underneath the cardboard platform. She kept the shape and area of the base the same for all columns in each experiment. Her data for the three experiments are summarized in the table below.

Triangular Columns		Square Columns		Circular Columns	
Number of Columns	Weight (kg) Supported	Number of Columns	Weight (kg) Supported	Number of Columns	Weight (kg) Supported
1	1.7	1	2.1	1	3.3
2	3.5	2	4.1	2	6.4
3	5.1	3	6.4	3	10.0
4	7.0	4	8.5	4	13.2
5	8.3	5	10.4	5	16.6

3. The scatterplots will vary, but should all show that as the number of sides increases, the maximum weight supported increases also. Shown below is our data from Trial 1.

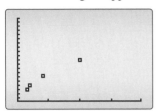

L₁	L₂	L₃
3	3	- - - - - -
4	4	
8	6	
20	10	
		- - - - - -

L₁(5) =

```
WINDOW
Xmin =0
Xmax =40
Xscl =10
Ymin =0
Ymax =20
Yscl =1
Xres =1
```

a. Most students probably will choose to put the circle at the far right of the plot because the weight it supports is more than the others or because they think of a circle as having an infinite number of sides. Look for good explanations of their choice. The graph is misleading if students choose 0 or 1 for the number of sides of a circle; be sure to clarify this if necessary.

b. The maximum weight supported seems to get larger as the number of sides increases. The rate of change of the maximum weight does not seem to be constant. The scatterplot seems to indicate that a curve will fit the data better than a line.

c. Responses will vary based on their table or graph. Their estimates should be between the maximum weights supported by the square and the octagonal columns. Be sure that students check their estimate by doing the experiment.

Checkpoint

See Teaching Master 136.

ⓐ The ancient Greeks probably chose cylindrical columns because they were the strongest and possibly easier to construct than a many-sided polygon column. Also, the cylinder supports the greatest weight. You may wish to have students express views on why the cylinder is better than the other space-shapes, but it is good not to arrive at definitive conclusions at this time.

ⓑ Some possible questions are:
- How does increasing the number of columns affect the weight they will support?
- Using the same perimeter for a base, does a regular-based prism support more or less weight than one with an irregular base?
- Will a column made with 2 sheets of paper hold twice as much as a column made with 1 sheet of paper?
- If the column is a filled space-shape and the radii are equal for different shapes (the radii for a regular polygon are the segments connecting the centroid and a vertex), which shape would support the most weight?
- If the column is a filled space-shape and the area of the bases are equal for different shapes, which shape would support the most weight?

CONSTRUCTING A MATH TOOLKIT: To help students summarize their results and extend them when possible, you may wish to have students record a summary of procedures and results from Activities 2 and 3 in their toolkits.

Master 136

Checkpoint

In this investigation, you explored the weight-bearing capacity of differently-designed columns.

ⓐ Why do you think the ancient Greeks chose to use cylindrical columns?

ⓑ What are some other questions about column design that seem important and which you could answer by experimentation?

Be prepared to share your group's thinking and questions with the class.

Unit 5

MORE
ASSIGNMENT   *pp. 335–340*

Students who finish early can begin work on Extending Task 2 from the MORE assignment following Investigation 2.

►On Your Own

a.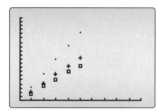

WINDOW
Xmin =0
Xmax =10
Xscl =1
Ymin =0
Ymax =20
Yscl =1
Xres =1

☐ Triangular Columns
+ Square Columns
● Circular Columns

b. As the number of columns increases for all three shapes, the weight supported increases.

c. The maximum weight supported for all three types of columns increases as the number of columns increases. They all seem to have an approximately constant rate of change. However, the weight increases the fastest per increment for circular columns and the slowest for the triangular columns.

d. Students probably will extend the graph or table and estimate. Using linear regression on a calculator to find equations for the lines that fit these data sets gives the following:

Triangular columns: $y = 1.67x + 0.11$
Square columns: $y = 2.1x$
Circular columns: $y = 3.34x - 0.12$

Using these equations, the predicted number of columns are 12, 10, and 7 for triangular, square, and circular columns, respectively.

MORE
ASSIGNMENT   *pp. 335–340*

Students can now begin Modeling Task 1 or 2 from the MORE assignment following Investigation 2.

INVESTIGATION ▶ 2 Recognizing and Constructing Space-Shapes

In Investigation 1, students began to realize that space-shapes have characteristics that make them useful. In this investigation, students classify and construct space-shapes. They also investigate planes of symmetry for three-dimensional figures. This investigation could be introduced with a whole-group discussion of the many space-shapes seen in our everyday world. Ask students to give examples of some space-shapes and to describe the features of those examples. The discussion may be given more focus if you indicate that the purpose of the investigation is to identify the characteristics of space-shapes that can be used to classify them. Students then can work through Activities 1 and 2 as a full class.

In Activities 1 and 2, encourage students to describe the space-shapes using mathematical terms such as *base, edge, face, plane faces, parallel edges, rectangular faces, congruent bases, parallel bases, circular bases, rectangular bases,* and *hexagonal bases*.

NOTE: Even though it is not explicitly noted, the words *prism, pyramid, cone,* and *cylinder* refer to *right,* but not necessarily *regular,* space-shapes. Oblique space-shapes are introduced only in the Extending tasks.

See additional Teaching Notes on page T418D.

a. Make a scatterplot of Latoya's data. Use a different symbol for the data from each of the three experiments.

b. What do you think is true about the relationship between *number of columns* and *weight supported*?

c. How are the patterns of change in *weight supported* as the *number of columns* increases similar for the different types of columns? How are they different?

d. For each type of column, estimate the number of columns needed to support a weight of 20 kg. Explain your method.

INVESTIGATION 2 Recognizing and Constructing Space-Shapes

The columns studied in Investigation 1 are examples of space-shapes. Most everyday space-shapes are designed with special characteristics in mind.

1. As a class, examine the space-shapes depicted below.

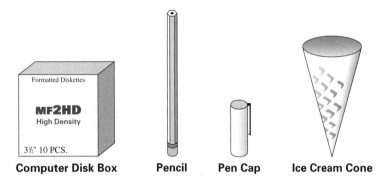

Computer Disk Box   **Pencil**   **Pen Cap**   **Ice Cream Cone**

a. Which shapes above have common characteristics? What are those characteristics?

b. In what ways might the word "parallel" be used to describe characteristics of some of the space-shapes?

2. On the following page are pictures of structures built through the centuries by various cultures. Describe the different space-shapes you see in these photographs. Name those that you can. Are some forms of space-shapes more common in some cultures than in others?

a.

Igloo in the Arctic

b.

Pyramid at Chichen Itza, Mexico

c.

Native American Tepees

d.

Stave Church, Norway

e.

Himeji Castle, Japan

f.

Taj Mahal, India

2. **a.** The igloo is formed by half a sphere and part of a cylinder.

    b. There are rectangular prisms that are placed on top of each other in order to form a truncated pyramid shape.

    c. Responses may vary. Students may suggest that a cone is the basic construction shape in the picture, or they may suggest a many-sided, polygon-based pyramid.

    d. There are space-shapes formed from triangles, trapezoids, and rectangles.

    e. Rectangles, triangles, and trapezoids are used to make this castle in Japan.

    f. These shapes are rounded but not circular or spherical. Rectangles are also used.

3. Student responses may vary. Responses should reflect careful thinking but they do not need to be expressed in formal mathematical terms.

    a. The prisms are A, F, G, I, J, and L because they have two equal, parallel bases that are connected by rectangular sides.

    b. The pyramids are C, H, and K because they have polygon bases with triangular faces that meet at a point.

    c. B is not a prism because parallel faces are not connected by rectangular faces; it is not a pyramid because there is no one face connected to all the other faces.

    D is not a prism because any parallel faces are not connected solely by rectangular faces. It is not a pyramid because the vertex does not connect with the vertices of the base.

    E is not a pyramid or a prism because it has a non-polygonal base.

4. a. Responses may vary. Pyramids have polygonal bases with triangular faces that meet at a point.

    b. Responses may vary. Prisms have two congruent and parallel polygonal bases that are connected by rectangular faces.

NOTE: The term "polygon" should be familiar from middle school mathematics. In Lesson 3, the idea of a polygon is more fully developed.

Unit 5

3. Two important classifications of space-shapes are **prisms** and **pyramids**. In your group, study the examples and non-examples below.

Examples	Non-examples
Prisms	**Not Prisms**
Pyramids	**Not Pyramids**

a. Which of the space-shapes below are prisms? Explain your reasoning.

b. Which of the space-shapes below are pyramids? Explain your reasoning.

c. Explain why the remaining space-shapes are neither pyramids nor prisms.

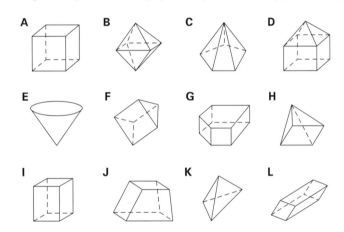

4. Now try to describe the distinguishing features of pyramids and prisms.

a. What are the characteristics of a space-shape that make it a pyramid?

b. What are the characteristics of a space-shape that make it a prism?

5. **Cones** and **cylinders** are two other common space-shapes. How are they similar to pyramids and prisms? How are they different?

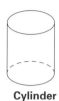

Cone   **Cylinder**

6. Develop a method for naming types of prisms and types of pyramids. Could you use the shape of the base in your naming procedure? Try it.

   a. Use your method to name a cube as a type of prism.

   b. Cardboard boxes are usually prisms. What would you name such a prism?

Checkpoint

In this investigation, you discovered identifying characteristics of prisms and pyramids.

a How are pyramids similar to prisms? How are they different?

b Sketch a prism in which the bases are five-sided. Name the prism.

c What space-shape best describes a Native American tepee?

Be prepared to share your descriptions and sketch with the class.

▶ On Your Own

An "A-Frame" is a style of architecture sometimes used in building houses. What space-shape is basic to the "A-Frame" construction?

Space-shapes can be modeled in three different ways. One way is as a *solid object* such as a brick, a cake, or a sugar cube. Another is as a *shell* such as a paper bag, a house, or a water pipe. The third way is as a *skeleton*, which includes only the

5. Responses may vary.

 Cones are similar to pyramids in that they both come to a point. Cones are different from pyramids in that cones have a circular base and pyramids have a polygonal base.

 Cylinders are similar to prisms because they both have two parallel, congruent bases. In the cylinder the bases are circles, but in the prism the bases are polygons.

6. Responses may vary, but most students will choose to name a prism or a pyramid by the shape of its base.

 a. A cube would be a square prism whose height is the same length as a side of the square base.

 b. Cardboard boxes would be rectangular prisms.

Master 137

MASTER 137   Transparency Master

Checkpoint

In this investigation, you discovered identifying characteristics of prisms and pyramids.

ⓐ How are pyramids similar to prisms? How are they different?

ⓑ Sketch a prism in which the bases are five-sided. Name the prism.

ⓒ What space-shape best describes a Native American tepee?

Be prepared to share your descriptions and sketch with the class.

Use with page 332.   UNIT 5 • PATTERNS IN SPACE AND VISUALIZATION

Unit 5

SHARE AND SUMMARIZE   full-class discussion

Checkpoint

See Teaching Master 137.

Again, after students do the Checkpoint items in their small groups, you can assess results with a full-group discussion. As part of the full-group discussion, after the Checkpoint items have been shared, you may want to assess understanding quickly and informally by asking, for example:

I am thinking of a prism with 8 plane-shapes as faces, including the bases. What kind of prism is this?

Give groups a few minutes to discuss this, and then ask them to explain their solutions. You then could continue:

What if there were 9 plane-shapes as faces? What shape would the prism be? Is it possible for a pyramid to have 9 plane-shapes for faces, including the base? What shape would the pyramid base be?

ⓐ Pyramids are similar to prisms in that both have only polygonal faces, and both are named by their bases. They are different in that pyramids have one base and triangular sides (lateral faces) that meet at a point, whereas prisms have two parallel, congruent bases and rectangular sides (lateral faces).

ⓑ Students will probably call it a pentagon (or pentagonal) prism.

ⓒ The Native American tepee is a pyramid which may have a variety of types of bases. Ask students what shape describes each of the faces of a tepee regardless of the number of sides of the base (a triangle). If students think the base of the tepee is circular then *cone* is the best name for the space-shape.

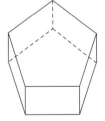

APPLY   individual task

 On Your Own

The space-shape is a triangular prism lying on one face.

Begin this next group of activities (7–9) with a full-class discussion of the differences among solids, shells, and skeletons. Note that the shape and its properties are evident across models. The differences are within the type of model itself. Before assigning these activities, you might have students construct the models described in Activity 8.

To provide valuable experiences in spatial visualization, have students use a variety of model types for these activities. In Activity 7, Play-Doh® or cheese can be substituted for clay, and you might wish to use dental floss to slice the solids. Another alternative is to have students build a Plexiglas cube with one side partially open, or purchase a set of transparent solids with an aperture. Fill the transparent model to varying levels with water that has been tinted with food coloring. Rotating the model allows students to visualize the various shapes formed when planes intersect the three-dimensional model.

It is important to have students construct three-dimensional models to develop spatial thinking and visualization. However, constructing models can be a time-consuming process. Asking each student to construct *one* model prism and *one* model pyramid will allow students more time to explore relationships and discover patterns.

If students are working with pre-cut straws in Activity 8, their task is to select the correct number of edges of each length and connect them. If they have to cut their own straws they will take much longer, and the models may not be as accurately made. Students will find it helpful to use these models for reference in future activities, so you may want to save them. The pentagonal prism, cube, and triangular prism are used again in Investigation 4 (page 345), so you will want to have multiple copies of these made (one for each group).

You will need 10-cm, 12-cm, and 16-cm pieces of straw. (See the materials list in the introduction to this unit.) To assemble a model, double over the pipe cleaner segment to connect two straws at a common vertex, as shown below. At the same vertex, insert a second pipe cleaner segment, double over the extended portion of the pipe cleaner, and connect a third straw as pictured below. Continue the process to complete the model.

While the students are making their models, it will help if you circulate among the groups and ask questions that focus students' attention on the properties of their space-shapes. For example, ask, "How many differently-shaped faces does your model have?", "How are your shapes similar to the shapes being made by other members of your group?", or "How are your shapes different from the models being constructed by others in your group?"

See additional Teaching Notes on page T418E.

NOTE: Commercial products are available for constructing space-shapes to assist students in visualizing and drawing. However, if these shapes are rigid, you may still need to construct some pipe cleaner models for Investigation 4.

edges like a jungle gym. A solid model can be made of material such as clay, wood, or plastic foam. A shell model can be made of paper or cardboard and tape, for example. A skeleton model can be made with things like toothpicks and clay or straws and pipe cleaners.

7. Use a piece of modeling clay or Play-Doh to make a cube.

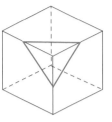

   a. How many flat surfaces or *faces* does it have?

   b. Imagine slicing a corner off. Now how many faces are there? What would you see as the shape of the new face on the cube? This is a **plane slice** since the new face is flat. Slice your cube to check your prediction.

   c. Imagine a line joining two opposite corners of a face. Make a plane slice all the way through to the corresponding line on the opposite face. What is the shape of the new face formed? Check by slicing your cube. What do you notice about the two pieces of the cube?

   d. Think of two other ways of slicing your cube (remade, of course). Predict and sketch the shape of the new face. Do the slicing to check your predictions.

8. Get a collection of straws and pipe cleaners from your teacher. Your group will need about 75 of the 10-cm straws, 27 of the 12-cm straws, and 6 of the 16-cm straws. Cut the pipe cleaners into 5- or 6-centimeter length pieces and bend them in half. These pieces will be used to connect two straw edges at a vertex, as shown here. Carefully cut the straws into the lengths given in Part a.

   a. Make the following models from straws and pipe cleaners. Divide the work among the group members. Each student should build at least one prism and one pyramid.

   - cube: 10-cm edges
   - triangular prism: 10-cm edges on bases, 12-cm height
   - square prism: 10-cm edges on bases, 12-cm height
   - pentagonal prism: 10-cm edges on bases, 12-cm height
   - hexagonal prism: 10-cm edges on bases, 12-cm height
   - triangular pyramid: 10-cm edges on bases, other edges 10 cm
   - square pyramid: 10-cm edges on bases, other edges 12 cm
   - pentagonal pyramid: 10-cm edges on bases, other edges 12 cm
   - hexagonal pyramid: 10-cm edges on bases, other edges 16 cm

b. Imagine slicing your triangular prism with a single plane slice. What is the shape of the new face produced by a single plane slice? Check by slicing a clay model if you have any doubts.

c. Think about the shapes of faces that are created when the triangular prism is sliced. Identify as many *different* shapes of these faces as you can. Sketch the shape of each new face. Check each with clay models if it is helpful.

d. Now imagine slicing each of the other prisms with planes. What new face shapes do you get with a single plane slice? Sketch each, and check with clay models if group members are not all in agreement.

e. Do any of your plane slices produce two halves that are identical space-shapes? If so, describe the slice location(s)?

Some planes may slice a space-shape into two identical mirror-image halves. When this is possible, the space-shape is said to have the property of **reflection symmetry**. The plane is called a **symmetry plane** for the space-shape. For example, when you want to share a piece of cake fairly, you cut it into two identical mirror-image halves.

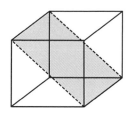

9. Which of the space-shapes constructed in Activity 8 have reflection symmetry? Find and describe all the symmetry planes for each shape. Compare your results with those of other groups.

Checkpoint

Visualizing planes slicing a space-shape can help in identifying properties of the shape.

a Imagine a prism and a plane. Describe several ways the plane could slice the prism without intersecting either base.

b Think about how the symmetry planes for prisms and pyramids are related to the bases. Explain how the symmetry planes differ for the two kinds of space-shapes.

Be prepared to share your ideas with the entire class.

▶**On Your Own**

Imagine or construct a rectangular prism. Determine the number of symmetry planes for the shape. Describe their locations.

8. **b.** The new face could be a rectangle, a trapezoid, or a triangle.

    c. Same as Part b. A rectangle comes from slicing a face perpendicular to the base; the shape is a trapezoid if the slice is not perpendicular to the base. A triangle is formed if you slice across or parallel to the base or if you slice off a corner.

    d. Cube: various rectangles, triangles, pentagons, or hexagons.
Rectangular prism: various rectangles, trapezoids, pentagons, or triangles.
Pentagonal prism: various hexagons, pentagons, rectangles, trapezoids, or triangles.
Hexagonal prism: various heptagons, hexagons, rectangles, trapezoids, or triangles.

    e. Slices parallel to the bases at the midpoints of a lateral edge will give identical halves. See the answer to Activity 9 for other cuts that will produce two identical space-shapes.

9. **Student descriptions of planes of symmetry will be incomplete and unclear on their first attempts. As you circulate around the groups, you can help them clarify their descriptions by asking individuals to read their descriptions to you. Then demonstrate planes that fit the offered descriptions but are not the intended planes of symmetry. Encourage students to add refinements and corrections to their descriptions. You might want to point out that if they want the plane to pass through the midpoints of opposite edges, then they have to say so. If they want the plane to be perpendicular to the base, then they have to say so.**

A cube has nine symmetry planes: three are parallel to two faces or bases and contain the midpoints of the edges that are perpendicular to the symmetry plane. The remaining six contain the diagonals of the square opposite faces or bases.

The triangular prism has four symmetry planes. One symmetry plane is parallel to the bases and contains the midpoints of the lateral edges. Because the triangle is regular, it also has three symmetry planes that are perpendicular to the bases and contain the altitudes of the triangle.

A square prism (that is not a cube) has five symmetry planes. Three are parallel to two faces or bases and contain the midpoints of the edges that are perpendicular to the symmetry plane. The other two contain the diagonals of the square bases.

A regular pentagonal prism has six symmetry planes. One symmetry plane is parallel to the bases and contains the midpoints of the lateral edges. Each of the other five contains a vertex of the pentagon, the midpoint of its opposite side, and is perpendicular to the bases.

A regular hexagonal prism has seven symmetry planes. One is parallel to the bases and contains the midpoints of the lateral edges. Three of them are perpendicular to the bases and contain the midpoints of opposite sides of each hexagonal base. The last three symmetry planes are perpendicular to the bases and contain a pair of opposite vertices of each hexagonal base.

The regular triangular pyramid (tetrahedron) has six symmetry planes. Each plane is perpendicular to one edge through its midpoint, and contains the two vertices that are not connected to that edge.

The square pyramid has four symmetry planes. Two are perpendicular to two sides of the base at the midpoints and contain the pyramid vertex. The other two contain opposite vertices of the base (*i.e.*, cut along the base's diagonal) and go through the pyramid vertex.

> **See additional Teaching Notes on page T418F.**

CONSTRUCTING A MATH
TOOLKIT: Ask students to add
a definition or description of
reflection symmetry for space-
shapes to their Math Toolkits
(Teaching Master 202).

MORE
ASSIGNMENT *pp. 335–340*

Modeling: 1 or 2, and 3*
Organizing: 1, 3, and 4
Reflecting: 3
Extending: Choose one*

*When choice is indicated, it is important to leave the choice to the student.
NOTE: *It is best if Organizing tasks are discussed as a whole class after they have been assigned as homework.*

MORE independent assignment

Modeling

1. **a–b.** Responses will vary. Some data for a sample experiment are shown below. The entries are the number of medium-sized paperback books supported by the columns. (The base perimeter or circumference is 10.5 inches, the overlap is 0.5 inch.)

Height (in inches)	Trial Number			
	1	2	3	4
8.5	5	4	4	4
6	5	4	6	5
4.25	5	5	6	6
2.125	4	5	4	4

Here is a scatterplot of the third trial data.

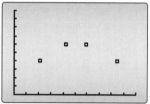 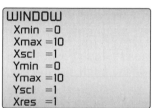

c. Notice that initially the weight supported increases as height decreases, but at some point the weight supported decreases as height decreases. You may need to combine class data to observe this relationship.

2. **a–b.** Sample data (in this case a height of 5.5 inches with an overlap of 0.5 inch) are shown below for a circular column.

Circumference (in inches)	Trial Number			
	1	2	3	4
8	10	8	8	11
6	7	6	6	7
5	5	5	4	4
3.75	3	4	4	4

Here is a scatterplot of the first trial data.

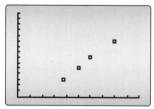

c. Increasing the circumference increases the weight that is supported. This relationship is partially due to the fact that as the circumference increases the "area" available for supporting the weight increases.

3. **a.** The base of the tower is a square prism. The next level is a square pyramid with the top cut off. Above this there is another square prism. A square pyramid is on the top.

b. A tetrahedron surrounds the carbon atom. There are planes of symmetry through each vertex which contain the altitudes of the face opposite the vertex. So there are six planes of symmetry.

MORE

Modeling • Organizing • Reflecting • Extending

Modeling

1. What do you think is true about the relationship between the height of a square column and the weight it can support?

   a. With a partner, investigate the weight-bearing capability of square columns of different heights. Vary the column heights, but keep the shape and area of the base the same.

   b. Organize your data in a table and display them in a graph.

   c. What appears to be true about the relationship between the height of a column and the weight it can support?

2. Make a conjecture about the relationship between the circumference of a circular column and the weight it can support.

   a. With a partner, conduct an experiment to test your conjecture about the weight-bearing capability of circular columns from this new perspective. Use columns of the same height, but with different circumferences.

   b. Organize your data in a table and display them in a graph.

   c. What appears to be true about the relationship between the circumference of a column and the weight it can support? Why do you think this happens?

3. Space-shapes form the basis of atomic structures as well as of common structures for work, living, and play. Often a single space-shape is not used, but rather a combination.

   a. Study this photograph of a tower in Europe. What space-shapes appear to be used in this tower?

   b. Scientists use space-shapes to model molecules of compounds. Shown at the left is a model of a methane molecule. Describe the space-shape whose skeleton would be formed by joining the four hydrogen atoms that are equally-spaced around the central carbon atom. Describe all possible planes of symmetry.

Big Ben clock tower in London, England

c. The square pyramids at Giza are pictured here. Describe one so that some-one who had never seen it could visualize it in his or her mind. Describe all the possible planes of symmetry of one of the pyramids.

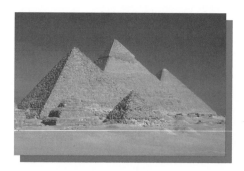

4. Examine the labeling of the faces of a die (one of several dice).

   a. How are the dots (called *pips*) on opposite faces related?

   b. Use cubes made of wood or clay to help you determine how many different ways the pips can be put on the faces so that opposite faces add to seven.

   c. Place your models on your desk so that the face with one pip is on the top and the face with two pips is toward you. How are the models related to each other?

Organizing

1. Refer to the model of a cube in Activity 7 of Investigation 2.

   a. How many faces, edges, and vertices does it have?

   b. Slice a corner off (as shown), making a small triangular face. Repeat at each corner so that the slices do not overlap. Make a table showing the number of faces, edges, and vertices of the modified cube after each "corner slice."

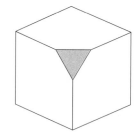

   c. Using *NOW* and *NEXT*, write a rule describing the pattern of change in the number of faces after a slice. Write similar *NOW-NEXT* rules for the number of edges and for the number of vertices after each slice.

   d. How many faces, edges, and vertices does the new solid have when all the corners are sliced off?

3. c. There are three pyramids in a row, with the center pyramid having the same shape as the others, but being larger. The base of each pyramid is a square and then the sides slant up so that they meet at a single point at the top of the pyramid. The planes of symmetry of one pyramid are perpendicular to the base of the pyramid and contain the top point. Two of the planes extend through opposite vertices of the square base. The other two planes of symmetry extend through midpoints of opposite sides of the square.

4. a. The sum of the number of pips on opposite sides of a standard die is 7.

b. There are only two different ways. Two pip arrangements are different when one die cannot be repositioned to be identical to the other. If you start with one pip on the top, then the front can be 2, 3, 4, or 5. If it's 2, then the back must be 5 and the remaining sides are 3 and 4. Putting 3 on the right gives a different arrangement from 3 on the left. All other arrangements will be identical to one of these two. For example, if you put 3 in front and 2 on the left, a quarter-turn to the right shows this is identical to 2 in front and 3 on the right.

c. The two models are mirror images of each other.

Organizing

1. This item connects geometry with the *NOW-NEXT* manner of summarizing a function rule (see Part c). It also emphasizes collecting data and seeking a pattern in those data.

a. There are 6 faces, 12 edges, and 8 vertices.

b. These results assume nonoverlapping slices as indicated in the student text.

	Faces	Edges	Vertices
Cube	6	12	8
First Slice	7	15	10
Second Slice	8	18	12
Third Slice	9	21	14
Fourth Slice	10	24	16

c. For faces, $NEXT = NOW + 1$.
For edges, $NEXT = NOW + 3$.
For vertices, $NEXT = NOW + 2$.

d. There will be 14 faces, 36 edges, and 24 vertices.

2. **a.** The image appears to walk toward the mirror.

   b. The image nose appears to be one meter from the mirror.

   c. The rubber band would be perpendicular to the mirror. The rubber band would remain perpendicular as your finger moves, because the image moves too. Also, the mirror would be at the midpoint of the rubber band.

3. **a.** Yes, segment *AB* would intersect the symmetry plane.

   b. Segment *AB* is perpendicular to the symmetry plane.

   c. The distances are the same.

   d. The line containing two symmetrically placed points is perpendicular to the symmetry plane (and thus to all lines in the symmetry plane which intersect with line *AB*).

4. **This is an item which helps students make connections among data collection, pattern recognition, and rule writing. A class discussion of this task will give students an opportunity to formalize and extend their individual thinking on these ideas.**

   a. Interlocking cubes, such as Multilink® cubes, can be used to construct models of the staircases. Constructing the models could help students develop visualization skills. Regular and isometric dot paper are available in the *Teaching Masters* as Masters 210 and 211, respectively. Your students may find these items helpful for sketching.

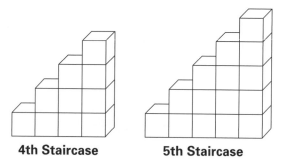

   4th Staircase   **5th Staircase**

   b. Add 5 more to the 10 blocks from the 4th staircase because you are adding a new row of 5 blocks on the bottom or on the right.

   c. The numbers in the next staircase would be $B + (n + 1)$. There would be a new row of $(n + 1)$ blocks.

   d. Look at the bottom cube of the tallest column. There is a symmetry plane that contains the diagonals of the front and back faces of this cube. Another symmetry plane runs vertically, cutting each cube in half.

2. A mirror acts like a symmetry plane for you and your "mirror" image.

   a. If you walk toward a mirror, what appears to happen to your image?

   b. If your nose is one meter from a mirror, how far does your "image" nose appear to be from the mirror?

   c. Imagine tying your index finger to its mirror image with a taut rubber band. How would the rubber band (a segment) be related to the mirror (a plane)? Would this relationship change as you moved your finger? Why or why not?

3. The figure at the right shows a space-shape and one of its symmetry planes. Points *A* and *B* are on the space-shape and are symmetrically placed with respect to the plane.

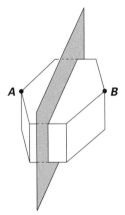

   a. If you connect *A* and *B* with a segment, would it intersect the symmetry plane?

   b. How is $\overline{AB}$ (segment *AB*) related to the symmetry plane?

   c. Compare the distances from *A* and from *B* to the symmetry plane.

   d. How can the word "perpendicular" be used in discussing a symmetry plane and any two symmetrically placed points such as *A* and *B*?

4. The first three elements of a sequence of staircases made from cubes glued together are shown here.

  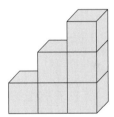

   a. Sketch the 4th and 5th staircases.

   b. If the 4th staircase has 10 blocks, how can you determine the number of blocks in the 5th staircase without counting?

   c. If the staircase in the *n*th position has *B* blocks in it, how many blocks are in the next staircase?

   d. Describe any symmetry planes for the staircases.

e. Imagine taking a staircase and fitting a copy of it on top to form a rectangular prism. In this way, form rectangular prisms from pairs of the first, second, fourth, and fifth staircases. Answer the following questions.

- How many blocks are in each prism?

- How is the number of blocks in each prism related to the number of blocks in each original staircase?

- How can you use the number of blocks on the bottom row of a staircase to predict the number of blocks in the prism?

- How can you use the number of blocks on the bottom row of a staircase to predict the total number of blocks in the staircase?

f. Write a formula for predicting the number of blocks in a staircase with n blocks on the bottom row.

- Use your formula to predict the total number of blocks in a staircase with 10 blocks on the bottom row.

- Use your result in Part c to help check your answer.

- How many blocks are on the bottom row of a staircase made up of 276 blocks?

g. What happens when you fit a staircase to the one immediately following it in the sequence of staircases?

Reflecting

1. Pyramids were built by the Egyptians as tombs for their rulers. What other cultures built structures shaped as pyramids? What purposes did they serve?

2. Every prism has at least one symmetry plane.

a. Draw a prism, then sketch in a symmetry plane whose description could involve the idea of *parallel*.

b. The symmetry plane you drew for Part a could also be described using the idea of *perpendicular*. To what is the symmetry plane perpendicular?

4. e.

Staircase Number	1	2	4	5
Number of Blocks in Prism	2	6	20	30

- The number of blocks in a prism is twice the number in the original staircase.
- Multiply the number of blocks on the bottom row by the height of the prism, which is 1 more than the number of bottom-row blocks. (Another interpretation of the prism-creating procedure would result in the length being one greater than height rather than *vice versa*. The end result would remain the same.)
- The staircase has half the blocks of the prism. So, the number of blocks on the bottom times the next integer and then divided by 2 is the total number of blocks in the staircase.

f. If n is the number of blocks on the bottom row of a staircase, then $\frac{n(n+1)}{2}$ is the total number of blocks in the staircase.

- 10 blocks on the bottom row gives $\frac{(10)(11)}{2}$ or 55 blocks.
- Extending the table by adding $n + 1$ each time gives the following:

Staircase Number	1	2	3	4	5	6	7	8	9	10
Number of Blocks	1	3	6	10	15	21	28	36	45	55

- An integer multiplied by the next larger integer, and then divided by 2, must be 276. So to undo that, $276 \times 2 = 552$. Since $23 \times 24 = 552$, there must be 23 blocks on the bottom row. (Note: $\sqrt{552} \approx 23.5$)

g. A rectangular prism, whose height is the same as its length, is formed.

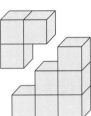

Reflecting

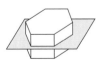

1. Responses may vary. For example, pyramids were built by the Mayan Indians in Mexico and used for religious purposes.

2. **a.** This symmetry plane is parallel to the two bases of the prism.

> NOTE: The ideas of parallel and perpendicular will arise in nearly every geometry unit throughout this curriculum.

b. This symmetry plane is perpendicular to the rectangular faces of the prism.

3. **a–b.** Responses may vary. Two possible post-packing arrangements are shown below.

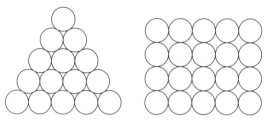

    c. Straws, crayons, felt-tip markers, chalk, metal pipes, and so on.

4. Responses will vary. Some examples are animals, leaves, butterflies, molecules, and some cells.

Extending

1. **a.** A plane could intersect only the corner point of the cube.

    b. A plane could intersect in a single edge of the cube.

    c. A plane could cut off only one corner of the cube.

    d. A plane could cut off equal lengths of three edges that meet at a corner of the cube.

    e. A plane parallel to a face intersects the cube in a square.

    f. A plane could intersect opposite faces of the cube and not be parallel to a side of the cube. Also, a plane could intersect two adjacent faces, perpendicular to the bases but not parallel to any face.

    g. A plane intersecting the top, four sides, and a vertex is a pentagon. Imagine, in the drawing of the hexagon below, that the two lower points meet at the lowest vertex.

    h. A plane could intersect each of the six faces of the cube by cutting off opposite corners of the cube. (See the diagram below.)

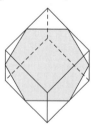

2. **a.** Responses may vary. For example, we found that two sheets folded into a triangular column supported 6 books and three sheets supported 10 books. Two sheets folded into a square column supported 11 books and three supported 15 books. Due to the number of folds, it is difficult to make an octagonal column out of multiple sheets.

    b. Responses may vary. In general, as the number of columns increases, the weight they can support increases.

3. Cedar posts are circular columns often used for building fences.

   a. How could you pack cedar posts for shipment? Sketch your arrangement (the end view).

   b. Are other post-packing arrangements possible? Illustrate those you find with sketches.

   c. In your experience, what consumer goods have you seen packaged in the manner of Part a? In the manner of Part b?

4. Reflection symmetry (sometimes called *bilateral symmetry*) is often found in nature. What examples of bilateral symmetry in nature have you seen in your science classes?

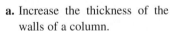

Extending

1. A cube is a square prism with all faces and bases congruent. For each figure below, describe how a plane and a cube could intersect so that the intersection is the figure given. If the figure is not possible, explain your reasoning.

   a. a point   **b.** a segment

   c. a triangle   **d.** an equilateral triangle

   e. a square   **f.** a rectangle

   g. a five-sided shape   **h.** a six-sided shape

2. Recall your column-building experiment in Investigation 1. Can you improve the weight-bearing capability of the poorest-performing column to equal the capability of the best-performing column? Choose one of the two methods below. Describe a procedure you could use to see if the method will improve the column's performance. Conduct the experiment and write a summary of your findings.

   a. Increase the thickness of the walls of a column.

   b. Increase the number of columns used to support weight.

3. The prisms you examined in Investigation 2 are right prisms because the edges connecting the bases are perpendicular to the edges of the bases. Use your skeleton models to help you visualize prisms where these edges are *not perpendicular* to the edges of the bases. These prisms are called **oblique**.

    a. What shapes are the faces of an oblique prism?

    b. Look up the definition of a prism in the dictionary. Is a particular kind of prism defined? If so, what kind?

    c. Do oblique prisms have symmetry planes?

    d. Given an oblique prism with five or fewer faces, imagine its intersection with a plane. What is the shape of the intersection? Find as many such shapes as you can. Name each of them.

4. Suppose each face of a cube is painted one of six different colors. How many cubes with different coloring patterns are possible?

5. Make six cubes with different coloring patterns, as described in Extending Task 4. Is it possible to join them together in a row so that all faces along the row are the same color, the colors of the touching faces match, and the colors of the two end faces match? If so, display your solution.

INVESTIGATION ▶ 3 Visualizing and Sketching Space-Shapes

Models of space-shapes are valuable for several reasons. For an architect, a scale model of a building gives the client a visual impression of the finished product. When the characteristics of a space-shape need to be understood, models allow those characteristics to be more easily visualized and verified.

Model of Biosphere 2

However, it is not always practical to construct models of space-shapes. For example, you cannot fax a scale model of an off-shore oil rig to a Saudi engineer. Rather, the space-shape needs to be represented in two dimensions and still convey the important information about the shape. In this investigation, you will explore various ways of drawing and sketching space-shapes.

3. **a.** The faces are parallelograms.

   b. Answers may vary. Usually oblique prisms are defined because the faces are required to be parallelograms, but not necessarily rectangles. In a right prism, the faces are always rectangles.

   c. For oblique prisms, there are no symmetry planes that are parallel to the bases. A symmetry plane exists if the plane contains the altitude of the prism and passes through corresponding symmetry lines in the bases.

   d. Responses will vary depending on the type of prism. Shapes include point, segment, triangle, trapezoid, and parallelogram. It is always possible to get an intersection congruent to the base of the prism by slicing the prism with a plane that is parallel to the bases.

4. One side will be a given color. There are 5 colors which could go opposite this color. If you continue in this manner, you would calculate that the four remaining sides could be colored in 4! ways. However, this counts each arrangement four times. Recall the die in Modeling Task 4: a quarter turn will give an identical, but seemingly different, cube. Thus, there are only $\frac{4!}{4}$ or 6 ways to arrange the remaining 4 colors. This gives 6×5, or 30 possible cubes with different coloring patterns.

5. Yes, it is possible.

   Additional questions which expand on Task 4 are:

   a. Choose 8 such cubes and make a $2 \times 2 \times 2$ cube that is a model, twice as high, of the original cube. In addition to the 6 faces of the larger cube having the same colors as the original cube, touching faces of adjacent cubes must match. Once you find a solution, rearrange the same 8 cubes to find a different solution. Describe how the two solutions are related. (Note: Only one set of 8 cubes will work. It will help to determine a systematic way to find those 8 cubes.)

   b. Try making each of the following $2 \times 2 \times 2$ cube models which must have touching faces match in color.

   ■ One color on two opposite faces, different colors on the other four

   ■ One color on the left and right faces, second color on the front and back, third color on the top, fourth color on the bottom

   ■ One color on the left and right faces, second color on the front and back, the remaining four colors on the top (each square a different color), and the same four colors on the bottom.

   ■ Each face has four colors, the same four colors on every face.

EXPLORE small-group investigation

INVESTIGATION 3 Visualizing and Sketching Space-Shapes

This investigation is a continuation of the previous one in terms of using constructed space-shapes and developing ideas of reflectional symmetry. The student-constructed models should be on display and available at all times. Many of the ensuing activities involve hands-on experiences using the student-made models from Investigation 2.

The introduction to this investigation gives one example for the need to represent space-shapes in two-dimensions. You can expand this into a class discussion; students will be able to give examples of two-dimensional drawings of space-shapes. Some examples are advertisements, directions for assembling an item, blueprints for construction, illustrations in textbooks, video game images, cartoon drawings, and landscaping plans. Let students know that, in addition to continuing to build spatial-visualization skills by working with space-shapes, in this investigation they will learn three ways to draw space-shapes. These are face views, isometric drawings, and perspective drawings (with or without hidden edges).

Many students have trouble visualizing how plane surfaces relate to each other and to the three-dimensional model. Ask students which lengths on the two-dimensional house drawings must match. From their efforts to think about which edges must match, or which measurements should coincide, you will have an informal assessment of the progress students are making with these ideas. The activities in Investigation 3 will give students more opportunities to develop their visualization skills.

Activity 3 begins a sequence of three activities in which the students are asked to sketch three-dimensional shapes on the plane. The method of Activity 3 often is used by architects when they provide elevations of their work. Working in small groups, students should complete Activities 3–5 and the accompanying Checkpoint. You may suggest that students compare sketches within each group and then make any needed revisions.

Activities 4 and 5 contain two related sketching problems. Each asks for a representation of a space-shape that gives the impression of three dimensions in the plane. In Activity 4, the sketch is constructed so that:

- visible parallel lines in the object are drawn parallel;
- visible parallel edges with equal lengths are drawn with equal lengths;
- most visible faces are drawn as parallelograms when they are actually rectangular;
- diagonal (back-to-front) lines in the drawing are shorter than the horizontal and vertical lines in the drawings; and
- hidden edges are shown as dotted segments.

It is important to have the constructed space-shapes from Investigation 2 available for student use during these activities.

The instructions explicitly ask students to draw a space-shape from a specific point of view. Instead, you may want to ask students to draw a figure (for example, a rectangular prism) and then change dotted segments, using one drawing to represent different views of the space-shape. This extended activity may be particularly helpful for students who are having difficulty in visualizing and drawing space-shapes.

1. **a.** There are 8 cubes in this model.
   b. Students should build the model and verify that their models have the provided top, front, and right side views.
   c. Using only the top and side views would allow you to construct the three-dimensional model correctly. An extension of this problem is to ask students how they can change the model (by changing only one view) so that the two views are not enough to determine the shape. (One way is to add a cube on the bottom layer behind the right-most cube.)

One way to depict space-shapes is to sketch the shape from various views. A method commonly used by architects is to draw **face-views**. For the house at the right, a *top view*, a *front view*, and a *right-side view* are shown below. Together, these views display the width, depth, and height of the building. (You'll notice the top view is different from the other two. Frequently, floor plans such as this are used instead of an exterior top view.)

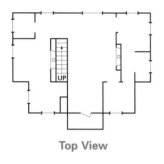

Top View

Front View

Right-Side View

1. Below are three face-views of a simple model of a hotel made from cubes.

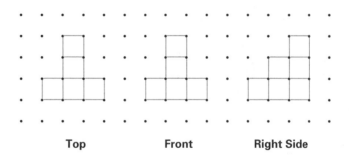

| Top | Front | Right Side |

   a. How many cubes are in the model?

   b. Use blocks or sugar cubes to make a model of this hotel. Build your model on a sheet of paper or poster board that can be rotated.

   c. Could you make the model using information from only two of these views? Explain your reasoning.

2. Shown here is a corner view of a model hotel drawn on *isometric* dot paper.

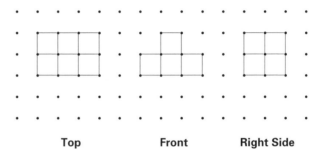

  a. Try to rotate your model from Activity 1 so that it appears as in this **isometric drawing**.

  b. Describe as completely as possible the vantage point from which the model is being viewed in this drawing.

  c. On your own, use isometric dot paper to draw a *top-front-right corner view* of your model. Compare your drawing with those of others in your group.

  d. Use dot paper to draw an isometric view of a model hotel that has top, front, and right-side views as shown below.

Top   **Front**   **Right Side**

  e. Compare your drawing with those of other group members.

   ■ Does each drawing accurately depict the hotel? If not, work together to modify any inaccurate drawings.

   ■ Describe as well as you can the vantage point from which the hotel is viewed in each drawing.

  f. Draw top, front, and right-side views for the model hotel below.

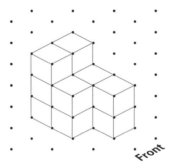

Front

2. a. Students will rotate their own models.

b. The provided drawing is from a top-front-left corner view.

c.

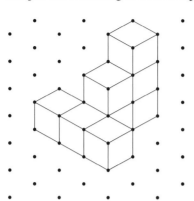

NOTE: In drawings on isometric dot paper, squares are represented as rhombi. The word "isometric" means "the same measure." The congruent sides of the cubes are also congruent in an isometric drawing.

Unit 5

d. Students' drawings may differ depending on the point of view they choose to use. Shown below is the top-front-right corner view.

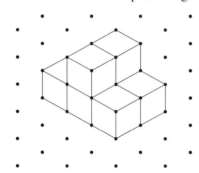

e. Responses may vary. This is an opportunity for students to see a variety of drawings of the same object.

f.

Top

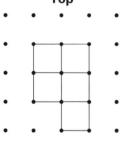

Front

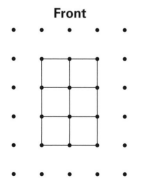

Right Side

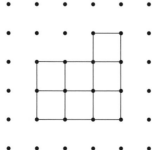

NOTE: The general practice in drafting and in drawings in magazines is to provide the views in the order Top, Front, Side. This allows for much easier visualization and dimensioning. You may wish to have your students use this layout.

NOTE: In perspective drawings, squares or rectangles may appear as their actual shape or as parallelograms. Congruent lengths are not always represented as congruent in a perspective drawing.

3. **a.** The box is a rectangular prism.

    b. The shapes shown in the three views are similar in shape to the actual faces of the box, but may be scaled up or down.

    c. ■ The front face appears to be a rectangle, but the side and top appear to be parallelograms. (Students frequently give the incorrect response that the top and side appear to be rectangles.) All faces of the box are actually rectangles.

        ■ Vertical and horizontal edges are drawn to scale, but the diagonal (back-to-front) lines are shortened to produce a three-dimensional effect.

        ■ Opposite sides of the faces and bases are parallel and should be drawn parallel. Since they do not really intersect, they should not meet in the drawing.

    d. All measurements are in centimeters. The right side shown implies a 90° clockwise turn to the space-shape. Students may not have the skill to calculate the lengths shown; estimates are acceptable. You may want to ask your students to explain how they made their drawings.

       Students may consider the "right side" to be the first face to the right, which gives the following:

Cube:

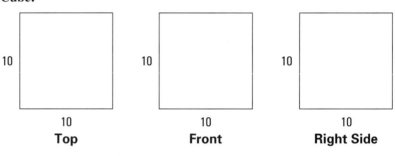

Triangular prism:

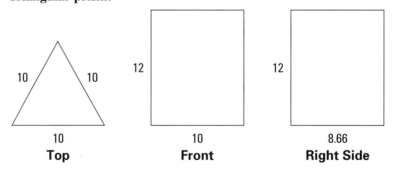

See additional Teaching Notes on page T418G.

3. Shown below is another way to depict a space-shape such as a box of computer disks. This **perspective drawing** provides a top-front-right corner view of the box.

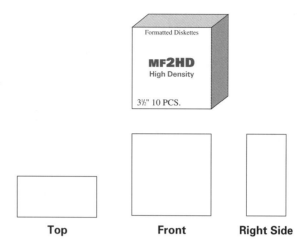

a. What space-shape is a box of computer disks?

b. How are the shapes shown in the three face-views related to the actual faces of the box?

c. Examine the drawing showing the box from the top-front-right corner view.

- What appear to be the shapes of the three faces as shown in the drawing? What are the true shapes of the three faces on the box itself?

- In this type of drawing, how do you know how long to draw each edge?

- What edges are parallel in the real object? Should they be drawn parallel? Explain your reasoning.

d. Draw top, front, and right-side views of the straw prisms you constructed for Activity 8 on page 333.

e. Now sketch each of your prism models from a top-front-right corner view.

f. Each member of your group should select a different prism. Sketch your prism from a top-front-left corner view. Check the other sketches and suggest modifications as necessary.

g. Compare representations of space-shapes by sketching face-views, by making isometric drawings, and by making sketches from particular perspectives. What are the advantages and drawbacks of each method?

4. Sometimes edges of the shape are *hidden* by your viewing angle. In these situations, it is helpful when sketching a space-shape, to represent the hidden edges with *dotted lines*. For example, the box of disks in Activity 3 would appear like this from a top-front-right corner view.

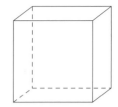

   a. Which faces in the drawing have true shape? That is, which faces have the same shape as their shape on the box itself?

   b. In this type of drawing, how do you know how long to make the dotted edges?

   c. Modify the sketches you made in Parts e and f of Activity 3 to show the hidden edges.

5. For this activity, refer to your pyramid models made in Activity 8, page 333.

   a. Sketch each of these pyramid models from a view in front and above the base. Show all hidden edges.

   b. How does drawing hidden edges help you visualize the entire space-shape?

Checkpoint

A space-shape can be represented in two dimensions by a face-views drawing, an isometric drawing, or a perspective drawing.

ⓐ Make a model of a space-shape that is two square pyramids sharing a common base. Sketch the two-piece shape using the drawing method you think is best.

ⓑ Explain your reasons for using the method you did.

Be prepared to share your sketch and discuss reasons for your choice of drawing method.

▶ On Your Own

Sketch the space-shape formed when a pentagonal pyramid is placed on top of a pentagonal prism. Describe a possible real-world application of a shape with this design.

4. **a.** The front and back faces are the true rectangular shape.
   b. The dotted edges should be the same length as the solid edges to which they are parallel.
   c.

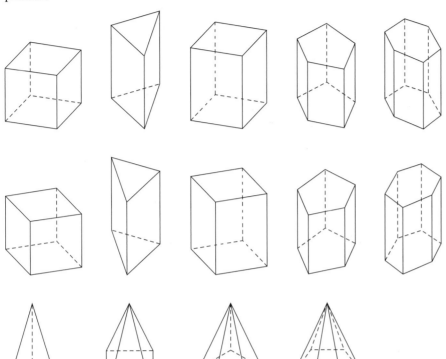

Master 139

MASTER
139 ▸   Transparency Master

Checkpoint

A space-shape can be represented in two dimensions by a face-views drawing, an isometric drawing, or a perspective drawing.

ⓐ Make a model of a space-shape that is two square pyramids sharing a common base. Sketch the two-piece shape using the drawing method you think is best.

ⓑ Explain your reasons for using the method you did.

Be prepared to share your sketch and discuss reasons for your choice of drawing method.

UNIT 5 · PATTERNS IN SPACE AND VISUALIZATION

Unit 5

5. **a.**

b. Drawing hidden edges helps to visualize the back of the space-shape, as if it were constructed of clear plastic.

SHARE AND SUMMARIZE   full-class discussion

Checkpoint

See Teaching Master 139.

Each group could select one student to put the group's sketch on the blackboard and a second student to present the reason this type of drawing was selected. Teachers should be looking to see that the figures are drawn correctly and that the explanations utilize appropriate terminology.

ⓐ One possible sketch is shown at the right.

ⓑ Student responses will vary.

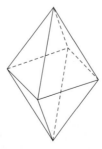

See additional Teaching Notes on page T418H.

INVESTIGATION 4 Rigidity of Space-Shapes

During this investigation, students will explore the rigidity of space-shapes. Students will learn to construct simple space-trusses and to make rigid space-shapes by combining or altering space-shapes which were not originally rigid. Each group of students should have at least a triangular prism, a cube, and a pentagonal prism. These were some of the models made in Activity 8 of Investigation 2 (page 333).

NOTE: Students need to explore rigidity in the case where a base is resting on a plane surface and also in the case where the shape does not rest on a plane surface.

---

1. **a.** A triangle is the most fundamental shape in both frames.
   b. This shape is the basis of his design since you can't alter the shape of a triangle. It is determined by the lengths of the three sides.
2. **a.** The triangular pyramid is the only rigid shape when not resting on a plane surface. In the case where the base is resting on a plane surface, all the pyramids are rigid.
   b. Yes, the faces are triangular, which makes them rigid.

INVESTIGATION 4 Rigidity of Space-Shapes

Buildings, bridges, and other outdoor structures must withstand great forces from the environment. While there are many types of space-shapes, only certain kinds of shapes are used to make structures which do not collapse under pressure.

1. As a class, examine the frameworks used to design the Statue of Liberty and the Eiffel Tower, as shown.

   a. What simple plane shape is fundamental to these frames?

   b. Why do you think Gustave Eiffel used this shape as the basis for his design of both structures?

2. Working in groups, examine the *rigidity* of your models from Activity 8 of Investigation 2, page 333.

   a. Which of these space-shapes are **rigid**? That is, which of the shapes will not change form when a force is applied to any part of it? Consider cases where a base of the shape rests on a plane surface and where the shape does not rest on a surface.

   b. Do the rigid space-shapes have anything in common? Explain.

3. Add reinforcing straws to your model of a triangular prism to make it rigid.

   a. How many reinforcements did you use? Describe where you placed them and why you placed them there.

   b. Could you have placed the reinforcements in different positions and still made the triangular prism rigid? Explain and illustrate.

4. Add reinforcements to your model of a cube so that it becomes a rigid structure.

   a. Note the number of reinforcing straws that you used and describe the position of each straw.

   b. Find a different way to reinforce the cube so that it becomes a rigid structure. Describe the pattern of reinforcing straws.

   c. Of the methods you used to reinforce the cube, which could be used to make a rectangular building stand rigidly?

5. Now consider your straw model of a pentagonal prism.

   a. Predict the minimum number of reinforcing straws needed to make it rigid.

   b. Make the prism rigid and compare the number of reinforcing straws needed with your prediction. Can you find a way to make the prism rigid with fewer reinforcements?

Checkpoint

Rigidity is often an important consideration in designing a space-shape.

ⓐ What is the simplest rigid space-shape?

ⓑ What reinforcement patterns are used to make a space-shape rigid?

Be prepared to share your group's findings with the class.

▶On Your Own

How many reinforcing straws would be needed to make a straw model of a hexagonal prism rigid? Where would you place the reinforcements? Draw a sketch of the prism with reinforcements.

3. **a.** Responses may vary.
    - ■ Subdividing the three rectangular faces into triangles makes the triangular prism rigid.
    - ■ If two of the rectangular faces are triangulated and the prism is lying on the third rectangular face, then it will be rigid.

    b. Either diagonal of each face may be used. If the prism is resting on one of its faces, either diagonal on each of the other two faces will make it rigid.

4. **a.** Responses may vary. If the cube is resting on a plane, triangulating the other five faces of the cube would make it rigid. This method would use five reinforcements. If it is not resting on a plane, you must triangulate each face.

    b. Responses may vary. Another way to make the cube rigid would be to place four reinforcements as diagonals through the center of the space-shape.

    c. Reinforcements for the faces are typically used so that a beam does not run through the interior of the building and cause design problems.

5. In this activity and in the "On Your Own" tasks, we have assumed that reinforcements do not go through the middle of the prism. If such reinforcements are allowed, the minimum number of reinforcements necessary will decrease. For example, it is possible to make a pentagonal prism rigid using only eight reinforcements, if the reinforcements are allowed to go through the prism. Nine are required otherwise.

    a. Responses may vary. (The minimum is nine if a base is not resting on a plane and seven if a base is on a plane.)

    b. One way to make the prism rigid is to reinforce each of the rectangular faces and add two reinforcements to each base for a total of nine reinforcements. If a base is resting on a plane, then triangulating the other base and each of the faces will make it rigid.

SHARE AND SUMMARIZE   full-class discussion

Checkpoint

See Teaching Master 140.

ⓐ The tetrahedron is the fundamental rigid space-shape. Its faces are all triangles and all vertices are connected to each other. For example, diamonds are composed of four carbon molecules bonded together into a tetrahedron-shaped crystal. This explains why diamonds are so strong.

ⓑ To reinforce a space-shape you can: (1) triangulate each face; (2) triangulate each face except one; or (3) put reinforcements through the middle of the space-shape.

APPLY   individual task

▶On Your Own

A hexagonal prism not resting on a plane would need at least six reinforcements for the rectangular faces and three more reinforcements for each base to make it rigid.

Modeling

MORE
ASSIGNMENT *pp. 347–354*

Modeling: 1 or 3, and 5*
Organizing: 2 and 5
Reflecting: 1
Extending: Choose one*

*When choice is indicated, it is important to leave the choice to the student.
NOTE: It is best if Organizing tasks are discussed as a whole class after they have been assigned as homework.

Unit 5

1. a. Four different models are possible. (Rotations of space-shapes do not give different patterns. Also, common sense dictates that a room above the foundation level must have a room below it.)

b.

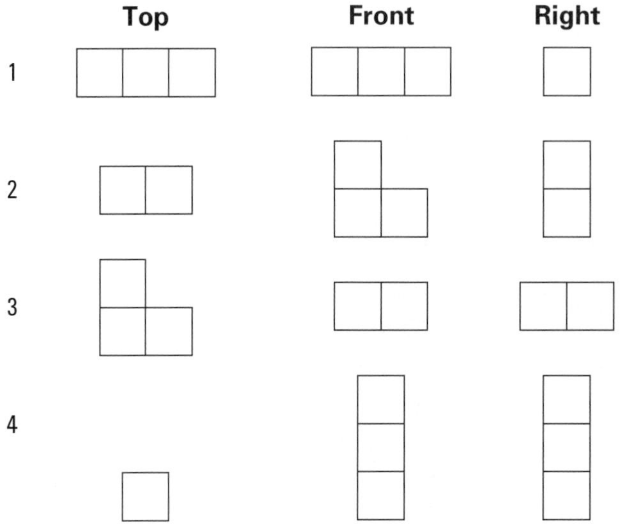

	Top	Front	Right

c.

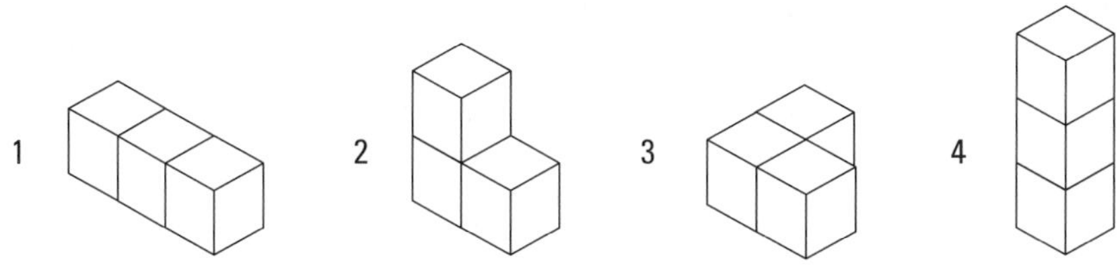

Responses may vary. The vantage point shown above is the top-right-front view. Constructing models from interlocking cubes, such as Multilink® cubes, could help students develop visualization skills.

d. The three-story single column motel would be the least costly to construct. It requires the least land, the smallest foundation, and the smallest roof.

2. a. Including motels which are "mirror images," 15 are possible. As many as 45 structures could be created, but 30 of these are simply 90°, 180°, or 270° rotations of the 15 possibilities given in Part b. Students may replace some of the figures with a rotated version.

See additional Teaching Notes on page T418I–T418J.

MORE
Modeling • Organizing • Reflecting • Extending

Modeling

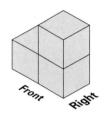

1. Designers of structures like motels can test their designs by using identical cubes to represent the rooms. They can use the cubes to try various arrangements of rooms. Suppose you have a three-room motel and that cubes must join face-to-face. A sample model is shown at the right.

   a. How many different three-room motels can you construct?

   b. Make top, front, and right-side view sketches of each possible motel.

   c. Make isometric drawings of the same motels. What vantage point did you use for the drawings?

   d. Which motel would be the least costly to construct? Why?

2. Increase the number of rooms in your motel from three to four.

   a. Find all the four-room motels you can build if rooms must connect face-to-face. How many did you find?

   b. Make face-view sketches or isometric drawings of each motel.

   c. How many of your motels form an L-shape?

   d. Land in and around cities is very expensive. Which of your motels would require that the least amount of land be purchased? The greatest amount? Explain your reasoning.

3. Study this perspective drawing of a cube motel.

   a. How many cubes are there in the model?

   b. Draw the top, front, and right-side views of this shape.

   c. Suppose this model is half of a twin towers structure. The towers are symmetrically built about the plane of the right side. Make a perspective drawing or an isometric drawing of the complete structure.

   d. Provide top, front, and right-side view sketches of the completed building.

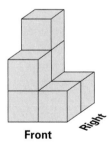

Front   Right

4. Below are three views of a cube model of a hotel.

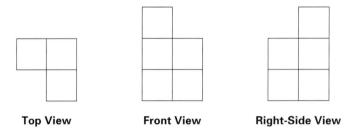

Top View   **Front View**   **Right-Side View**

   a. Construct cube models which match these views.

   b. Can you construct more than one model? If so, explain how they differ.

   c. Make a three-dimensional drawing of your model. Choose a vantage point that shows clearly all the characteristics of your model.

5. Both portability and rigidity are design features of a folding "director's chair."

   a. How are these features designed into the chair shown at the right?

   b. Identify at least two other items which must remain rigid when "unfolded" and analyze their designs.

Organizing

1. In Investigation 3, you learned how to represent three-dimensional space-shapes in two dimensions. Another way to do this with a rectangular prism is illustrated below.

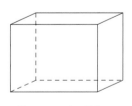 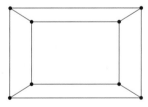

Rectangular Prism   **Vertex-Edge Graph**

4. **a–b.** There are two possible models, with either 1 or 2 cubes in the back right corner. Have students construct models with interlocking cubes if available.

   c.

   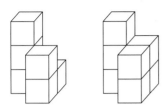

5. **a.** When opened and placed on the ground, the legs are positioned so that the director can sit on two rigid triangles connected at the vertices. The seat of the chair is made of fabric so that when the chair is picked up and collapsed, the rigid triangles formed by the ground and the legs of the chair are gone.

   b. A ping-pong table and a fold-out TV tray are two examples. The legs of a ping-pong table usually are connected to the table top by cross bars running from the middle of each leg to the table top, forming a triangle. For TV trays, the tray and the legs usually snap together to create a triangle.

Organizing

1. **This task introduces students to representing three-dimensional figures with graph models. Students will need to recall that graph models do not represent size and location. In this case, they do represent the connectedness of three-dimensional shapes.**

   a. Responses will vary. Some shared properties include the following:
      - no edges cross;
      - neither figure is rigid;
      - each figure has twelve edges;
      - each figure has eight vertices.

   b.
         i   ii   iii

     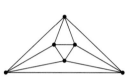

2. a. The sum of the number of vertices and the number of faces is two more than the number of edges ($V + F = E + 2$). This formula was first discovered by Leonard Euler and is commonly known as Euler's Formula.

   b. F simply replaces R and the equation relating the number of vertices V, faces F, and edges E is $V + F - E = 2$.

   c. Some students may prefer $V + R = E + 2$ so all terms are positive, but any equivalent form is acceptable.

3. a.
      - There are four centers.
      - Six segments are needed to connect all four centers.
      - Each face is a triangle and there are four of them.
      - The space-shape formed is a tetrahedron.

a. The figure on the right at the bottom of page 348 is a representation of a rectangular prism as a vertex-edge graph with no edge crossings. You can think of this graph resulting from "compressing" a rectangular prism with elastic edges down into two dimensions. The graph does not look much like the three-dimensional prism, but it shares many of the prism's properties. Name as many shared properties as you can.

b. Use the idea of *compressing* illustrated in Part a to draw vertex-edge graphs representing the following polyhedra. After compressing the octahedron, non-intersecting edges in the octahedron should not intersect in the graph. You will need to stretch the edges that go to one vertex to be sure this does not happen.

i.   **ii.**   **iii.**

2. In this task, you will re-examine the straw space-shapes you constructed. Count the edges, vertices (points where two or more edges meet), and faces of each space-shape. Organize your data in a table.

a. Look for a pattern relating the number of faces, vertices, and edges for each shape. Describe any patterns you see.

b. In Organizing Task 2 (page 262) of the "Graph Models" unit, you may have discovered that the numbers of vertices V and regions R formed by edges E of certain graphs are related by the formula $V + R - E = 2$. Compare this pattern to your pattern for the shapes in Part a. Write a similar equation relating the numbers of vertices V, faces F, and edges E of each of your space-shapes.

c. Write two equations that are equivalent to the equation $V + R - E = 2$. Which form of the equation would be easiest to remember? Why?

3. There are interesting and useful connections between pairs of special space-shapes.

a. Examine the triangular pyramid constructed from six equal-length straws. It is called a **tetrahedron**. Imagine the centers of each face.

- How many such centers are there?

- Imagine connecting the centers with segments. How many such segments are there?

- Visualize the space-skeleton formed by the segments. What are the shapes of its faces?

- What space-shape would be formed by the segments?

b. Examine visually the straw model of a cube. Imagine the centers of each face.

- How many such centers are there?
- Imagine connecting, with segments, each center to the centers on the four **adjacent faces**. Adjacent faces are faces that have a common edge. How many such segments are there?
- Visualize the space-skeleton formed by the segments. What are the shapes of its faces? How many faces are there?

c. Make a straw model of the space-skeleton in Part b. This shape is called an **octahedron**.

4. Bridge trusses are examples of rigid space-shapes. Shown here is a Parker truss in Elizabeth, New Jersey.

In addition to the Parker truss, there are several other types of trusses that vary in cost, strength, and other factors. Three of them are illustrated below.

i.   **ii.**   **iii.**

Pratt Truss   **Warren Truss**   **Howe Truss**

a. Determine if it is possible to make a model of each using a single piece of wire. If possible, draw sketches showing the manner in which you would bend the wire.

b. Explain your results in terms of vertex-edge graphs and Euler paths.

3. **b.** ■ There are 6 centers.

      ■ In this case, 12 segments are needed.

      ■ There are 8 triangular faces.

   c. Students will build models.

4. **a.** None of the trusses shown can be modeled by a single piece of wire.

   b. If we consider the line segments of the trusses as *edges*, and their intersections as *vertices*, a truss may be modeled by a single piece of wire only if the graph modeling it has an Euler path. Because each of the trusses shown has more than two vertices of odd degree, none of the graphs has an Euler path.

NOTE: Tasks 5 and 6 introduce students to simulation and probability, which will be explored more deeply in the units "Simulation Models" in Course 1 and "Patterns in Chance" in Course 2.

5. Students will make a tetrahedron.

   a. Theoretical probability tells us that each number is equally likely, so that we would expect to toss 25 of each. However, most students' experimental probabilities will only be close to this.

   b. The histogram should resemble a rectangle.

   c. The histogram should resemble a rectangle.

6. **a.** Responses may vary. For example,

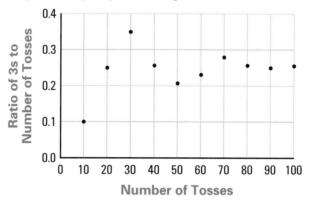

   b. Initially, the ratio may fluctuate. As the number of tosses gets close to 100, it is probable that the ratio will approach 0.25.

Reflecting

1. Responses for all parts may vary. Some possible responses are:

   a. In Investigation 1, they did an experiment to determine which shape column supported the most weight.

   b. Students searched for patterns when developing the definition of a polygon.

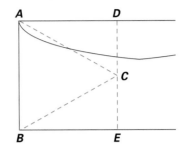

5. Here is a quick way to make a tetrahedron from a sealed letter envelope.

■ Find point *C* so that segments *AB*, *AC*, and *BC*, are the same length. (*Hint:* Try folding, measuring, or using a compass.)

■ Cut along $\overline{DE}$ parallel to $\overline{AB}$.

■ Fold back and forth along $\overline{AC}$ and $\overline{BC}$.

■ Open the envelope at the cut, and then pinch the envelope so that points *D* and *E* are together. Tape along the cut edge.

a. Label the faces of the tetrahedron 1, 2, 3, and 4 to make a tetrahedral die. Toss the die 100 times. Record the number of times each face lands down.

b. Make a histogram of your data.

c. Describe the shape of the histogram.

6. Obtain or make a tetrahedral die as described in Organizing Task 5. Gather data on the following experiment. Use a table to organize your work.

■ Toss the die 10 times; record the number of times the face labeled 3 lands down. Determine the ratio: number of 3s ÷ total tosses (10).

■ Toss 10 more times and determine the ratio: number of 3s (in both sets of tosses) ÷ total tosses (20).

■ Repeat until you have 100 tosses.

a. Create a graph with "number of tosses" on the horizontal axis and "ratio of 3s to number of tosses" on the vertical axis.

b. What does the graph tell you?

Reflecting

1. In this lesson, as well as in previous units, you have engaged in important kinds of mathematical thinking. From time to time, it is helpful to step back and think about the kinds of thinking that are broadly useful in doing mathematics. Look back over the four investigations in this lesson and consider some of the mathematical thinking you have done. Describe an example where you did each of the following:

a. experiment;

b. search for patterns;

c. formulate or find a mathematical model such as a function rule;

d. visualize;

e. make and check conjectures;

f. make connections

  ▪ between mathematics and the real world;

  ▪ between mathematical strands (between geometry and algebra, geometry and statistics, or geometry and graph theory).

2. Which of the methods of drawing space-shapes is most difficult for you? Why?

3. Which drawing method provides the most complete information regarding a space-shape? Explain your reasoning.

4. A particular space-shape is symmetrical about a plane cutting the front of the shape. What can you conclude about the front view of the shape? Why?

5. Buildings in areas that are subject to the stresses of earthquakes must have "flex" built into them. How can a space-shape have both rigidity and flex?

Extending

1. Models of solids can be made by folding a pattern drawn on paper and taping or gluing the edges. Here is such a pattern for a square pyramid. Find and sketch two other patterns that would fold into a square pyramid. How many straight cuts are needed in order to cut out your patterns?

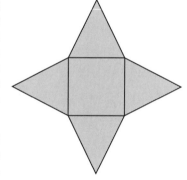

2. Try to imagine a space-shape that has a rectangle as its front view, a triangle as its side view, and a circular top view. Is such a space-shape possible? If so, sketch it. If not, explain why it is impossible.

3. Use your results from Modeling Tasks 1 and 2 to identify all the three- and four-room motels with right-angle bends in them. If possible, make a model of each motel using cubes taped or glued together. For some of the motels, there is another that is actually the same space-shape. Only include one of these motels.

1. **c.** Students may have drawn modeling lines or found modeling equations in the experiments in Investigation 1.

    d. Students visualized the shapes of motels in order to draw them in Investigation 3.

    e. Students made conjectures about what reinforcements were necessary to make shapes rigid, and then checked to see if they were correct.

    f. The experiments in Investigation 1 provide connections between mathematics and the real world as well as between geometry and algebra and between geometry and statistics.

2. Responses may vary.

3. Responses may vary. The top, side, and front views may not be enough to fully identify the figure. The perspective drawing that shows hidden edges eliminates this problem.

4. The front view of the shape is line symmetric.

5. Earthquake-resistant structures are built with some flexibility in their connecting joints and beams. For example, walls can be reinforced with steel, which is somewhat flexible. Structural architects refer to this ability to flex as "ductility." In addition, some buildings in earthquake zones have "base isolation," which means their foundations are built with the ability to roll or slide.

Extending

1. Responses may vary. Some examples are shown at the right. The pattern in the left diagram requires eight straight cuts, and the one on the right requires only seven.

    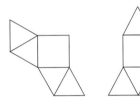

2. Begin with a circular cylinder. Mark parallel diameters in the top and bottom and the perpendicular diameter in the top. Use the planes determined by the diameter in the bottom and the points of intersection of the perpendicular diameter and the top base to determine slicing planes. The resulting space-shape will have the desired characteristics.

3. a. There are 6 such pieces (when duplicate shapes are omitted): the three-cube shape number 2 and the four-cube shapes numbers 2, 3, 7, 8, 9, and 10.

  b. 27 individual cubes are needed.

  c. The three-cube shape has two symmetry planes.
  The four-cube number 2 has one symmetry plane.
  The four-cube number 3 has two symmetry planes.
  The four-cube number 7 has one symmetry plane.
  The four-cube number 8 has one symmetry plane.

  d. The four-cube shapes numbers 9 and 10 are mirror images.

NOTE: Other extensions to Extending Task 3 would be to:

 i. Use the models to construct other shapes. In particular, make a cube using all the shapes.

ii. Investigate the origin of the "Soma cube."

---

4. a. A geodesic is "the shortest line between two points on any mathematically defined surface, such as a sphere." (*The American Heritage Dictionary*, Third Edition. Boston: Houghton Mifflin Company, 1994.) Fuller may have used this term since the dome is formed by using straight pieces of building material to connect two points that are close to each other on the surface.

  b. The Expo dome's fundamental unit is the triangle. Students may also notice parallelograms and hexagons.

  c. The Epcot dome's fundamental unit is also a triangle.

a. How many motels with right-angle bends are there?

b. How many individual cubes are needed to make the whole collection of these shapes?

c. Which of the shapes have reflection symmetry? For shapes that are symmetric, write the number of planes of symmetry.

d. Are any two of your shapes related by symmetry? If so, identify them.

4. One of the strongest types of structures is a dome. However, it is very difficult to build a dome without the weight of the building material being too great. To lighten the weight, dome-like space frames are used to approximate the shape of a true dome. These dome-like space frames are generally referred to as *geodesic domes*. The work of R. Buckminster Fuller greatly influenced the popularity of the dome. A picture of Fuller's dome at the Montreal Exposition in 1967 is shown below.

R. Buckminster Fuller, left, discusses geodesic design with an artist.

Montreal Exposition, 1967

a. Look up the meaning of the roots of the word "geodesic." Explain why you think Fuller used this term to describe the dome.

b. What are the fundamental units of the Expo dome? What other polygons do you notice in this dome?

c. Conduct research on other geodesic domes such as the Epcot Center at Disney World in Orlando, Florida. What are the fundamental units of those domes? What other polygons do you notice in the domes?

5. Some space-shapes can be made by weaving strips of paper together. Obtain a copy of the following patterns.

a. Cut along segment ST, making two strips of five equilateral triangles. Letter the corners as shown. Fold along the sides of the triangles. Try to weave these strips into a tetrahedron. If you need assistance, use the instructions below the figures. "$A_2 \rightarrow A_1$" means face A_2 goes under face A_1 with the letters on top of each other.

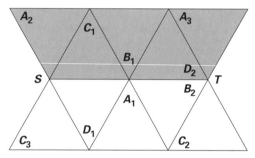

Weaving Procedure: $A_2 \rightarrow A_1$; $C_2 \rightarrow C_1$; $B_2 \rightarrow B_1$; $A_3 \rightarrow A_1$ and A_2; slide C_3 through the open slot so $C_3 \rightarrow C_1$ and C_2, and $D_2 \rightarrow D_1$.

b. You can also weave a cube. Cut out the 3 strips from a copy of this pattern and follow the weaving procedure below the figure. "$A_2 \rightarrow A_1$" means face A_2 goes under face A_1 with the letters on top of each other. "$D_2 (D_3)$" means face D_2 with face D_3 under it.

	D_1	A_2	B_1	
F_2				F_3
E_3		A_1	E_2	
	F_1	C_2		
	C_1	B_2		
D_2		E_1	D_3	

Weaving Procedure: $A_2 \rightarrow A_1$; $B_2 \rightarrow B_1$; $C_2 \rightarrow C_1$; $E_2 \rightarrow E_1$; $D_3 \rightarrow D_2$; $D_2 (D_3) \rightarrow D_1$; $F_3 \rightarrow F_2$; slide E_3 in the slot so that $E_3 \rightarrow E_1 (E_2)$ and $F_2 (F_3) \rightarrow F_1$.

MORE *continued*

5. a–b. Weaving Procedure
  See Activity Master 141.

See Assessment Resources, pages 171–176.

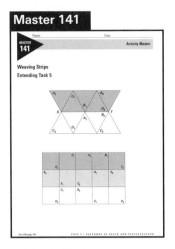

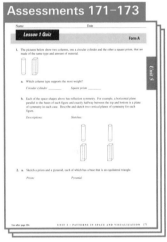

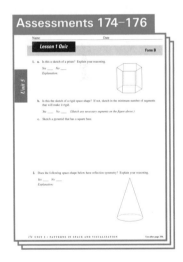

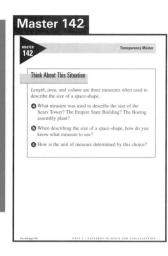

MASTER
142   Transparency Master

Think About This Situation

Length, area, and *volume* are three measures often used to
describe the size of a space-shape.

ⓐ What measure was used to describe the size of the
Sears Tower? The Empire State Building? The Boeing
assembly plant?

ⓑ When describing the size of a space-shape, how do you
know what measure to use?

ⓒ How is the unit of measure determined by this choice?

Use with page 355.   UNIT 5 • PATTERNS IN SPACE AND VISUALIZATION

Lesson 2 *The Size of Things*

LESSON OVERVIEW Lesson 1 of "Patterns in Space and Visualization" introduced students to geometric concepts from a three-dimensional perspective. This
lesson focuses students on two-dimensional shapes and space-shapes and their
measurements. Students will (re)develop the concepts of area, perimeter, volume,
and computational techniques to calculate these measures. Next, students will
explore relationships between area and perimeter, and then (re)develop and apply
the Pythagorean Theorem for right triangles. Finally, they will find measures of
space-shapes and investigate relations between volume and surface area. In these
materials, "surface area" refers to the area of the surface of a space-shape, including the bases. A piece of paper like those used for the column investigation will
make a good model to show part of the flattened shape. The point here is to motivate the need to compute or otherwise determine areas of plane-shapes.

Lesson Objectives

- ■ To use geometric shapes and their properties to make sense of situations
  involving data, change, chance, and discrete structures
- ■ To (re)develop and use formulas to find perimeter and area of plane-shapes
- ■ To (re)develop and use the Pythagorean Theorem to find lengths
- ■ To (re)develop and use formulas to compute surface area and volume of space-
  shapes

LAUNCH · full-class discussion

A major objective of this lesson is for students to be able to measure space-
shapes or parts of space-shapes. It may be both motivating and helpful for students
to briefly discuss specifically what is meant when asked to select a "largest building" in their area. A full-class discussion should help you emphasize once again the
need to be specific when communicating. Also, the discussion probably will give
students an opportunity to distinguish between area, perimeter, and volume in
advance of the investigation.

When making the selection of the "largest building" in your area (as suggested on
page 355), students will need to select criteria on which to base their choice. After
some discussion of criteria has occurred, you may want to point out that this selection criterion is somewhat arbitrary and in the real-world it will vary depending on
the people involved and their purposes. Ask students to describe situations where
one might use each type of measurement (height, width, surface area, and volume)
as the criterion for "largest." For example, real estate agents would be most likely to
consider the amount of floor space (area) that can be rented, whereas a storage
company would be most likely to consider overall capacity (volume) because they
can rent space based on cubic feet. Build these ideas into the discussion of the
"Think About This Situation" to determine student depth of understanding of the
measurement process for areas. (The data in the introduction can be found in
Guinness Book of World Records and most reference almanacs. These are good
sources of such information.)

See additional Teaching Notes on page T418K.

Lesson 2 — *The Size of Things*

If you were asked to identify the largest building in the area where you live, how would you respond? Deciding which of the buildings in your area is largest might be easy. If all the buildings in the United States were included, it may be difficult to decide. The Sears Tower in Chicago might be a candidate since it has a height (without antenna) of 1,454 feet. The Empire State Building in New York City has a height (without lightning rod) of 1,224 feet, but it could be considered since it has 2,248,370 square feet of rentable space.

Sears Tower

Empire State Building

The Boeing aircraft assembly plant in Everett, Washington, could be considered since it contains 472 million cubic feet of space. However, its maximum height is only 115 feet.

Think About This Situation

Length, *area*, and *volume* are three measures often used to describe the size of a space-shape.

a What measure was used to describe the size of the Sears Tower? The Empire State Building? The Boeing assembly plant?

b When describing the size of a space-shape, how do you know what measure to use?

c How is the unit of measure determined by this choice?

INVESTIGATION 1 Describing Size

Length, perimeter, area, and volume are ideas used to describe the size of geometric shapes. These measures commonly are used in daily life as well as in manufacturing and technical trades. This investigation will help you review and deepen your understanding of these basic measurement ideas.

1. Obtain measuring equipment from your teacher and individually select a box such as a cereal or laundry detergent box.

   a. Make a sketch of your box. What technique did you choose? Why?

   b. Working with a partner, compare your boxes. Which do you think is larger?

   c. What characteristics of the boxes did you use to predict which was larger?

2. Working individually, measure your box in as many different ways as you can. Use your measurements to answer each of the following questions.

   a. What is the total length of all the edges? Describe the procedure you used to determine this total. Is there a shortcut? If so, describe it.

   b. Suppose the box could be formed by simply attaching the faces along their edges. How much material would be needed to make it? Describe how you found your answer and note any shortcuts taken.

   c. About how many sugar cubes could your box hold? How did you find your answer?

   d. With your partner, review the prediction you made in Part b of Activity 1. Do all your measures in this activity support your choice? Explain why or why not.

3. Now connect your work in Activity 2 to the sketch of the box you prepared in Activity 1.

   a. On your sketch of the box, write only the lengths that are *absolutely* necessary to answer Parts a through c of Activity 2.

   b. Explain how the lengths you wrote are used to obtain the measures asked for in Activity 2.

   c. If you used any formulas in completing Activity 2, write them down. Then explain how each formula works.

INVESTIGATION 1 Describing Size

Students should work in small groups to complete Activities 1, 2, and 3. As you move from group to group, you can check to see what students know and do not know about perimeter, area, and volume concepts and how these concepts are determined. Hopefully, much of these activities will be review for students. Discuss the ideas of perimeter, area, and volume using words like "distance around," "covering," "holding," and "filling." Some students may still have a difficult time with these concepts. When students have completed Activities 1–3, a class discussion of the techniques used and the student ideas of perimeter, area, and volume can help clarify any remaining misconceptions. Emphasize student responses that use characteristics of the space-shapes that help determine the various measures. This is also a good time to review terminology of surface area and volume.

NOTE: You may want each student to provide one box (cereal, Quaker Oats, shoebox, *etc.*) for the first measurement activities so you don't have to provide them all yourself.

1. **a.** This part reviews the sketching skills developed in the previous investigation. Any of the three techniques is appropriate, but the choice should be supported with a rationale.

   b. Responses will vary. Some students may consider volume while others might consider height and width. Students should state why they think their choice is the largest.

   c. A variety of characteristics of each box may be used to determine size, some good, some bad. For example, some students may initially think of size in terms of edge length or surface area.

2. As you circulate among groups, you may find it helpful to have one box which has been opened along its edges to form a flat shape. Some students still may have trouble keeping track of the measurements they need to calculate surface area. The flat shape may help them see what the goal is.

   Be sure that students are attempting to measure the volume of the *box*, not the volume of the *contents*, for Part c. The concepts of surface area and volume both receive further attention later in this lesson.

   a. Responses will vary. Shortcuts depend upon the box itself. However, most will be rectangular prisms, so each has 3 sets of 4 parallel and equal edges which can be used for a calculation shortcut.

   b. Responses will vary. Again shortcuts depend upon the nature of the box. One that may be suggested is cutting along edges and measuring the flattened plane-shape or shapes. Another would be to note congruent faces that have the same areas.

   c. Responses will vary. Make sure students are thinking in terms of volume. Ask groups how they could use one layer of sugar cubes to help them determine the total. If they need further prompting, you might ask what else they would need to know.

   d. It is anticipated that not all the measures made will support the declarations of "largest." If this is not so, it may be appropriate to choose examples to show the class. For example, choose boxes such that surface area of one is greater than the surface area of another but the volume or total edge length of one box is smaller.

See additional Teaching Notes on page T418K.

4. Students should have measuring tools available. This might include string, rulers, measuring tape, and centimeter grids. It is not necessary to distribute these tools; just mention what is available (on a counter or desk) and leave the decisions on what to use to students.

    Many students will believe that the diagonal of a square is the same length as the edges of the square. If you see students counting slant heights as if they were the same length as horizontal edges, you might ask them to check with a ruler or piece of string. A large version of a plane-shape, such as figure *D*, could be drawn on the board. The sloping edge at the left of figure *D* crosses four columns of the square grid, but is much longer than the horizontal equivalent; comparing these lengths on the enlarged blackboard example might be necessary to convince some students.

    Another common error is to confuse perimeter and area. Students may count the length of the diagonal of a square as one-half unit because they focus on the one-half square unit created by the diagonal. Returning to the use of string to measure lengths is a visual reminder that the relation between length and area is not quite so simple.

    a. Student estimates may vary, but should be close to those in the table below. Students may need to be reminded that they are using a 0.5 cm grid, so they can't just count the grid spaces.

Figure	Perimeter (cm)
A	14
B	8
C	12
D	11.5
E	13.5
F	14.5
G	9.5
H	11.5
I	16.5

The number you were asked to find in Part b of Activity 2 is the *surface area* of your box. The **surface area** of a space-shape is the sum of the areas of each face—top, bottom, and *lateral* faces. In Activity 2, Part c, you were asked to find the *volume* of your box.

4. The perimeter and area of some plane-shapes are not as easy to find as those for the faces of the boxes. Shown below are several plane-shapes drawn on a background grid. The grid squares have a side length of 0.5 cm.

   a. Find the perimeter of each plane-shape to the nearest 0.5 centimeter. Divide the work among your group. Which shape has the greatest perimeter?

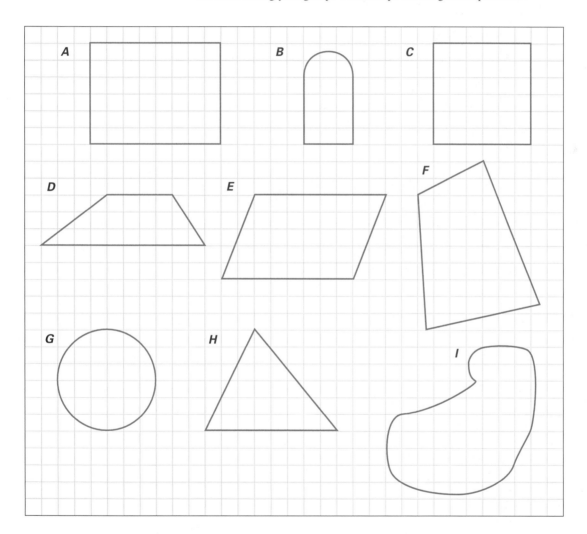

b. Describe the procedure you used to determine each perimeter. If you used any formulas to help you, include them and describe how they were used.

c. Of the procedures you identified in Part b, could any be used for all the plane-shapes? If so, which ones? Why don't the other procedures work for all shapes?

The area of a plane-shape can be measured in different ways. One way is to find the number of same-sized square regions needed to completely cover the enclosed region.

5. Refer back to the plane-shapes in Activity 4.

a. Explain why the area of each grid square is 0.25 square centimeter.

b. For each of the plane-shapes, estimate its area to the nearest 0.25 square centimeter. Again, divide the work among the members of your group. Describe the method you used to determine the area of each region. If you used formulas, note them in your descriptions and explain how they were used.

c. Which of your methods will work for all plane regions? Why won't the other methods work for all regions?

Checkpoint

Often you can find the perimeter and area of a plane-shape in more than one way.

ⓐ Describe two ways in which you can find the perimeter of the parallelogram shown here. Use each method to find the perimeter.

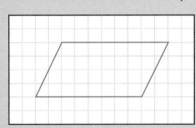

ⓑ Describe two ways in which you can find the area of the parallelogram. Find the area using both methods.

Be prepared to explain to the class the procedures used by your group and the results you obtained.

4. b. *A*: Students might simply "count unit segments" to determine distance around; a quicker way is to count the segments whose total length comprise the base (*b*) and the height (*h*), then compute $2(b + h)$.

B: This shape's perimeter is more easily figured when it is considered to be a semi-circle resting on a rectangle. Students might first count segments to determine the perimeter of the "untopped" rectangle, then add an estimate of the lengths of the arcs in each square $\left(\frac{1.25}{2} + \frac{0.75}{2} + \frac{1}{2} + \frac{0.75}{2} + \frac{1.25}{2} = \frac{5}{2} \text{ cm}\right)$. They also might use their knowledge of how to compute a semicircle's circumference $\left(\frac{1}{2}\pi d\right)$, then add the perimeter of the untopped rectangle.

C: Again, students may simply count segments or, upon noticing the figure itself is a square, they may count the segments comprising one side and multiply this number by four.

D: For the trapezoid, students could begin by determining the lengths of the two parallel line segments. To determine the lengths of the non-parallel line segments, they might cut a piece of string the length of the side in question, then align the string with the grid to measure its length. A 0.5-cm square grid copied onto a small piece of a clear overhead transparency works well, as does a ruler marked in 0.5 cm. Visual estimation is another method. Some may remember the Pythagorean Theorem and use it to find the lengths of the nonparallel sides.

E: Again, students may wish to use string or a transparency grid to determine one side, and simply count to determine the length of the base. Visual estimation is another method. These figures may then be summed and the resulting total doubled. The Pythagorean Theorem could be used here as well.

F: For this arbitrary quadrilateral, students will want to use either estimation techniques, string, or a transparency grid. Determine the side lengths one at a time, then total the four lengths. The Pythagorean Theorem applied to each side is another possibility.

G: Students may wish to use string, visual estimation, or prior knowledge of the method for finding a circle's circumference from its diameter.

H: Again use string, a transparency grid, visual estimation, or a ruler.

I: As the perimeter of this shape cannot be figured by conventional methods (counting, Pythagorean Theorem, *etc*.), accurate estimation proves quite difficult. If done square by square, a close estimate can be obtained. Students might be encouraged to think of alternative methods to determine perimeter. One possibility is to lay a piece of string so that it matches the shape's border, then straighten out the string and measure its length.

c. The last procedure outlined (using string) or visual estimation of each little "segment" is general enough to be used on any plane-shape. The other methods will not work in general due to their dependence on straight lines and alignment with the underlying grid.

NOTE: See Constructing a Math Toolkit prompt on page T418M.

See additional Teaching Notes on page T418L–T418M.

APPLY **individual task**

▶**On Your Own**

Using a string, we find the perimeter is about 630 m. (600 m to 650 m is an appropriate range.)

By adding squares, we find the area is about 15,500 m². (15,000 m² to 16,000 m² is an appropriate range.)

EXPLORE **small-group investigation**

6. **a.** Triangle:

a, b, and c are arbitrary sides of the triangle.

h represents the triangle's height.

Parallelogram:

a and b are two nonparallel sides.

h represents the parallelogram's height.

Circle:

r represents the circle's radius.

b. A: 4 cm $\times$ 3 cm $=$ 12 cm²

C: 3 cm $\times$ 3 cm $=$ 9 cm²

E: 4 cm $\times$ 2.5 cm $=$ 10 cm²

G: $\pi(1.5$ cm$)^2 \approx 7.1$ cm²

H: $\frac{1}{2}(3.0$ cm$) \times 4$ cm $=$ 6 cm²

c. The estimates should be very close to the computed values.

d. Thinking of figure B as a rectangle with a semicircle attached to it, we get

Area $=$ (1.5 cm $\times$ 2 cm) $+ \frac{1}{2}(\pi)(0.75$ cm$)^2 = 3 + 0.88$ cm² $=$ 3.88 cm².

Figure D could be divided in several different ways. One possibility is a rectangle and two triangles. In this case, the area is computed as follows:

Area $=$ (2 cm $\times$ 1.5 cm) $+ \frac{1}{2}(2$ cm $\times$ 1.5 cm) $+ \frac{1}{2}(1$ cm $\times$ 1.5 cm)

$=$ 3 cm² $+$ 1.5 cm² $+$ 0.75 cm² $=$ 5.25 cm²

These areas should be close to those obtained in Activity 5.

► **On Your Own**

Consider this scale drawing of Mongoose Lake. Using the given scale, estimate the perimeter to the nearest 10 meters and the area to the nearest 100 square meters.

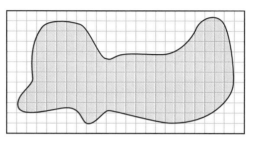

Mongoose Lake
Scale: ⊢—⊣ = 10 meters

Six formulas used to calculate the perimeter and area of common plane shapes are summarized below. You should be familiar with these from your study of mathematics in middle school.

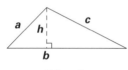 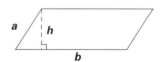

Triangle	**Parallelogram**	**Circle**
Perimeter: $P = a + b + c$	$P = 2(a + b)$	$P = 2\pi r$
Area: $A = \frac{1}{2}bh$	$A = bh$	$A = \pi r^2$

6. Examine the perimeter and area formulas above.

   a. For each formula, what is the meaning of the letters a, b, c, h, or r?

   b. Use the formulas above to compute the areas of figures A, C, E, G, and H of Activity 4. Recall that each grid square has side length 0.5 cm.

   c. Compare your results in Part b with those you obtained for Part b of Activity 5.

   d. Illustrate how you could use the formulas above to compute the areas of figures B and D of Activity 4. Compare your results with those obtained previously.

7. Now examine more closely the formulas for the perimeter and area of a triangle and of a parallelogram.

   a. Write a formula for the perimeter of an equilateral triangle that is different from the formula for a general triangle. Write a similar formula for the perimeter of a square.

   b. If you only remember the area formula for a parallelogram, how could you figure out the area formula for a triangle?

   c. How could you modify the formula for the area of a parallelogram so that it applies only to squares? Illustrate with a sketch.

8. In your group, investigate whether each of the following statements is true.

   ■ If two rectangles have the same perimeter, then they must have the same area.

   ■ If two rectangles have the same area, then they must have the same perimeter.

   a. Begin by dividing your group into two approximately equal subgroups, A and B.

   Subgroup A: Develop an argument supporting the first statement or provide a counterexample. (A **counterexample** is an example showing that a statement is not true.) Use rectangles with the same perimeter (such as 40 cm) and make a data table showing length, width, and area.

   Subgroup B: Develop an argument supporting the second statement or give a counterexample. Use rectangles with the same area (such as 48 cm^2) and make a data table showing length, width, and perimeter.

   b. Share and check the findings of each subgroup. Then compare your group's final conclusions with those of other groups.

   c. Would your group's views on the two statements be the same or different if "rectangles" were replaced by "squares"? Explain.

9. Jacob has 30 meters of fencing to enclose a garden plot in the shape of a rectangle.

   a. Find the dimensions of all possible gardens Jacob could make using whole-number sides.

   b. Find the areas of the gardens in Part a. Put all your information in a table. Of your sample garden dimensions, which give the largest garden?

Length

Width

7. a. For an equilateral triangle, $P = 3a$ where a represents the length of one side. For a square, the perimeter can be found by using the formula $P = 4s$ where s represents the length of one side.

b. Every triangle can be thought of as half a parallelogram, as shown in the diagram. The area of the triangle is half of a parallelogram having the same base and height as the triangle. So the area formula for a triangle is $A = \frac{1}{2}bh$.

c. Since the base has length s and the height has length s as well, the formula is $A = s^2$.

$h = s$
$b = s$

8. Students may find grid paper helpful for this activity.

a–b. Students should begin by making the suggested tables shown below.

Subgroup A

Perimeter (cm)	Length (cm)	Width (cm)	Area (cm²)
40	10	10	100
40	15	5	75
40	12	8	96
40	14	6	84

Subgroup B

Perimeter (cm)	Length (cm)	Width (cm)	Area (cm²)
28	6	8	48
28	8	6	48
32	12	4	48
52	24	2	48

These tables provide counterexamples for both statements.

c. If the word "rectangle" in Part a is replaced by the word "square," then both statements become true.

If the two squares have the same perimeter, where one has side length x and one has side length y, so $4x = P = 4y$, then $x = y$. Thus $x^2 = y^2$; that is, their areas are the same.

Similarly, if their areas are the same, $x^2 = A = y^2$, and since $x > 0$ and $y > 0$, this means $x = y$, so $4x = 4y$; that is, their perimeters are the same.

9. a–b. The dimensions of gardens with a perimeter of 30 m are shown in the following table:

Length (m)	14	13	12	11	10	9	8
Width (m)	1	2	3	4	5	6	7
Area (m²)	14	26	36	44	50	54	56

The garden with the largest area has dimensions 8 m by 7 m.

EXPLORE *continued*

9. **c.** Finding an algebraic representation for area is very challenging for many students. Students will be unable to finish Activity 9 without expressing the length and area algebraically.

length = (15 − x) meters

area = [x(15 − x)] square meters

d. Using graphs or table values, we find the maximum area is 56.25 square meters. The dimensions of the garden are 7.5 m by 7.5 m.

NOTE: If students make a table of whole number values from the equation $A = W(15 − W)$ [or $y = x(15 − x)$], they will think that the gardens with the largest area are 8 m by 7 m, or 7 m by 8 m. Encourage them to look at the graph also, where they can see that other dimensions exist between these two examples.

---

e. Be sure that students verify their answer to Part d as you observe the groups.

f. Students will need to represent the area in terms of the lengths of the sides. If x represents the width, then the length is $\left(\frac{75}{2} - x\right)$ meters and the area is $\left[x\left(\frac{75}{2} - x\right)\right]$ square meters. The graph or table generated by the rule for area indicates that dimensions of 18.75 m × 18.75 m result in a maximum area of about 352 square meters.

g. Both of the largest garden plots are square plots.

SHARE AND SUMMARIZE **full-class discussion**

Checkpoint

See Teaching Master 144.

ⓐ You cannot conclude anything about the perimeters of two rectangles that have equal areas.

ⓑ You cannot conclude anything about the areas of two rectangles that have equal perimeters.

ⓒ For a given perimeter P, the rectangle with the largest area will be a square with side length $\frac{P}{4}$.

APPLY **individual task**

▶On Your Own

This task assesses students' understanding that when the perimeter of a rectangle is held constant, area varies with the change in dimensions and is maximized by a square.

a. If $P = 126$, then length (l) + width (w) = 63. Since $l \geq 1$ and $w \geq 1$, this means there are 62 whole-number combinations for which ($l + w$) = 63. However, if we consider an ($a \times b$) rectangle as the same as a ($b \times a$) rectangle, we have double counted each rectangle. Hence there are 31 rectangles with whole number dimensions and a perimeter of 126 units.

b. The rectangle with dimensions 31 × 32 has the greatest area.

c. 31.5 × 31.5

MORE
ASSIGNMENT *pp. 366–372*

Students can now begin Reflecting Task 3 or 4 from the MORE assignment following Investigation 2.

c. Let x represent the width of a garden whose perimeter is 30 meters.
  - ▪ Write an expression for the length of the garden.
  - ▪ Write an expression for the area of the garden.

d. Use your graphing calculator or computer software to find the dimensions of the largest rectangular garden that can be enclosed with 30 meters of fencing. Find the dimensions to the nearest 0.1 meter.

e. Did you use tables of values or graphs in Part d? Verify your answer to Part d using the other form of representation.

f. Suppose Jacob has 75 meters of fencing. What is the largest rectangular garden he can enclose? Support your position.

g. What is similar about the shape of the two largest garden plots in this activity?

Checkpoint

Look back at your work calculating perimeters and areas of rectangles.

a If two rectangles have equal areas, can you conclude anything about their perimeters? If so, what?

b If two rectangles have equal perimeters, can you conclude anything about their areas? If so, what?

c For a given perimeter, can you say anything about the shape of the rectangle having the largest possible area? If so, what?

Be prepared to share and defend your group's conclusions.

▶On Your Own

Consider possible rectangles with a perimeter of 126 units.

a. How many different rectangles with whole number dimensions and a perimeter of 126 units can you create?

b. Of the rectangles in Part a, which has the maximum area?

c. To the nearest 0.1 unit, find the dimensions of the rectangle with a perimeter of 126 units that has the largest possible area.

INVESTIGATION ▶ 2 Television Screens and Pythagoras

Television manufacturers often describe the size of their rectangular picture screens by giving the length of the diagonal. The set pictured here has a 25-inch diagonal screen. Several companies also advertise a 50-inch diagonal color stereo television. How well does giving the measure of the diagonal describe the rectangular screen?

1. For this activity, consider a 20-inch TV picture screen.

a. Model the 20-inch diagonal by drawing a 5-inch segment on your paper. (Each member of your group should do this.) In your drawing, each inch represents 4 inches on the picture screen. This is done so that the drawing will fit on your paper. Your drawing has a 1 to 4 (1:4) scale.

b. Draw a rectangle with the segment you drew as its diagonal. One way to do this is to place a piece of notebook paper with a 90° corner over the segment. Carefully position the paper so that its edges just touch the ends of the segment. Mark the corner. Describe how the entire rectangle can be drawn from this one point and the segment.

c. Compare your rectangular screen with those of others in your group. Are they the same? How do they compare in perimeter? In area?

d. Draw a scale model of a TV screen that is 4 inches wide and has a diagonal of 20 inches. What are the lengths of the other sides? What is its area?

e. Make a scatterplot of at least eight (*width*, *area*) data pairs for 20-inch diagonal screens. Use your plot to estimate the 20-inch diagonal screen with the greatest viewing area.

f. How well does the length of the diagonal of a TV screen describe the screen? Give reasons for your opinion.

INVESTIGATION 2 Television Screens and Pythagoras

In this investigation, students continue thinking about size by considering what the length of the diagonal of a rectangle can reveal about the shape of the rectangle. Students also use the Pythagorean relationship to find a missing side length in a right triangle. One way to introduce this investigation is to ask students if they know how TV screen size is advertised and then have them consider the screen of a graphing calculator. Have students measure the diagonal in centimeters (the TI-82 and TI-83 have about 7-cm diagonals) and suggest that if it were a TV screen it would be a 7-cm screen. Ask someone to read the first paragraph and ask all students to measure the diagonal of the TV in the student text in centimeters (4.7 cm) and also in inches (1.75 inches). If this is a scale drawing, what is the scale? The scales are approximately 1 to 14. This activity can be used to motivate and set up the work on Activity 1.

The students may need assistance with the procedure described in Part b, but once they have it, it provides a simple way to draw "half-rectangles" with a given diagonal. You may wish to provide a blank transparency for student use in drawing the rectangle. A class discussion of Activity 1, Part f, is a good way to summarize the work in Activity 1. Continuing in the same mode as the previous Checkpoint, you might ask the following:

If two rectangles have the same diagonal length, can we conclude their perimeters are equal?

If two rectangles have the same diagonal length, can we conclude their areas are the same?

Activity 2 does not assume students already know and understand the Pythagorean Theorem. The point here is that if we know the length and width of a rectangle, we can sketch the rectangle, perhaps to scale, and measure the diagonal. The result is unique and depends on the length and width. Some students may apply the Pythagorean Theorem if they remember it. However, rote application is not the desired focus. Activities 3–5 continue the review/development of the Pythagorean Theorem. Note that Activity 5 asks students to investigate other triangles and the squares of their side lengths. In future work, the Law of Cosines will generalize the Pythagorean Theorem for nonright triangles.

Initially, some students find it difficult to use the abstract symbolic representation of the Pythagorean Theorem (that is, $a^2 + b^2 = c^2$) to solve problems. Consider encouraging those students to use a diagram to represent the relationship. Suggest that they continue to draw the right triangle with a square annexed to the legs and hypotenuse, as in the figures in Activity 3. The students can label the known lengths of the legs and hypotenuse and the areas of the squares. They then can refer to their diagrams to solve problems. Have group members explain to each other the Pythagorean relationship. After they come to understand and are comfortable applying the Pythagorean relationship, they should be encouraged to make the transition to the algebraic rule.

1. **a.** Student work

See additional Teaching Notes on page T418N.

2. The diagonal of the TV screen is 10 inches. Students may need to make an accurate drawing of the TV screen and measure the length of the diagonal. In this case their answer should be close to 10 inches but may not be exactly 10 inches.

3. a.

	Area of Square on Short Side 1	**Area of Square on Short Side 2**	**Area of Square on Longest Side**
i.	1	4	5
ii.	4	4	8
iii.	16	9	25

2. A manufacturer of small personal TVs thinks that a screen measuring 6 inches by 8 inches is a nice size for good picture quality. What diagonal length should be advertised?

3. You can calculate the diagonal lengths of screens by considering the right triangles formed by the sides. To see how to do this, examine the figures below in which squares have been constructed on the sides of right triangles.

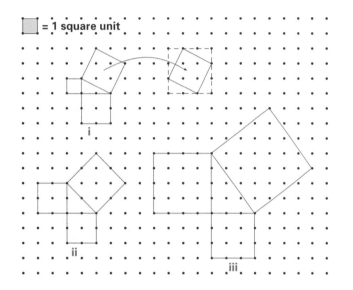

a. For each right triangle, calculate the areas of the squares on the triangle's sides. Use the unit of area measure shown. To calculate areas of squares on the longest side, you may have to be creative as suggested by the first figure. Record your data in a table like the one below.

	Area of Square on Short Side 1	Area of Square on Short Side 2	Area of Square on Longest Side
i.	_____	_____	_____
ii.	_____	_____	_____
iii.	_____	_____	_____

b. Describe any pattern you see in the table. Check to see if the pattern holds for other right triangles. Have each member of your group draw a different test case on a sheet of square dot paper. Record these data in your table as well.

c. Now examine the figure at the right. Explain how this figure illustrates the general pattern in the table of data you prepared in Part b.

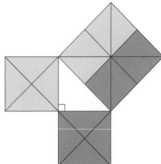

d. In general, how are the areas of the squares constructed on the two shorter sides of a right triangle related to the area of the square on the longest side? Compare your discovery with those made by other groups.

e. Represent the lengths of the two shorter sides of the right triangle by *a* and *b*. How could you represent the area of each of the two smaller squares? If the length of the longest side is *c*, what is the area of the largest square?

f. Write an equation expressing the conjecture you made in Part d using *a*, *b*, and *c*.

The discovery you made in Activity 3 was based on a careful study of several examples. The Greek philosopher Pythagoras is credited with first demonstrating that this relationship is true for all right triangles. The relationship is called the **Pythagorean Theorem**. Historians believe that special cases of this relationship were discovered earlier and used by the Babylonians, Chinese, and Egyptians.

4. Now investigate how the Pythagorean Theorem can help in sizing television screens.

a. Recall the 6-by-8 inch TV screen.

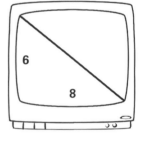

- Find the square of the diagonal.
- How can you find the length of the diagonal when you know its square? What do you get in this case?
- How do you think the manufacturer advertises the size of the 6-by-8 inch TV set? Compare this answer to what you proposed in Activity 2.

b. Use your calculator or computer to find the length of a diagonal whose square is 56.

3. **b.** The sum of the first two columns is equal to the third column. This pattern will hold for any right triangle.

   c. If we take apart the two boxes constructed on the shorter legs, their pieces may be combined to build the box constructed on the longest side. Simply by moving triangles we see the area is a perfect match.

   d. The sum of the areas of the squares on the two shorter sides of the right triangle is equal to the area of the square on the longest side.

   e. a^2, b^2, c^2

   f. $a^2 + b^2 = c^2$

4. **Students should be using the Pythagorean Theorem to complete this activity.**

   a. ■ If d represents the length of the diagonal, then $6^2 + 8^2 = d^2$. Thus, $d^2 = 100$.

   ■ The length of the diagonal may be found by taking the square root of d^2. In this case, the response is $\sqrt{100} = 10$.

   ■ The manufacturer probably advertises a 10-inch diagonal screen TV. This should agree with the response in Activity 2.

   b. $\sqrt{56} \approx 7.5$

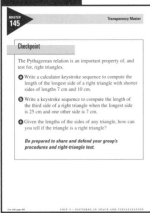

EXPLORE *continued*

4. **c.** $13^2 + b^2 = 20^2$, so $169 + b^2 = 400$. Thus $b^2 = 231$, so $b \approx 15.2$. Students may not solve this algebraically. Rather they may use their table or their scatterplot from Activity 1 Part e.

    d. Responses may vary. (27, 42.1), (30, 40), (35.71, 35), (38, 32.5), and (43.3, 25) are possible dimensions. If students give an ordered pair such as (10, 48.99), you may want to discuss the reasonableness of those dimensions.

5. The Pythagorean Theorem does not work for other triangles.

6. **a.** Yes the numbers 8, 15, and 17 satisfy the Pythagorean Theorem. A right triangle is formed.

    b. Responses may vary. Some acceptable sets of lengths are 3, 4, 5; 5, 12, 13; 4, 5, 6.4; 10, 14, 17.2; and 24, 7, 25. While the third and fourth sets will not produce a right triangle exactly, students are unlikely to be able to provide more precise measurements. This may be a good time for a short discussion of precision and acceptable error.

SHARE AND SUMMARIZE   full-class discussion

Checkpoint

See Teaching Master 145.

You may wish to ask groups for alternative procedures after one group's response to a part of this Checkpoint. You might want to end the summary discussion by asking for a calculator keystroke sequence that will calculate the length and width of a rectangle if you know its diagonal. Of course, this is not possible, but it does return students to the beginning of the lesson. If we know the diagonal there are many combinations of lengths and widths which will work. We need to know two out of three of the length, width, and diagonal in order to calculate the third.

ⓐ Responses may vary. For the TI-82 or 83, two possible responses are:

    i. $\boxed{\text{2nd}}$ $\boxed{x^2}$ $\boxed{(}$ 7 $\boxed{x^2}$ $\boxed{+}$ 10 $\boxed{x^2}$ $\boxed{)}$ $\boxed{\text{ENTER}}$

    ii. 7 $\boxed{x^2}$ $\boxed{+}$ 10 $\boxed{x^2}$ $\boxed{\text{ENTER}}$
       $\boxed{\text{2nd}}$ $\boxed{x^2}$ $\boxed{\text{2nd}}$ $\boxed{(-)}$ $\boxed{\text{ENTER}}$

ⓑ Responses may vary.

    $\boxed{\text{2nd}}$ $\boxed{x^2}$ $\boxed{(}$ 25 $\boxed{x^2}$ $\boxed{-}$ 7 $\boxed{x^2}$ $\boxed{)}$ $\boxed{\text{ENTER}}$

ⓒ Responses may vary. Students may suggest summing the squares of the two smaller numbers and comparing it to the square of the larger number. If the triangle is a right triangle, then these two numbers will be equal. Others may suggest choosing the two smaller lengths, squaring each one, adding them, and then taking the square root of the sum. If the triangle is a right triangle, this number will match the given length of the longest side.

CONSTRUCTING A MATH TOOLKIT: Students should add the Pythagorean Theorem to their Toolkits as a relationship. You may also wish to have them record an example that illustrates the use of the Pythagorean Theorem to find the length of a leg of a right triangle.

---

c. In Activity 1, the diagonal of the TV screen was 20 inches. Suppose one of the sides of the screen is 13 inches. Find, to the nearest 0.1 inch, the length of the other side.

d. For a 50-inch TV, find five possible length-width pairs that would be reasonable dimensions for a rectangular screen.

5. In Part f of Activity 3, you wrote an equation relating the squares of the lengths of the sides of a right triangle. Jonathan wondered if that *Pythagorean relation* is true for triangles without a right angle. Draw several triangles, measure the sides, and test the Pythagorean relation. Does it work for such triangles? Divide the work among your group and summarize your findings.

6. Now consider cases of other triangles for which the Pythagorean relation does hold.

a. Verify that the numbers 8, 15, and 17 satisfy the Pythagorean relation. Use tools such as a compass or pieces of uncooked spaghetti to draw a triangle whose lengths, in centimeters, are 8, 15, and 17. What kind of triangle is formed?

b. Find four more sets of three numbers that satisfy the Pythagorean relation. Make triangles with these lengths as sides. Divide the work and report the kind of triangles you get.

Checkpoint

The Pythagorean relation is an important property of, and test for, right triangles.

ⓐ Write a calculator keystroke sequence to compute the length of the longest side of a right triangle with shorter sides of lengths 7 cm and 10 cm.

ⓑ Write a keystroke sequence to compute the length of the third side of a right triangle when the longest side is 25 cm and one other side is 7 cm.

ⓒ Given the lengths of the sides of any triangle, how can you tell if the triangle is a right triangle?

Be prepared to share and defend your group's procedures and right-triangle test.

In a right triangle, the longest side (the one opposite the right angle) is called the **hypotenuse** and the shorter sides are called **legs**. The Pythagorean Theorem can be stated in the following form:

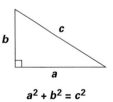

$$a^2 + b^2 = c^2$$

The sum of the squares of the legs of a right triangle equals the square of the hypotenuse.

> ## On Your Own

The Morgan family made a garden for perennial flowers in the corner of their lot. It was a right triangle with legs of 8 and 10 meters.

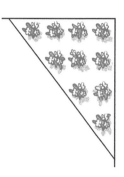

a. Find the perimeter of the garden and explain how this information might be used by the Morgans.

b. Find the area of the garden and explain how this information might be used in care of the garden.

MORE
Modeling • Organizing • Reflecting • Extending

Modeling

1. A TV manufacturer plans to build a picture screen with a 15-inch diagonal.

  a. Find the dimensions of four possible rectangular picture screens.

  b. Find all picture screens with whole number dimensions. Describe the procedure you used to do this.

  c. Of all possible 15-inch screens, which design would give the largest viewing area? Do you think this would be a good design? Why or why not?

2. The Alvarez family purchased twenty 90-cm sections of fencing to protect their planned garden from the family dog. They plan to use an existing wall as one of the borders. The 90-cm sections can not be cut or bent.

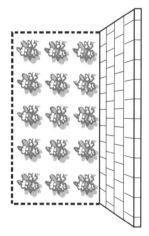

  a. Make a table of the dimensions and areas of gardens that can be enclosed by the 90-cm sections.

  b. What is the largest garden area that can be enclosed with these sections of fence?

  c. For a garden with the largest area, how many sections of fence should be used for each width of the border? For the length of the border?

APPLY individual task

▶On Your Own

a. The length of the hypotenuse is approximately 12.8 meters. The perimeter of the garden is approximately 30.8 meters. The Morgans might use this information if they buy decorative fencing to enclose the flower garden.

b. The area of the garden is 40 m². This information would be crucial in planning the number of plants or seeds to buy and in determining the amount of topsoil or fertilizer needed.

MORE independent assignment

Modeling

1. a. Responses will vary. One procedure is to compute the third side using $\sqrt{15^2 - s^2}$ where s takes on different values. Several possibilities are 6 by 13.75; 8 by 12.69; 10 by 11.2; and 12 by 9.

   b. One procedure is to use integers for one dimension and compute the other by use of the Pythagorean Theorem. The screen with dimensions 9 by 12 is the only screen with whole number dimensions.

   c. The largest viewing area is obtained when the screen is a square. In this case, the length of a side would be approximately 10.6 inches. Responses will vary as to whether this is a good design. Look for valid reasoning and good support for a student's position.

2. a.

Dimensions in Fence Units Width × Length	Dimensions (cm) Width × Length	Area (cm²)	Area (m²)
1 × 18	90 × 1,620	145,800	14.58
2 × 16	180 × 1,440	259,200	25.92
3 × 14	270 × 1,260	340,200	34.02
4 × 12	360 × 1,080	388,800	38.88
5 × 10	450 × 900	405,000	40.50
6 × 8	540 × 720	388,800	38.88
7 × 6	630 × 540	340,200	34.02
8 × 4	720 × 360	259,200	25.92
9 × 2	810 × 180	145,800	14.58

   b. The largest garden area is 405,000 cm².

   c. Use 5 sections of fencing for the width and 10 sections for the length.

MORE
ASSIGNMENT   pp. 366–372

Modeling: 3 and 4
Organizing: 1, and 3 or 4*
Reflecting: 3 and 4
Extending: Choose one*

*When choice is indicated, it is important to leave the choice to the student.
NOTE: It is best if Organizing tasks are discussed as a whole class after they have been assigned as homework.

2. d. Assuming the fencing could not be bent, even though they were buying the same total length of fencing, the Alvarez family could not have enclosed a garden of the same size as above, and certainly not a larger one.

   The dimensions 450×900 yield the largest possible area, regardless of incrementation of fencing. However, these dimensions cannot be achieved with 120 cm sections of fencing. The best we can do is 480 cm $\times$ 820 cm for an area of 393,600 cm^2.

   e. Responses may vary. They might not want it jutting too far out into the yard, so they might choose to make it long and narrow.

3.

| | Area (in square yards) | | |
	Blue	Red	White
Czech Republic	1.5	2.25	2.25
Switzerland	0	5.3	0.7
Thailand	2	2	2
Japan	0	1	5
Total Area (sq yd)	3.5	10.55	9.95
Total Area (sq ft)	31.5	94.95	89.55

Since 32 ounces of paint covers 110 square feet, then one ounce of paint will cover 3.4375 square feet. To paint the flags, the museum will need at least $\frac{31.5}{3.4375}$ or 9.16 ounces of blue paint, $\frac{94.95}{3.4375}$ or 27.62 ounces of red paint, and $\frac{89.55}{3.4375}$ or 26.05 ounces of white paint. Without the prices of the different sizes, we can't tell what would be the most economical way to buy the necessary paint. Two possibilities are: one 16-ounce can of blue and one 32-ounce can each of red and white; or 8-ounce and 4-ounce cans of blue and 16-ounce, 8-ounce, and 4-ounce cans of red and white.

4. a. The buckling will occur so that the highest point of the buckle is in the middle of the 220-foot-long rail.

   b. Responses will vary. After answering Part c, students should see that a gym bag definitely would fit under the rail.

d. The Alvarez family could have purchased fifteen 120-cm sections of fencing for the same price as the shorter sections they bought. Could they have enclosed a larger garden area using these sections? Explain your response.

e. What else might influence the decision about how to set up the garden?

3. A historical museum plans to paint a mural on its walls illustrating different flags of the world. The flags of the Czech Republic, Switzerland, Thailand, and Japan use some combination of red, white, or blue as shown below. Each of the flags is to be 3 yards long and 2 yards wide. A quart (32 ounces) of paint covers approximately 110 square feet. Paint can be purchased in cans of 32, 16, 8, and 4 ounces. How much paint of each color should be purchased to paint these flags?

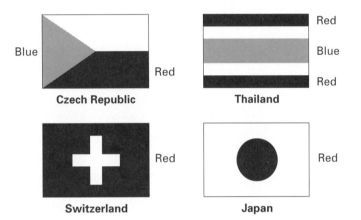

Czech Republic   **Thailand**

Switzerland   **Japan**

4. Materials tend to expand when heated. This expansion needs to be considered carefully when building roads and railroad tracks. In the case of a railroad track, each 220-foot-long rail is anchored solidly at both ends. Suppose that on a very hot day a rail expands 1.2 inches, causing it to buckle as shown below.

a. At what point along the rail do you think the buckling will occur?

220 ft

b. Do you think you could slide a gym bag between the raised rail and the track bed?

c. Model this situation using right triangles, and then calculate an estimate of the height of the buckle.

d. Would you expect your estimate of the height of the buckle to be more or less than the actual value? Explain your reasoning.

e. Research *expansion joints*. How does the use of these joints in railroad tracks and concrete highways minimize the problem you modeled in Part c?

5. In Lesson 1, Investigation 1, you used an 11-inch-long sheet of paper to model a rectangular prism column.

   a. If 0.5 inch is used for overlapping before taping the seam, how should the paper be folded to make the area of the rectangular base as large as possible?

   b. Does the paper folded as in Part a produce the rectangular prism column with the largest possible surface area? Organize your work and provide evidence to support your answer.

Organizing

1. Carefully trace the figure shown here.

   a. Cut out the square labeled *A* and the pieces labeled *B*, *C*, *D*, and *E*.

   b. Can you use the five labeled pieces to cover the square on the hypotenuse of the right triangle? If so, draw a sketch of your covering.

   c. This puzzle was created by Henry Perigal, a London stockbroker who found recreation in the patterns of geometry. How is Perigal's puzzle related to the Pythagorean Theorem?

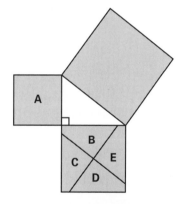

   d. After studying the puzzle, Anne conjectured: "Every square can be dissected into five pieces which can be reassembled to form two squares." Do you think Anne is correct? Explain your reasoning.

4. c. Using the Pythagorean theorem:
$$(1{,}320.6)^2 = 1{,}320^2 + h^2$$
$$1{,}584.36 = h^2$$
$$39.8 \approx h$$

The height of the buckle is approximately 39.8 inches.

1,320.6 in.

1,320 in.

h

   d. Since the railing is curved, the straight line from end to middle actually would be less than 1,320.6 inches. Our estimate of the height of the buckle is slightly more than the actual value.

   e. Expansion points allow the rails to expand without buckling.

5. a. For a fixed perimeter, the rectangle with the largest possible area is a square, so the 10.5 inches should be divided by 4. That is, after making a $\frac{1}{2}$-inch seam allowance, fold the paper every $2\frac{5}{8}$ (or 2.625) inches.

   b. If the base and the top are considered in figuring the surface area, then this paper folding arrangement yields the greatest surface area. Area of bases is maximized while total area of the sides is constant.

Organizing

1. a–b.

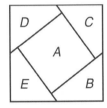

   c. The area of the square on the hypotenuse is equal to the sum of the areas of the squares on the two legs. This can be seen because the big square is exactly covered by pieces comprising the two smaller squares.

   d. Anne is correct; we can work backwards. For a given square, choose one side and construct a right triangle for which that side is the hypotenuse and the legs do not lie on the square diagonals. Repeat with each side of the square, creating identical (congruent) triangles on each side. A smaller or equal-sized square will be formed in the center. Then leave the smaller (or equal-sided) square whole and partition the larger square as shown by your drawing.

2. **This task connects to the previous units on linear functions.**

   a. $h = \frac{3w}{4}$

   b. $h^2 + w^2 = 19^2$

   c. $\left(\frac{3w}{4}\right)^2 + w^2 = 19^2$ or $(0.75w)^2 + w^2 = 19^2$

   $\frac{9w^2}{16} + w^2 = 361$ $0.5625w^2 + w^2 = 361$

   $\frac{25w^2}{16} = 361$ $1.5625w^2 = 361$

   $25w^2 = 5{,}776$ $w = \sqrt{\frac{361}{1.5625}}$

   $w^2 = 231.04$ $w = 15.2$

   $w = 15.2$

   Now, $h = \frac{3w}{4} = \frac{3(15.2)}{4} = 11.4$ inches.

   The television screen measures 11.4 inches $\times$ 15.2 inches.

   d. Student work

3. **Since students will be choosing Task 3 or 4 as homework, the class discussions are important to extend all students' understanding. This task draws on the data analysis work done earlier.**

   a.

Side Length (cm)	Diagonal (cm)
2	2.8
4	5.7
7	9.9
8	11.3
10	14.1
11	15.6

   b.

   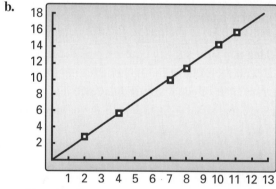

   c. Yes, the plot appears to be linear. Students can draw in the line containing the points or use the linear regression line from their calculator or computer software.

   d. Responses may vary. The equation should be approximately $y = 1.4x$.
   - The slope (1.4) gives the approximate ratio of diagonal to side length. It also means that for every 1-cm increase in side length, the diagonal length increases by 1.4 cm.
   - The y-intercept is 0. This makes sense because if the side length is 0, the diagonal's length must be 0.

   e. The length of the diagonal is approximately 1.4(55) + 0, or 77 cm.

   f. Using the Pythagorean Theorem, the diagonal is found to be 77.78 cm. The differences are due to rounding error and variation in the linear models used.

4. a–c. Answers will vary according to cylinders selected. Students should get a linear graph that has slope approximately π and y-intercept 0.

2. The television industry has set a standard for the sizing of regular television screens. The ratio of height *h* to width *w*, called the *aspect ratio*, is 3:4. That is $\frac{h}{w} = \frac{3}{4}$.

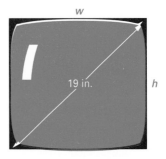

a. Write an equation expressing *h* as a function of *w*.

b. Use the Pythagorean Theorem to write an equation relating *h*, *w*, and the diagonal length 19.

c. Use your equations in Parts a and b to find the standard dimensions of a 19-inch TV screen.

d. Check the dimensions you obtained against actual measurements of a 19-inch TV screen.

3. Draw squares of side lengths 2, 4, 7, 8, 10, and 11 centimeters on centimeter grid paper.

a. Measure the diagonals to the nearest 0.1 cm. Record your data in a table.

b. Make a plot of your (*side length, diagonal*) data.

c. Does the plot appear to have a linear pattern? If so, find a linear model that you believe fits the trend in those data.

d. Find an equation for your line.

■ What is the slope? What does it mean?

■ What is the *y*-intercept? Does it make sense? Explain.

e. Predict the length of the diagonal of a square with side length of 55 cm.

f. Compare your predicted length to that computed by using the Pythagorean Theorem. Explain any differences.

4. Locate six cylindrical shapes of different sizes. Cans and jar lids work well.

a. Measure the circumference of each cylinder to the nearest 0.1 cm. Record your data in a table.

b. On a sheet of paper, trace around the base of each cylinder. Then measure, to the nearest 0.1 cm, the diameter of each tracing and record it in your table.

c. Make a plot of your (*diameter, circumference*) data.

LESSON 2 • THE SIZE OF THINGS **369**

d. Find a line and its equation that you believe models the trend in these data.

■ What is the slope of the line? What does it mean?

■ What is the *y*-intercept? Does it make sense? Explain.

e. The diameter of a small fruit-juice can is approximately 5.5 cm. Use your linear model to predict the circumference of the can.

f. Compare your predicted circumference to that computed by using the formula for the circumference of a circle. Explain any differences.

5. Imagine a plane intersecting a cube.

a. Describe the shape of the intersection of a cube and a plane that has the largest possible area.

b. Describe the shape of the intersection of a cube and a plane that has the smallest possible area.

c. Find the least and greatest possible areas of shapes formed by the intersection of a plane with a cube 5 cm on a side.

6. Draw a segment 10 cm long on a sheet of paper.

a. Imagine a right triangle that has the segment as its hypotenuse. If one side is 0.5 cm long, where would the vertex of the right angle be? Locate that point and make a mark there. (Use a technique similar to the one in Activity 1 of Investigation 2, page 362.) Where would that vertex be if the side is 1 cm long? Mark that point. Now increase the side length in steps of 0.5 cm and plot those vertices of the resulting triangles. Stop when the side length is 10 cm.

b. Examine your plot of the points. What shape do they appear to form?

c. Support your view by citing appropriate measurements from your model.

Reflecting

1. Architects use many design principles. For example, tall buildings will always provide more daylight, natural ventilation, and openness than low buildings of the same floor area. Explain why this is the case.

New York City

4. **d.** The equation should be approximately $y = 3.14x$.

　■ The slope should be close to 3.14. It is the ratio of the circumference to the diameter. It also means that the circumference increases (or decreases) 3.14 cm for every increase (or decrease) in diameter of 1 cm.

　■ The y-intercept should be close to zero, since a circle with no diameter also has no circumference.

e. The model should predict a circumference close to 17 cm.

f. $C = \pi \times d = \pi(5.5) \approx 17.28$ cm. Differences may occur due to variety in the linear model.

5. **a.** The shape of the intersection with the largest possible area is a rectangle with one side that shares an edge of the cube and the diagonal of a face of the cube as an adjacent side.

b. One shape of an intersection with the smallest area is a point; it occurs when a plane intersects the corner (vertex) of a cube. Since a line segment has no area, another zero-area solution is a plane that intersects an edge of the cube and contains no other points of the cube.

c. Least area:　$A = 0$ when the intersection is at a point or along an edge.

Greatest area: $A \approx 7.07 \times 5 = 35.35$ cm^2

6. **a.** See student drawings.

b. The points appear to lie on a circle.

c. Find the midpoint of the segment. Measurements from this point to each of the plotted points is close to 5 cm, supporting the fact that all points lie on a circle.

Reflecting

1. Responses may vary. For example, space in office buildings is generally leased by the square foot. If two buildings have the same square footage but differ in height, the taller building may be designed as a rectangular prism where each office has a window for sunlight and air. However, in order for the shorter building to have the same office space, it may require some offices to be in the center of the building where there are no windows.

2. The circle encloses more area than the square.

   Square: A perimeter of 42 inches implies that the side length is 10.5 inches, so the area enclosed is 110.25 in^2.

   Circle: A circumference of 42 inches implies the diameter is $\frac{42}{\pi}$. Thus, the radius is $\frac{21}{\pi}$, so the area enclosed is $\pi \times \left(\frac{21}{\pi}\right)^2$, or approximately 140.37 in^2.

3. Area is measured in square units. Since π has no units (it is the ratio of measurements in the same units), the formula πr^2 results in square units (for example, cm^2 if the radius is measured in cm). Computing $2\pi r$ gives a response in terms of the same unit used for the radius (for example, centimeters), which is a linear measure.

4. a. The number of regions doubles when another point is added to the circle.

   b. Anthony's prediction is incorrect. The maximum number of regions it is possible to get is 31 regions. It is also possible to get only 30 regions, when the six points are evenly spaced around the circle.

   c. One has to be careful when generalizing from only a few data values.

NOTE: Be sure that students recognize the danger in generalizing from a few data values.

Extending

1. Yes, this method will establish the relation for any right triangle.

   a. It is parallel to the hypotenuse.

   b. They are perpendicular.

Unit 5

2. Which shape encloses more area: a square with perimeter 42 or a circle with perimeter (circumference) 42? Justify your reasoning.

3. In what kind of units is area measured? How can you use this fact to avoid confusing the formulas $2\pi r$ and πr^2 when computing the area of a circle?

4. Experimenting, collecting data, and searching for patterns is a powerful way to discover important mathematical relationships. However, it also has limitations. Consider the following example.

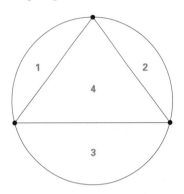

On the circle at the right, three points are marked. Each point is connected to all the others. Four nonoverlapping regions are formed.

Anthony investigated what happened when differing numbers of points were marked on a circle and each was connected to all the others. He summarized his findings in the table below.

Number of Points	1	2	3	4	5
Number of Regions	1	2	4	8	16

a. Do you see any pattern in the table?

b. Anthony predicted that the number of nonoverlapping regions formed by six points would be 32. Check his prediction.

c. What lesson can be learned from this example?

Extending

1. Examine more closely the *dissection* method of "proof" of the Pythagorean Theorem in Organizing Task 1. Will this method establish the relation for *any* right triangle?

   a. There are two "cut lines" dividing the square on the longer leg of the triangle. Is one of those lines related in a special way to the hypotenuse of the right triangle? Explain.

   b. How are the two "cut lines" related to each other?

2. The circle at the right has been dissected into eight sections. These sections can be reassembled to form an "approximate" parallelogram.

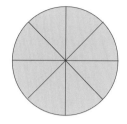

a. How is the base of this "approximate" parallelogram related to the circle?

b. What is the height of the "approximate" parallelogram?

c. How could you dissect the circle into sections to get a better approximation of a parallelogram?

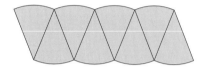

d. Use the above information to produce the formula for the area of a circle.

3. Suppose you are designing a hexagonal flower garden for which all sides are the same length and all angles are the same size.

a. How much decorative fencing is needed to enclose the garden if it measures 4 meters between opposite vertices?

Dimension for Part b

b. Suppose the distance between opposite *sides* is to be 4 meters. How much fencing is needed?

Dimension for Part a

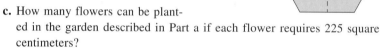

c. How many flowers can be planted in the garden described in Part a if each flower requires 225 square centimeters?

d. How many flowers can be planted in the garden described in Part b?

e. Suppose the 4-meter length measured the length of other segments through the center of the hexagon. What can you say about the amount of fencing needed? Explain your reasoning.

4. In order for kites to fly well, they need to have a high ratio of *lift area* to weight. For two-dimensional kites, the lift area is just the area of the kite. Find the lift area of the traditional kite shown with cross pieces of lengths 0.8 m and 1.0 m.

2. **a.** The base length is half the circle's circumference.
    b. The height is equal to the length of the radius of the circle.
    c. Cut the circle into smaller wedges.
    d. Area $= b \times h$
    $$= \tfrac{1}{2}C \times r$$
    $$= \tfrac{1}{2}(\pi \times d) \times r$$
    $$= \tfrac{1}{2}(\pi \times 2r) \times r$$
    $$= \pi r^2$$

3. **a.** By dividing up the garden into six equilateral triangles with sides of length 2 meters, students can determine the perimeter is 12 meters.
    b. In a regular hexagon, the lengths of the edges and of the segments from the vertices to the center are equal. The (dashed) segment described bisects the base. Thus, the length of the base can be found by solving $2^2 + \left(\tfrac{x}{2}\right)^2 = x^2$ for x. So each base has length $\sqrt{\tfrac{16}{3}}$, and the perimeter is $8\sqrt{3}$ or approximately 13.9 meters.
    c. The area is approximately 10.39 m² or 103,923 cm². Therefore, the approximate number of flowers that can be planted is 461.
    d. For one equilateral triangle the area is $\sqrt{\tfrac{16}{3}}$, so the total area is about 13.86 m² or 138,600 cm². Hence 615 flowers can be planted.
    e. The amount of fencing would be between 12 and 13.9 meters. When the distance from center to side is measured at the midpoint of a side as in Part b, all sides are as far from the center as possible. This makes each equilateral triangle as large as possible. When the distance from center to side is measured at a vertex, the equilateral triangles are as small as possible (2 meters on a side). If the distance from center to side is measured to a point between these two, the equilateral triangles are also intermediary in size.

4. Lift area $= 2(0.5 \times 1 \times 0.4)$
    $\qquad\quad = 0.4$ square meters

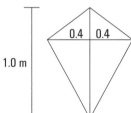

INVESTIGATION 3 Size Measures for Space-Shapes

NOTE: Some middle school programs include a similar development of the surface area and volume of three-dimensional shapes. Your students may not need to do this investigation, but may benefit from a review doing some of the MORE tasks.

In the last two investigations, most of the measurement was with two-dimensional figures. During this investigation, students will explore surface area and volume for a variety of space-shapes. They also will develop formulas to compute these measures.

Some students may continue to confuse the concepts of area and volume. You can help them by having flattened-out prisms, paper shapes pasted on to some faces of straw prisms, and boxes partially filled with unit cubes. Reminders such as these help students focus on the concept, not on the formula. Likewise, discussions about student-produced formulas should focus on making sense of the formulas. Volume is a measure of three-dimensional space, so if a student suggests measuring the perimeter of the base and multiplying by the height to find the volume (a common misconception), you can point out that each of these is a measure of one dimension. Multiplying them might produce the measure of some two-dimensional area, but it can not produce a measure of three-dimensional space.

1. Responses will vary. Examples are given.
    a. When remodeling a house, you may need to know how much wallpaper or paneling, siding for a house, *etc.* to buy.
    b. When wrapping a present, painting an object, and so on, the total surface area is important.
    c. You may need to determine how much storage space you will need or, when buying a heater or air conditioner, you need to know the space that you will heat or cool.

2. a. *Cube*: Each face is 10 cm $\times$ 10 cm or 100 cm^2, so the lateral area is 4(100) or 400 cm^2.

    Triangular prism: The three faces each are 10 cm $\times$ 12 cm or 120 cm^2, so the lateral area is 3(120) or 360 cm^2.

    Square prism: The four faces each are 10 cm $\times$ 12 cm or 120 cm^2, so the lateral area is 4(120) or 480 cm^2.

    Pentagonal prism: The five faces each are 10 cm $\times$ 12 cm or 120 cm^2, so the lateral area is 5(120) or 600 cm^2.

    Hexagonal prism: The six faces each are 10 cm $\times$ 12 cm or 120 cm^2, so the lateral area is 6(120) or 720 cm^2.

    b. Since each face is a rectangle, the base and height of each face must be measured in order to compute *Area = base $\times$ height, or A = b $\times$ h*. This will give the area of one face. The area of all faces is the sum of the areas of the individual faces. For a prism with a regular *n*-sided polygonal base, the total area of the lateral faces is $LA = n \times b \times h$.

    Since the sum of the base edges of a prism is the perimeter of the prism, another equation is $LA = p \times h$ where *p* is the perimeter of the base and *h* the common height of the rectangular faces. (Note: It should not be expected that the use of the perimeter will be suggested by many students. The idea is brought out in Part d of this problem.) This formula will work with nonregular bases, such as a nonsquare rectangular prism.

INVESTIGATION ▶ 3 Size Measures for Space-Shapes

Prisms model the shape of most office buildings. Among the prisms, the rectangular prism is the most common. This fact is demonstrated in an aerial photo of a portion of New York City, shown below at the left. Other prisms well suited to architecture generally have numbers of sides that are multiples of four. One building in the Crown Zellerbach Plaza in San Francisco (shown below at the right) is based on a 40-gon prism. (A 40-gon is a polygon with 40 sides.) Regardless of the shape of the base, the other faces (*lateral faces*) of a prism are rectangles. These facts permit easy measuring of the surface area and volume of space-shapes commonly found in architecture.

1. In your group, discuss possible real-life situations where you would want to know:

   a. the areas of the lateral faces of a prism;

   b. the surface area (total area of the bases and lateral faces) of a prism;

   c. the volume of a prism.

2. Now try to discover a formula for calculating the total area of the lateral faces of a prism.

   a. Refer to the skeleton models of the five prisms that you made in Activity 8 of Investigation 2 (page 333). Imagine covering each prism with paper. Describe how you would find the total area of the lateral faces of each of those prisms.

   b. Based on your descriptions in Part a, write a general formula for finding the total area of the lateral faces of any prism. Describe what each variable in your formula represents.

c. Suppose you have an octagonal prism whose bases have sides of length 4 cm and all angles the same size. The edges connecting the bases are 10 cm long. Apply your formula to this prism.

d. Could you use the concept of perimeter to simplify your formula in Part b? If you can, do so; if not, explain why not.

e. How could you simplify your formula for the special case of a cube?

3. Modify your formula of Activity 2 to give a formula for the *surface area* of a prism.

a. Apply your formula to find the surface area of one of the boxes you analyzed in Activity 1 of Investigation 1 (page 356).

b. Apply your formula for surface area to the following prisms.

■ Square prism: 5-cm edges on bases, height is 6 cm.

■ Triangular prism: 5-cm edges on bases, height is 6 cm.

c. The base of a hexagonal prism with 4-cm edges and all angles the same size can be divided into 6 equilateral triangles as shown here.

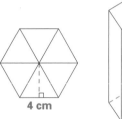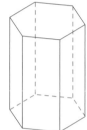

■ How can you calculate the altitude of one of the equilateral triangles?

■ Calculate the area of a base.

■ Find the surface area of this prism if the height is 9 cm.

Surface area gives you one measure of the size of a space-shape. *Volume* gives you another. Just as area can be found by counting squares (hence *square units*), volume can be found by counting cubes (hence *cubic units*).

4. Look at the figure below showing one layer of unit cubes in a prism.

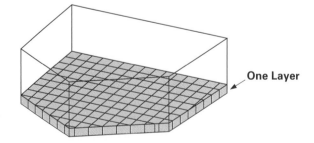

One Layer

2. **c.** Octagonal prism: $n = 8$, $b = 4$, and $h = 10$
   The lateral area is $LA = 8 \times 4$ cm $\times 10$ cm $= 32$ cm $\times 10$ cm $= 320$ cm^2.

   d. Yes, instead of computing the area for each face separately, imagine removing the bases of the prism, then cutting it and flattening it out. The length of the resulting rectangle is the perimeter of the prism. Therefore, the area of all faces combined would be *Lateral Area = perimeter × height* or $LA = p \times h$.

   e. Since the perimeter of the cube is $p = 4s$ (where s is side length), then
   $LA = 4s \times s = 4s^2$.

3. To get a formula for surface area we need to add the area B of each base. Since the bases are identical, the formula for the surface area is *Surface Area = 2B + ph*.

   a. Responses will vary depending on the box used in Activity 1.

   b. ■ Square prism: $2 \times (5 \times 5) + 20 \times 6 = 2 \times 25 + 120$
   $$= 50 + 120$$
   $$= 170 \text{ cm}^2$$
   ■ Equilateral triangular prism: $(2 \times 0.5 \times 5 \times 4.33) + (15 \times 6) \approx 111.65$ cm^2

   c. ■ The height of the equilateral triangle can be found using the Pythagorean Theorem.

   $$h^2 + 2^2 = 4^2$$
   $$h^2 = 12$$
   $$h = \sqrt{12} \approx 3.5$$

   The altitude of the equilateral triangle is approximately 3.5 cm.
   ■ The base can be divided into 6 equilateral triangles each with an area of approximately $0.5 \times 4 \times 3.5$ or 7 cm^2. So the area of the base is approximately 6(7) or 42 cm^2.
   ■ The surface area of the prism is 2(42) + 24(9) or 300 cm^2.

4. **a.** 84 cubes

   b. $84 \times 6 = 504$ cubic units

   $84 \times 134 = 11,256$ cubic units

   c. 13 cubes

   $13h$ cubic units

   d. $B \times h$

5. Student work should include a sketch of each prism.

   a. $V = (4 \times 5) \times 6 = 20 \times 6 = 120$ cm^3

   b. $V = (8 \times 8) \times 8 = 64 \times 8 = 512$ cm^3

   c. $V = (0.5 \times 3 \times 2.6) \times 8$

   $\quad = 3.9 \times 8$

   $\quad = 31.2$ cm^3

   d. $V = 6(0.5 \times 6 \times 5.2) \times 3 = 93.6 \times 3 = 280.8$ cm^3

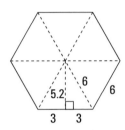

6. Students may need to be reminded that surface area includes all faces and both bases.

   a. $S = 2(4 \times 6) + 2(5 \times 6) + 2(4 \times 5)$

   $\quad = 48 + 60 + 40$

   $\quad = 148$ cm^2

   b. $S = 6(8 \times 8)$

   $\quad = 384$ cm^2

   c. $S = 3(3 \times 8) + 2(0.5 \times 3 \times 2.6)$

   $\quad = 72 + 7.8$

   $\quad = 79.8$ cm^2

   d. $S = 6(6 \times 3) + 2(6 \times 0.5 \times 6 \times 5.2)$

   $\quad = 108 + 187.2$

   $\quad = 295.2$ cm^2

7. **a.** The bases of a cylinder are circles. The shape of the lateral face, when flattened out, is a rectangle.

   b. $S = LA + 2B$ $\qquad\qquad\qquad V = \pi r^2 h$

   $\quad = (2\pi \times 4) \times 7 + 2(\pi \times 4^2)$ $\qquad = (\pi 4^2) \times 7$

   $\quad \approx 175.93 + 100.53$ $\qquad\qquad\quad \approx 351.86$ cm^3

   $\quad \approx 276.46$ cm^2

   c. $S = 2\pi rh + 2(\pi r^2)$

   d. $S = 2\pi r(h + r)$

   (The formula in Part c is probably easier for students to remember, but students may choose either one. You may wish to discuss why they think one formula will be easier to remember than the other.)

   e. $V = \pi r^2 h$

See additional Teaching Notes on page T418O.

a. If that layer has a base area of 84 square units, how many unit cubes are in it?

b. If there are 6 such layers, what is the volume of the prism? What is the volume if there are 134 layers?

c. Suppose the layer has a base area of 13 square units. How many unit cubes are in it? If there are *h* such layers, what is the total volume?

d. Write a formula for calculating the volume *V* of a prism which has a base area of *B* square units and a height of *h* units. Compare your formula with that of other groups. Resolve any differences.

5. Make a sketch of each prism with the given dimensions and then find its volume.

a. Rectangular prism: base is 4 cm by 5 cm, height is 6 cm.

b. Cube: edge is 8 cm.

c. Equilateral triangular prism: base edges are 3 cm, height is 8 cm.

d. Equilateral, equiangular hexagonal prism: base edges are 6 cm, height is 3 cm.

6. Find the surface area of each prism in Activity 5.

7. Some products like vegetables or fruit juice are packaged in cylindrical cans. A cylinder (shown here) can be thought of as a special prism-like shape.

Cylinder

a. What shape are its bases? Imagine removing the bases and cutting the lateral face from base to base as indicated in the diagram. If you flatten the cut lateral face, what shape is it?

b. Find the surface area and volume of a cylinder if the base has a radius of 4 cm and the height is 7 cm.

c. Write a formula for the surface area *S* of a cylinder with radius *r* and height *h*.

d. Write an equivalent expression for your formula for surface area. Which expression will be easier to remember?

e. Write a formula for the volume *V* of a cylinder with radius *r* and height *h*.

8. A can of diced tomatoes has a base with diameter 7.5 cm and height 11 cm. These cans are usually packaged for shipping in boxes of 24 (two layers of 12).

a. What space-shape usually is used for the shipping boxes?

b. What arrangements of the cans are possible for a box holding 12 in a layer?

c. For each arrangement of 12 cans, determine the dimensions of the smallest possible shipping box.

d. What arrangement of cans uses the greatest amount of available space in the box?

e. Which arrangement of cans requires the smallest amount of cardboard to make the box?

9. A $10\frac{3}{4}$ ounce can of soup has a height of 10 cm and a base with radius 3.3 cm. A $6\frac{1}{8}$ ounce can of tuna has a height of 4 cm and a base with radius 4 cm. Which metal can is more efficient in its use of metal for the weight of its contents?

Checkpoint

In this investigation, you explored methods and discovered formulas for finding the surface area and volume of space-shapes.

ⓐ How is the perimeter of a base of a prism useful in finding the area of the lateral faces?

ⓑ How are the formulas you developed for surface area and volume of cylinders similar to the corresponding formulas for prisms? How are they different?

ⓒ How is the Pythagorean Theorem helpful in computing surface areas and volumes of prisms with equilateral triangles or equilateral, equiangular hexagons as bases?

Be prepared to share your group's ideas with the entire class.

▶ On Your Own

A decorative candy tin used by Sorby's Candies and Nuts has an equilateral, equiangular hexagonal base with dimensions as shown. These tins are shipped from the manufacturer in boxes 20 cm by 17.5 cm.

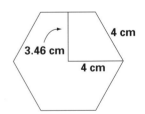

a. How many tins can be put in one layer of a box?

b. If the box and tin have the same height, how much of the available volume of the box is used by the candy tins?

8. c. For the 12×1 arrangement, length = 90 cm, width = 7.5 cm, height = 22 cm.
For the 6×2 arrangement, length = 45 cm, width = 15 cm, height = 22 cm.
For the 4×3 arrangement, length = 30 cm, width = 22.5 cm, height = 22 cm.

d. Volume of 24 cans = $24(\pi \times 3.75^2 \times 11)$
$\approx 11{,}663.16$ cm^3
Volume of 12×1 arrangement = $90 \times 7.5 \times 22$
$= 14{,}850$ cm^3
Volume of 6×2 arrangement = $45 \times 15 \times 22$
$= 14{,}850$ cm^3
Volume of 4×3 arrangement = $30 \times 22.5 \times 22$
$= 14{,}850$ cm^3
In each case, the percent of space used is $\frac{11{,}663.16}{14{,}850}$ or approximately 78.5%.

e. Surface area of 12×1 arrangement:
$S = 2[(90 \times 7.5) + (7.5 \times 22) + (90 \times 22)]$
$= 5{,}640$ cm^2
Surface area of 6×2 arrangement:
$S = 2[(45 \times 15) + (15 \times 22) + (45 \times 22)]$
$= 3{,}990$ cm^2
Surface area of 4×3 arrangement:
$S = 2[(30 \times 22.5) + (22.5 \times 22) + (30 \times 22)]$
$= 3{,}660$ cm^2
The 4×3 arrangement uses the smallest amount of cardboard.

9. Surface area of soup can = $2(\pi \times 3.3^2) + (2\pi \times 3.3 \times 10) \approx 275.8$ cm^2
Tin per ounce $\approx \frac{275.8 \text{ cm}^2}{10.75 \text{ oz}} \approx 25.7$ cm^2/oz
Surface area of tuna can = $2(\pi \times 4^2) + (2\pi \times 4 \times 4) \approx 201.06$ cm^2
Tin per ounce $\approx \frac{201.06 \text{ cm}^2}{6.125 \text{ oz}} \approx 32.8$ cm^2/oz
The soup can uses the tin most efficiently.

SHARE AND SUMMARIZE full-class discussion

Checkpoint

See Teaching Master 146.

ⓐ The perimeter of a base of a prism is equal to the sum of all the base lengths of the rectangular faces. Therefore, you can find the area of each face separately, then add them together, or you can simply multiply the perimeter of the base times the height of the prism.

CONSTRUCTING A MATH TOOLKIT: After completing the Checkpoint, ask students to summarize the concepts of surface area and volume that they explored in Activities 1–7. They could include why these measures are important, a definition of volume, and the formulas they used (Teaching Master 202).

See additional Teaching Notes on pages T418O–T418P.

MORE
ASSIGNMENT *pp. 377–382*

Modeling: 1 and 3
Organizing: 1, and 3 or 4*
Reflecting: Choose one*
Extending: Choose one*

When choice is indicated, it is important to leave the choice to the student.
NOTE: *It is best if Organizing tasks are discussed as a whole class after they have been assigned as homework.*

Unit 5

MORE independent assignment

Modeling

1. **a.** No, because the volume is $\pi 9^2 \times 55$ or approximately 13,996 ft³, but they need a volume of 20,000 ft³.

   b.
Diameter (in feet)	16	17	18	19	20	21
Height (in feet)	100	89	79	71	64	58

   c. The silos with 19-foot and 20-foot diameters would be suitable, since the height is below 75 feet and the diameter will fit on the prepared 20×20 piece of land.

2. **a.**
   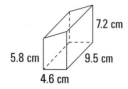

   7.2 cm
   5.8 cm   9.5 cm
   4.6 cm

NOTE: The base dimensions of the liner must be 0.2 cm smaller than the box in order to fit inside. The heights were measured to be 5.8 cm and 7.2 cm.

---

   b. Two reasonable answers are 601.4 cm² and 554.9 cm².
   The amount of cardboard needed for the box is:
   $$2(9.7 \times 4.8) + 2(4.8 \times 9.7) + 2(9.7 \times 9.7) = 374.42 \text{ cm}^2$$
   or, if the student considers the liner bottom to be the only bottom:
   $$(9.7 \times 4.8) + 2(4.8 \times 9.7) + 2(9.7 \times 9.7) = 327.86 \text{ cm}^2$$
   The amount of cardboard needed for the liner is:
   Rectangle $= 4.6 \times 9.5 = 43.7$ cm²
   Rectangle $= 9.5 \times 7.2 = 68.4$ cm²
   Rectangle $= 5.8 \times 9.5 = 55.1$ cm²

   Two trapezoids $= 2\frac{4.6(7.2 + 5.8)}{2} = 59.8$ cm²

   The total amount of cardboard needed for the liner is
   $43.7 + 68.4 + 55.1 + 59.8 = 227$ cm².
   The total amount of cardboard required for the box and liner is approximately 601.4 cm² (or 554.9 cm²).

   c. The inside dimensions of the box are 9.5 cm $\times$ 4.6 cm $\times$ 9.5 cm, so the volume is approximately 415.2 cm³.

   d. The inside dimensions of the liner are 9.3 cm $\times$ 4.4 cm $\times$ 5.7 cm on one side and they are 9.3 cm $\times$ 4.4 cm $\times$ 7.1 cm on the other side.
   The volume will be 5.7 cm $\times$ 4.4 cm $\times$ 9.3 cm plus the volume of the triangular prism, which is $\frac{1}{2}(4.4)(1.4)(9.3)$. So, the volume of the liner is $233.244 + 28.644 = 261.888$ cm³.

MORE
Modeling • Organizing • Reflecting • Extending

Modeling

1. Susan and John Sitzman are farmers who specialize in raising cattle. They need to build a new feed storage silo with an estimated volume of 20,000 cubic feet for the cylinder portion. They have prepared a square piece of land, 20 feet on each side, on which to build the silo.

   a. After shopping around, the Sitzmans found the "best buy" comes from a company which makes a type of silo with a diameter of 18 feet and a height of 55 feet. Would this type fit their needs? Why or why not?

   b. ACME Equipment Company makes silos with a range of diameters from 16 to 21 feet. They will custom-build their silos to any height the customer desires. If the Sitzmans require a volume of 20,000 cubic feet, how high would a silo of a given diameter have to be? Make a table like the one below to help organize your work.

Diameter (in feet)	16	17	18	19	20	21
Height (in feet)						

   c. The Sitzmans want to keep the height of their new silo below 75 feet, since they often have strong winds in their area. Which of the silos in your table would be suitable for these conditions?

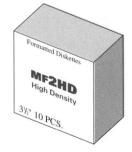

2. A computer disk box measures 9.7 cm by 4.8 cm by 9.7 cm. Inside, the bottom half of the box is an open-ended cardboard protective liner which measures 7.2 cm high at its back and 5.8 cm high at its front. The thickness of all material is 0.1 cm.

   a. Sketch the liner and give its dimensions.

   b. How much cardboard is needed to make the disk box and its liner?

   c. What is the volume of the box?

   d. What is the volume of the liner?

3. A container manufacturing company makes open-top storage bins for small machine parts. One series of containers is made from a square sheet of tin that is 24 cm on a side. Squares of equal size are cut from each corner. The tabs are then turned up and the seams are soldered.

 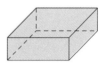

a. Using centimeter graph paper, cut out two squares 24 cm on a side. Make model bins by cutting squares of one and two centimeters on a side from the corners of the 24 × 24 squares. Fold up the tabs and tape the seams. What are the dimensions of the model which has the larger volume?

b. Let *x* represent the side-length of the cutout corner squares. Write an expression

- for the length of each side of the storage bin;
- for the volume of the bin.

c. What is the possible range of values for *x*, the side-length of the cutout squares?

d. Use the table-building capability of your graphing calculator or computer software to help find the dimensions of the container with the largest possible volume.

4. A swimming pool is 28 feet long and 18 feet wide. The shallow 3-foot-deep end extends for 6 feet. Then for 16 feet horizontally, there is a constant decline toward the 9-foot-deep end.

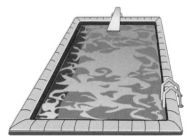

a. Sketch the pool and indicate the measures on the sketch. Is this a prism? If so, name it.

b. How much water is needed to fill the pool within 6 inches of the top?

c. One gallon of paint covers approximately 75 square feet of surface. How many gallons of paint are needed to paint the inside of the pool? If the pool paint comes in 5-gallon cans, how many cans should be purchased?

3. **a.** 1-cm cutouts:

   $V = 22 \times 22 \times 1 = 484$ cm^3

   2-cm cutouts:

   $V = 20 \times 20 \times 2 = 800$ cm^3

   The model with the larger cutout of 2 cm has the larger volume.

   b. The box height is x, so

   $L = 24 - 2x$

   $V = (24 - 2x)(24 - 2x)(x)$

   c. $0 < x < 12$

   d. When $x = 4$, the dimensions would be $16 \times 16 \times 4$ and would give the maximum volume of 1,024 cm^3.

4. **a.** This is a *hexagonal* prism.

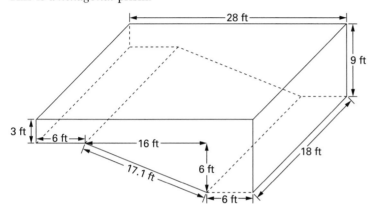

   b. The base, or the front of the pool as shown here, is comprised of a 2.5×28 rectangle, a right triangle with legs 16 and 6, and a 6×6 square. The area of this base is

   $2.5 \times 28 + 0.5 \times 16 \times 6 + 6 \times 6 = 70 + 48 + 36$

   $= 154$ square feet

   Volume of water = area of base $\times$ height

   $= 154$ ft$^2 \times 18$ ft

   $= 2{,}772$ ft^3

   c. The area of the two bases (or sides of the pool) is 2(154) or 308 square feet.

   There are 5 different rectangular surfaces to paint:

   (1) $3 \times 18 = 54$ ft^2

   (2) $6 \times 18 = 108$ ft^2

   (3) $17.1 \times 18 = 307.8$ ft^2

   (4) $6 \times 18 = 108$ ft^2

   (5) $9 \times 18 = 162$ ft^2

   The total surface area to paint is the sum of areas of the five rectangles plus the areas of the two bases (front and back of the pool), or 1,047.8 square feet. Since the value of $\frac{1{,}047.8}{75} \approx 14$, approximately 14 gallons of paint will be needed. They should purchase three 5-gallon cans of paint.

4. d. $32 \times 22 = 704$ square feet

  e. The perimeter of the pool is 92 feet. One row of six-inch tiles would require 184 tiles. In order to have 18 inches of tiling, you need three rows around the pool or 552 six-inch square tiles.

Organizing

1. a–b.

Length (cm)	Width (cm)	Height (cm)	Surface Area (cm²)
1	1	60	242
1	2	30	184
1	3	20	166
1	4	15	158
1	5	12	154
1	6	10	152
2	2	15	128
2	3	10	112
2	5	6	104
3	4	5	94

  c. The dimensions of the gift box that uses the least amount of paper are $3 \text{ cm} \times 4 \text{ cm} \times 5 \text{ cm}$.

  d. **This is a task asking students to exercise the habit of mind of checking evidence for a conjecture.**

  The statement is false. All of the above prisms are rectangular prisms with a volume of 60 cubic centimeters, but no two such prisms have the same surface area.

2. This task again emphasizes the importance and usefulness of the Pythagorean Theorem. Students will learn about simplifying radicals in the Course 2 unit, "Power Models." At this time, they may use approximations for square roots.

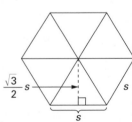

  a. Using the Pythagorean Theorem, the height of the triangle is

$$\sqrt{s^2 - \left(\frac{s}{2}\right)^2} = \sqrt{1s^2 - \frac{1}{4}s^2} = \sqrt{\frac{3}{4}s^2} = \sqrt{0.75}s, \text{ or about } 0.8665s \text{ units.}$$

  So the area is $A = 0.5(s)\left(\sqrt{\frac{3s^2}{4}}\right) = \frac{s^2\sqrt{3}}{4}$ or $0.4335s^2$ square units.

  b. Since a regular hexagon with side-length s can be divided into 6 equilateral triangles with side-length s, the area of the hexagon will be 6 times the area of the triangle from Part a.

$$A = 6(0.5)(s)\sqrt{\frac{3s^2}{4}} = 3s\sqrt{\frac{3s^2}{4}} = \frac{3\sqrt{3}}{2}s^2 \approx 2.6s^2$$

See additional Teaching Notes on page T418P.

    d. How much material is needed to make a pool cover that extends 2 feet beyond the pool on all sides?

    e. About how many 6-inch square ceramic tiles are needed to tile the top 18 inches of the inside faces of the pool?

Organizing

1. Imagine a rectangular gift box that has a volume of 60 cubic centimeters and whole number dimensions.

    a. Find the dimensions of all possible boxes. Use a table to organize your findings.

    b. What is the surface area of each gift box?

    c. What are the dimensions of the gift box that uses the least amount of paper?

    d. Express your view on the statement: *If two prisms with the same kind of bases (the same shape, not the same size) have identical volumes, then their surface areas are identical.* Explain your position.

2. To use the formula for the area of a triangle, you need to know the length of a side (the base) and the length of the altitude to that side (the height). In the case of some special triangles, it's sufficient to know the length of a side.

    a. Develop a formula for calculating the area A of an equilateral triangle with side-length s.

    b. Develop a formula for calculating the area A of an equilateral, equiangular hexagon with side-length s.

3. Ian's class had two prisms that were 20 cm high. One had a square base with 5-cm sides. The other had an equilateral triangular base with 5-cm sides. The class collected data on the amount of water needed to raise the water level to various heights in each prism. The data are summarized in the following table.

Height in cm	0	2	4	6	8	10	12	14	16	18	20
Volume of Square Prism (5-cm sides)	0	49	102	150	199	252	300	347	398	452	500
Volume of Triangular Prism (5-cm sides)	0	21	44	65	86	107	130	152	172	196	216

    a. Produce a scatterplot of the (*height, volume*) data for each prism.

    b. For which scatterplots would a linear model fit the trend in the data? Where appropriate, find an equation for the linear model.

    c. Describe the rate of change in the volume for each prism.

    d. How is the rate of change related to the base of the space-shape?

Modeling ● Organizing ● Reflecting ● Extending

4. Ian's class found the results of modeling the volumes of the prisms being filled with water (Organizing Task 3) very interesting. They extended the investigation and collected (*height*, *volume*) data for other 20-cm-tall space-shapes. The results are summarized in the following table.

Height in cm	0	2	4	6	8	10	12	14	16	18	20
Volume of Square Pyramid (5-cm sides)	0	17	33	50	66	84	99	115	133	149	167
Volume of Triangular Pyramid (5-cm sides)	0	7	16	22	28	36	44	50	57	66	72
Volume of Cylinder (2-cm radius)	0	25	49	75	101	123	149	177	200	227	252
Volume of Cone (2-cm radius)	0	8	17	26	34	41	49	59	66	76	84

a. Produce four scatterplots of the (*height*, *volume*) data in the table.

b. If appropriate, find a linear model for each scatterplot.

c. Compare the linear models for the cone and the cylinder. Make a conjecture about the relationship between the volumes of a cylinder and a cone with identical bases and identical heights.

d. Compare the linear models for the pyramids with those of a prism with a similar base in Organizing Task 3. Make a conjecture regarding the relation between the volumes of a prism and a pyramid with identical bases and identical heights.

Reflecting

1. Commodities sold in grocery stores come in many kinds of packages. Packages made of cardboard tend to be rectangular prisms. Packages made of metal or glass are more often cylinders. What reasons might you give for these trends?

2. What changes the volume of a cylinder more: doubling its diameter or doubling its height? Explain your reasoning.

3. In Investigation 3, you saw that the volume of a prism or a cylinder is found simply by multiplying the area of the base by the height. Explain why it would not be reasonable to calculate volumes of pyramids or cones in the same way.

4. In Unit 4, "Graph Models," you developed *algorithms* for finding Euler circuits and coloring the vertices of a graph. In this investigation, you developed *formulas* for calculating volumes of space-shapes. How is a formula similar to an algorithm? How is it different?

4. This task attempts to help students see how volumes of pyramids and cones are related to the volumes of like-based prisms and cylinders. This is a nice use of data analysis to introduce a relationship that is not always easy for students to understand.

a.
```
WINDOW
 Xmin =0
 Xmax =22
 Xscl =2
 Ymin =0
 Ymax =260
 Yscl =50
 Xres =1
```

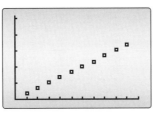

Volume of Square Pyramid

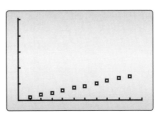

Volume of Triangular Pyramid

Volume of Circular Cylinder

Volume of Circular Cone

b. The linear models are as follows:

Volume of Square Pyramid: $y = 8.3x$

Volume of Triangular Pyramid: $y = 3.6x + 0.23$

Volume of Circular Cylinder: $y = 12.6x - 0.77$

Volume of Circular Cone: $y = 4.2x$

c. The slope of the cylinder graph is steeper; about three times that of the cone. (The volume of a cylinder is three times the volume of a cone with identical base and height.)

d. The slopes of the pyramid scatterplots are less steep; they are about one-third those of the corresponding prisms. The pyramid has volume about one-third that of the corresponding prism.

Reflecting

1. Responses may vary. For example, cardboard is easier to "bend" into rectangular prisms than metal or glass. Also metal or glass containers are more expensive to make and should, therefore, use less material than a prism to hold the same amount of a product. This occurs when cylindrical shapes are used.

2. Consider a cylinder with diameter d and height h.

$$\text{Volume} = \pi \times \left(\frac{d}{2}\right)^2 \times h = \frac{1}{4}\pi d^2 h$$

If the height is doubled, then the height is $2h$.

$$\text{Volume} = \pi \times \left(\frac{d}{2}\right)^2 \times 2h = \frac{1}{2}\pi d^2 h$$

See additional Teaching Notes on page T418Q.
See additional Teaching Notes on page T418Q.

Extending

1. a. The length of the side of the square base can range from 1 inch to 26 inches. Below is part of a table where:

L_1 is the length of the side of the square base, from 1 to 26.

L_2 is the length of the box, so $L_2 = 108 - 4 L_1$.

L_3 is the volume of the box, so $L_3 = L_2 \times L_1^2$.

L1	L2	L3
15	48	10800
16	44	11264
17	40	11560
18	36	11664
19	32	11552
20	28	11200
21	24	10584

L1 (15) = 15

From this table it appears that the maximum volume is obtained if the square has side of length 18 inches and the length of the box is 36 inches. The volume is 11,664 cubic inches.

Alternatively, students could write an equation for volume with the length of the side of the square x: $V = x^2(108 - 4x)$. They could graph this equation and find the maximum value for volume.

b. No. For a given perimeter, a square is the quadrilateral that encloses the maximum area. Since volume is area of the base times the height, the maximum volume will be obtained with a square base.

2. a. The shape of the flattened cone is outlined by the heavy lines in the figure below.

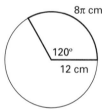

8π cm

120°

12 cm

Circumference of cone = 8π

Circumference of circle = 24π

b. The flattened cone is $\frac{1}{3}$ of a circle with radius 12 cm.

c. Area = $\frac{1}{3}(\pi \times 12^2) = 48\pi \approx 151$ cm^2 (NOTE: This assumes there is no base on this cone.)

NOTE: You may wish to have some students design and conduct an experiment similar to that in Extending Task 3 to describe a possible relationship between the volume of a pyramid and the volume of a prism that have the same base and height.

3. a. Students should see that they must pour the contents of the cone into the cylinder roughly three times to fill the cylinder. Therefore, the volume of the cylinder is about three times the volume of the cone.

b. Students should have similar results.

c. $V = \frac{1}{3} \times (\textit{volume of a cylinder}) = \frac{1}{3} Bh = \frac{1}{3}\pi r^2 h$.

4. More advanced students could be challenged further by this problem if you ask if this formula will work on *any* space-shape. A counterexample might be two congruent hourglass shapes stacked together.

a. $\dfrac{B + 4M + T}{6} = \dfrac{1}{6}B + \dfrac{4}{6}M + \dfrac{1}{6}T$

This shows that the "middle" cross section receives four times the "weight" that the base or top cross sections receive. This weighted average is very similar to the one used in Unit 4, "Graph Models." In "Graph Models," the most likely task time (also the middle of the three times) was weighted four times as much as the two extreme task times. The same weighting occurs here.

Extending

1. The U.S. Postal Service has requirements on the size of packages it will ship within the United States. The maximum size for parcel post packages is 108 inches in combined length and *girth*.

   a. Suppose you are shipping goods via parcel post that do not require a specific length shipping box. What are the dimensions of a square prism package that would allow you to ship the greatest volume of goods?

   b. Could you ship a greater volume of goods using a rectangular prism package? Explain your reasoning.

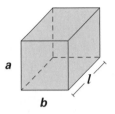

Girth = 2*a* + 2*b*

2. A cone has a circular base with a radius of 4 cm. To cut it open, you need to make a 12 cm cut from bottom to top.

   a. Sketch the shape of the cone when cut and flattened.

   b. The flattened shape is part of what larger shape? What fractional part of the larger shape is this surface?

   c. Find the area of the surface of the cone.

3. The diagram at the right suggests that a cone with the same base and height as a cylinder will have less volume. To see how much, use a cylindrical can or glass and a cone made from stiff paper as shown. Fill the cone with sand, rice, or birdseed and then pour the contents into the cylinder. Repeat until the cylinder is filled.

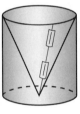

   a. What is the relationship between the volume of the cone and the volume of the cylinder?

   b. Compare your finding with that of other classmates who completed this experiment

   c. Write a formula for the volume *V* of a cone with radius *r* and height *h*.

4. The volume formulas in this unit can be viewed as special cases of the *prismoidal formula*:

$$V = \frac{B + 4M + T}{6} \cdot h$$

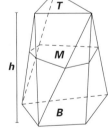

where *B* is the area of the cross section at the base, *M* is the area of the cross section at the "middle," *T* is the area of the cross section at the top, and *h* is the height of the space-shape.

   a. Explain why $\frac{B + 4M + T}{6}$ can be thought of as the "weighted" average area of the cross sections of the solid. Compare this formula for "weighted average" with the one used in Unit 4, "Graph Models," page 313.

LESSON 2 • THE SIZE OF THINGS   **381**

b. Use the prismoidal formula and the diagram below to show that the volume of a triangular prism is $V = Bh$, where B is the area of the base and h is the height.

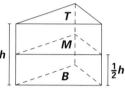 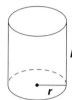

c. Examine the cylinder shown above.

- What is the shape of any cross section of a cylinder (parallel to the base)?

- As the number of sides in the base of a prism increases, the shape of the prism approaches that of a cylinder. Use this fact and the prismoidal formula to show that the volume of a circular cylinder with radius r and height h is given by $V = \pi r^2 h$.

d. As the number of sides in the base of a pyramid increases, the shape of the pyramid approaches that of a cone. Examine the cone shown above at the right. Use the prismoidal formula to help you discover a formula for the volume of a cone with base radius r and height h.

e. Locate an irregularly shaped vase or bottle. Use the prismoidal formula to approximate the volume of the container. Check your estimate by filling the container with water, then pouring it into a measuring cup.

4. Analysis of the formulas for the volume of a prism and for the volume of a cylinder suggests that multiplying the dimensions of the space-shape by a positive constant changes the volume in a predictable way.

a. One large juice can has dimensions twice those of a smaller can. How do the volumes of the two cans compare?

b. One cereal box has dimensions 3 times those of another. How do the volumes of the two boxes compare?

c. If the dimensions of one prism are 5 times those of another, how do the volumes compare?

d. If the dimensions of one prism are k times those of another, how do the volumes compare?

5. The dimensions of a model of a building are one-hundredth of the dimensions of the actual building.

a. How does the volume of the model compare to the volume of the actual building?

b. How does the surface area of the model compare to the surface area of the building?

MORE *continued*

4. **b.** In a triangular prism, $B = M = T$, so
$$V = \frac{B + 4M + T}{6} \times h = \frac{B + 4B + B}{6} \times h = \frac{6B}{6} \times h = B \times h$$

    c. ■ Every cross section is a circle.
       ■ In a cylinder, $B = M = T = \pi r^2$, so
$$V = \frac{B + 4M + T}{6} \times h = \frac{\pi r^2 + 4\pi r^2 + \pi r^2}{6} \times h = \frac{6\pi r^2}{6} \times h = \pi r^2 h$$

    d. In a cone, $T = 0$, $M = \pi\left(\frac{r}{2}\right)^2$, $B = \pi r^2$, so
$$V = \frac{\pi r^2 + 4\pi\left(\frac{r}{2}\right)^2 + 0}{6} \times h = \frac{2\pi r^2}{6} \times h = \frac{1}{3}\pi r^2 h$$

    e. Estimates will vary depending on the vase or bottle chosen.

5. Encourage students to first work with specific examples, and then to generalize and perhaps algebraically prove their results. This concept is further developed in "Power Models" and also "Geometric Form and Its Function" in Course 2.

    a. The volume of the large can is 8 times that of the small can.

    b. The volume of the larger box is 27 times that of the smaller box.

    c. The volume of the larger prism is 125 times that of the smaller prism.

    d. The volume of the larger prism is k^3 times that of the smaller prism.

6. **a.** The volume of the actual building is 1,000,000 times that of the model.

    b. The surface area of the actual building is 10,000 times that of the model.

See Assessment Resources, pages 177–182.

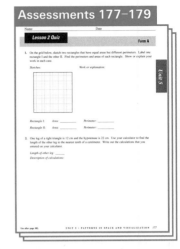
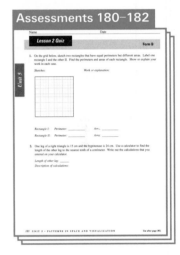

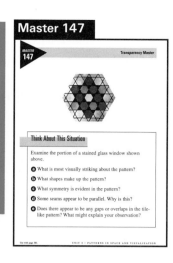

Master 147

NOTE: If your students have a good understanding of polygons from middle school studies, you might begin with the Checkpoint discussion on page 385.

Lesson 3 *The Shapes of Plane Figures*

LESSON OVERVIEW Now that students have developed visualization skills and measurement skills, they will extend their knowledge of plane-shapes by classifying polygons and using the concepts of line and rotational symmetry to discuss properties of polygons. Once students are able to classify polygons, they will investigate polygons which tile the plane and recognize and build nets for polygons. Investigation 3 introduces students to translational and glide reflection symmetries. Students will use transformations to analyze and create patterns in the plane. These transformations will be studied again in Course 2, Unit 2, "Patterns of Location, Shape, and Size," from a synthetic (coordinate) perspective.

To introduce this lesson, you may begin with a full-class discussion of various polygon shapes. If possible, bring in a sample of contemporary art with several distinct regions that are polygons. You also may ask students to bring in samples of art, architecture, or advertisements which contain identifiable regions they believe to be polygons. Ask what polygon names they already know and make a list on the board. Let students know that the purpose of the first investigation is to learn how to classify plane-shapes such as the ones they have listed and also how to define many of the plane-shapes. Students also will extend the concept of reflection symmetry from space-shapes to plane-shapes and will examine plane-shapes for rotation symmetry.

If your students have access to TI-92 calculators, you may wish to use "Geometric Investigations for the Classroom using the TI-92" from Texas Instruments as an alternative way to help students understand or extend the concepts in the investigation.

Lesson Objectives

- To classify polygonal plane-shapes, including special quadrilaterals
- To recognize line and rotational symmetry in plane-shapes
- To identify regular polygons that will tile a plane
- To interpret and draw nets for space-shapes
- To recognize and create translation and glide reflection symmetries
- To use isometric transformations to analyze and create symmetric patterns in the plane

See additional Teaching Notes on page T418Q.

Lesson 3

The Shapes of Plane Figures

Space-shapes come in a wide variety of forms. Many of those forms are based on some very common shapes such as the rectangular prism, the pyramid, the cylinder, and the cone. All the faces of prisms and pyramids, as well as the bases of cylinders and cones, are *plane-shapes*. The most common shape of a face is the *polygon*. In this lesson, you will study the characteristics of polygons and explore how they are used in art, design, and other ways.

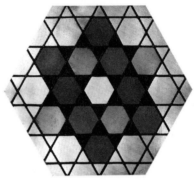

© 1977 Stained Glass Tessellation. Creative Publications Inc. Reprinted by permission of Creative Publications.

Think About This Situation

Examine the portion of a stained glass window shown above.

a What is most visually striking about the pattern?

b What shapes make up the pattern?

c What symmetry is evident in the pattern?

d Some seams appear to be parallel. Why is this?

e Does there appear to be any gaps or overlaps in the tile-like pattern? What might explain your observation?

INVESTIGATION ▶ 1 Polygons and Their Properties

The word "polygon" comes from Greek words *poly* meaning "many" and *gon* meaning "angle." This is descriptive, but it describes shapes that are not polygons as well as those that are. It will be helpful to have a more precise definition of "polygon" before investigating properties of various polygons.

1. Shown below are twelve plane-shapes.

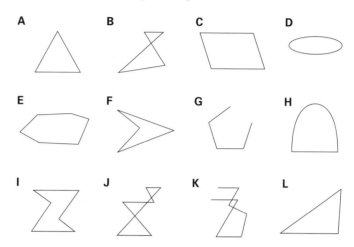

a. Working individually, sort these shapes into groups of shapes that are "alike" in some manner.

b. Share with your group the criteria you used to sort the twelve shapes.

c. Choose another set of sorting criteria for sorting the shapes. Re-sort and describe the criteria you used.

d. As a group, determine a criterion for sorting which would put all shapes except shapes D and H in one group.

e. What criterion would put shapes A, B, C, E, F, I, J, and L (no others) into one group?

f. What criterion would put shapes A, C, E, F, I, and L (no others) into one group?

g. What criterion would put shapes A, C, E, and L (no others) into one group?

h. What criterion would put shapes A and L in one group; B, C, F, and G in another group; and E, I, and J in a third group?

i. What criterion would put shapes A, D, G, and H (no others) into one group?

j. What criterion would put shapes A, C, and D (no others) into one group?

Your work in Activity 1 suggests that there are many ways that plane-shapes can be grouped or classified. One commonly used classification puts *polygons* into one group and all other shapes into another group (non-polygons). The criterion you developed for Part f above should have identified only shapes which are polygons.

As students work on Activity 1, move from group to group to ensure students attempt to write complete, thoughtful criteria for their groupings as requested in Parts a–c. Students may be surprised to see that plane-shapes can be grouped in so many different ways. (Students will prove many properties of special quadrilaterals using synthetic or analytic proofs in Course 3, Unit 4.)

NOTE: For Activity 1, Parts i and j, students should identify line symmetry and rotational (turning) symmetry as the key criteria for grouping those shapes together. If these ideas are new to many of your students, the items may deserve a whole-class discussion to ensure that the ideas are clear to every student. These concepts are used several times throughout the investigation, so it is important to make sure all students are comfortable with both line and rotational symmetry. This is a good place to point out that there frequently are opportunities for mathematicians to make choices. In this case, a decision was made as to how we will group various plane-shapes.

---

1. Answers will vary. Here are some possibilities:
   a–c. A, C, E, L (closed figure, boundary does not cross itself, boundary composed of line segments, all angles are less than 180°);
   D, H (closed figure, boundary does not cross itself, boundary contains curves);
   B, J (closed figure, boundary crosses itself);
   G, K (figure not closed);
   F, I (figure closed but some angles are greater than 180°, *i.e.*, it is not convex).
   Or:
   A, C, D, E, F, H, I, L (closed figure, boundary does not cross itself);
   B, G, J, K (boundary crosses itself or is not closed).
   d. All sides are line segments.
   e. All are closed figures with line segments for sides.
   f. All are closed figures bounded by three or more line segments that intersect exactly two other segments, once at each of its endpoints. (Note: The students' criterion for these figures should be equivalent to a definition for polygons which includes convex and concave polygons. Often when the word polygon is used it is assumed to be convex polygons, just as the prisms were assumed to be right prisms in Lesson 1.)
   g. Same as Part f, but also the line segments must intersect so that the interior angle formed is less than 180 degrees.
   h. Each set has plane-shapes made up of the same number of line segments.
   i. Each has line symmetry. It may be useful to illustrate line (reflection) symmetry with objects. A plane-shape has line symmetry when it appears unchanged before and after reflecting.
   j. Each has rotational symmetry. Similar comments are appropriate for rotational symmetry. Illustrate and find the center of rotation.

Master 148

NOTE: Students will prove
properties of special quadrilaterals using either synthetic or
analytic proofs in Course 3,
Unit 4, "Shapes and Geometric
Reasoning."

CONSTRUCTING A MATH
TOOLKIT: Once the class has
agreed on the various types of
quadrilaterals and their special
characteristics, these can be
entered in their Math Toolkits
(Teaching Master 202).

EXPLORE *continued*

2. With the review of the shapes in Activity 1, Part f, you also may want to ask groups to share their written criteria. Any definition of polygon tends to be cumbersome to write or express and often allows one to construct counterexamples to highlight inadequacies; therefore, a discussion of descriptions as an entire class could be quite useful.

   a. Shapes F and I often are questioned. Convex shapes and concave shapes may be introduced informally in discussions about shapes F and I.

   b. Answers will vary. Stress clear communication of ideas and careful listening by others.

   c. This is an informal assessment for students. Bring any major differences to the entire class for resolution.

3. a. Most groups will get square, rectangle, and parallelogram. Discussion between different groups may be needed to generate good sketches of rhombus, trapezoid, and kite.

   b. Consider having groups list conjectures about angle and side relationships for each quadrilateral. You can list student conjectures on poster or chart paper. On each list, leave room to add new ideas. Post the lists where students can see them. As students progress through the investigations, encourage them to add to the list of conjectures or to refute a conjecture by finding a counterexample.

   At the outset of this part of Activity 3, you may have to ask leading questions to get students started thinking about the characteristics of shapes. You might say that you want students to consider questions such as:

   Are there any equal sides?

   Are there any equal angles?

   Are there any other equal lengths or angles if we add diagonals?

   Are there any parallel or perpendicular segments?

   Are there any sides or angles cut in half?

   Is there anything special about the plane-shapes created by adding diagonals?

   Are there any other side or angle relationships that you think are worth investigating?

   Following the study of line and rotational symmetry, students should informally test their conjectures.

   Parallelogram:
   ■ Two pairs of opposite sides are parallel.
   ■ Opposite angles are congruent and adjacent angles add to 180°.
   ■ Diagonals bisect each other.

   Rhombus:
   ■ All parallelogram relationships hold.
   ■ All four sides are congruent.
   ■ Diagonals are perpendicular.

   Rectangle:
   ■ All parallelogram relationships hold.
   ■ All four angles are equal and all sides are perpendicular.
   ■ Diagonals are equal in length.

   Square:
   ■ All rectangle relationships hold.
   ■ All rhombus relationships hold.

See additional Teaching Notes on page T418R.

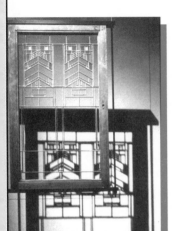

2. Review the shapes that were grouped together in Part f of Activity 1.

   a. Are there shapes in that group that did not fit your idea of a polygon? If so, which ones?

   b. What is it about these shapes that made you think they were not polygons?

   c. Draw a shape, either a polygon or not a polygon. Trade shapes with a partner and have each person identify the shape as a polygon or not. Explain why that choice was made.

One class of polygons commonly seen in architecture is the class of **quadrilaterals**, which are four-sided polygons.

3. You are familiar with many quadrilaterals from your previous work in mathematics. The diagram at the right shows a general quadrilateral. It has no special properties; just four sides and four angles.

   a. You may recall that there are six special kinds of quadrilaterals. They are the *square*, *rectangle*, *parallelogram*, *rhombus*, *trapezoid*, and *kite*. Draw a sketch of each of these polygons.

   b. For each quadrilateral sketched in Part a, list all the special properties you think it has. For example, are opposite sides parallel or equal in length? Are adjacent angles equal or supplementary (sum of their degree measures is 180)?

   c. Which of your shapes has the greatest number of special properties? Which has the least?

   d. Compare your analysis of properties of special quadrilaterals to those of other groups. Resolve any differences.

Checkpoint

Look back at your work classifying plane-shapes as polygons and as special quadrilaterals.

a Write a criterion (a definition) that will put all polygon shapes in one group and any other plane-shape in another group.

b Write criteria you would use to classify a quadrilateral as the following:

a kite	a trapezoid	a rhombus
a parallelogram	a rectangle	a square

Be prepared to compare your group's classification criteria with those of other groups.

▶ On Your Own

Classify each statement as *true* or *false*. Give a justification for your conclusion.

a. Shape A is a polygon.

b. Shape B is a polygon.

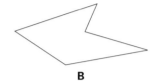

c. Every parallelogram is a rectangle.

d. Every rhombus is a kite.

e. Every trapezoid is a parallelogram.

A polygon with *n* angles and *n* sides is often called an *n-gon*. So another name for a quadrilateral is a *4-gon*. In the next activity, you will explore connections between the number of sides of a polygon and the measures of its angles.

4. Carefully draw polygons having 4, 5, 6, 7, 8, 9, and 10 sides. Share the work in your group.

a. Subdivide each polygon into *nonoverlapping* triangles by drawing line segments from one vertex to another. Try to make the *fewest* possible triangles in each polygon.

- Record your results in a table like the one below. Compare the number of sides of a polygon and the number of triangles into which it can be subdivided.

Number of Sides	Number of Triangles
4	

- Examine your table to find a pattern. Draw and test more polygons, if needed.

- Suppose a polygon has *n* sides. Into how many nonoverlapping triangles can it be subdivided? Use the pattern you discovered in your table to write a rule (formula) relating the *number of sides n* to the *number of triangles T.*

APPLY individual task

On Your Own

a. False: Two segments intersect in points that are not endpoints of other segments.

b. True: The five line segments intersect only at their endpoints, and it is a closed figure.

c. False: A parallelogram is a rectangle only if it contains right angles.

d. True: Since all sides are equal, the condition that two pairs of consecutive sides are equal is satisfied.

e. False: The condition of opposite sides parallel is not satisfied; using either definition, a trapezoid could have only one pair of parallel sides.

4. a.

Number of Sides	Number of Triangles	Angle Sum
4	2	360°
5	3	540°
6	4	720°
7	5	900°
8	6	1,080°
9	7	1,260°
10	8	1,440°

- Each polygon has two fewer triangles than it does sides.
- A polygon with n sides can be divided into $n - 2$ nonoverlapping triangles, so $T = n - 2$.

Unit 5

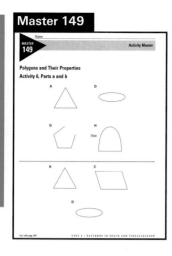

APPLY *continued*

4. **b.** See the "Angle Sum" column in the table for Part a.
    - $Sum = (n - 2) \times 180$
    - For a 12-gon, the sum is $(12 - 2) \times 180$ or $1,800°$.

    c. If x is the number of sides of a polygon and y is the measure of the sum of the interior angles, then $y = 180x - 360$. The y-intercept of -360 does not make sense since $x = 0$ implies a polygon has 0 sides. The slope of 180 means that for every additional side in a polygon, the interior-angle sum increases by $180°$.

5. **a.** Since $(6 - 2)(180°) = 720°$, each angle of a hexagon measures $\frac{720°}{6} = 120°$.
    The angle sum for a regular 10-gon is $(10 - 2)(180°)$ or $1,440°$. The measure of each angle of the 10-gon is $\frac{1,440°}{10} = 144°$.

    b. $A = \dfrac{(n - 2)(180)}{n}$ or $A = \dfrac{n(180) - 360}{n}$

NOTE: The results of Activities 4 and 5 should be recorded in students' Math Toolkits for later reference. The ideas will be used without comment in later work.

---

6. **See Activity Master 149.**

    In this activity, the concepts of line and rotational symmetry are explored. A whole-group discussion may be needed to clarify these ideas. Such a discussion might extend line symmetry to include the fact that a line of symmetry will bisect any segment determined by two points that are a pair of reflection-symmetric points. (This idea was introduced in Organizing Tasks 2 and 3 on page 337, which followed Investigation 2.) It will be important for students to understand that a shape with rotational symmetry has a center of rotation, and that you can talk about the "size" of the rotation by citing the measure of the angle determined by corresponding points (before and after rotation) and that center.

    a.   A   D   G   H

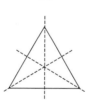

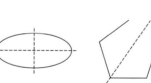
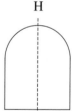

    b. A. The center of rotation is the intersection of the altitudes. Rotation angles are $120°$ and $240°$.

    C. The center of rotation is the intersection of the diagonals. Rotation angle is $180°$.

    D. The center of rotation is the intersection of the horizontal and vertical lines of symmetry. Rotation angle is $180°$.

    A   C   D

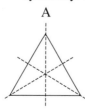
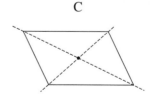

b. Recall that the sum of the measures of the angles of a triangle is 180 degrees.

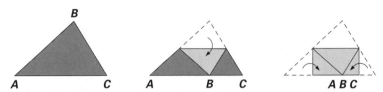

Use this fact to find the sum of the measures of the angles of each polygon listed in your table. Add a column "Angle Sum" to your table and record your results.

- Write a rule relating the number of sides of an *n*-gon to the sum of the measures of its angles.

- Use your rule to predict the sum of the measures of the angles of a 12-gon. Check your prediction with a sketch.

c. Do you think a line is a good model for the (*number of sides, angle sum*) data? If so, what is the slope and what does it mean in terms of the variables? Does the *y*-intercept make sense? Why or why not?

5. Now investigate how to predict the measure of one angle of a **regular polygon**. In a regular polygon, all angles are the same size and all sides are the same length.

a. Determine the measure of one angle of a regular hexagon. Apply your procedure to a regular 10-gon.

b. Write a rule relating the *number of sides n* to the *measure A of an angle* of a regular *n*-gon.

6. Polygons and other plane-shapes also may have other properties. For example, look at your grouping rules for Parts i and j of Activity 1 (page 384).

a. Shapes A, D, G, and H could be grouped together because they each have **reflection** or **line symmetry**. On a copy of each shape, draw a line through it so that one half is the reflection of the other half.

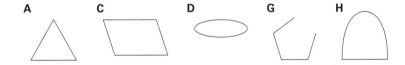

b. Shapes A, C, and D could be grouped together because they have **rotational symmetry**. This is also called **turn symmetry** because the amount of rotation is given as an angle in degrees. Locate the center of each shape and determine through what angles it can be turned so that it coincides with itself.

c. Which of the following figures have reflection (line) symmetry?

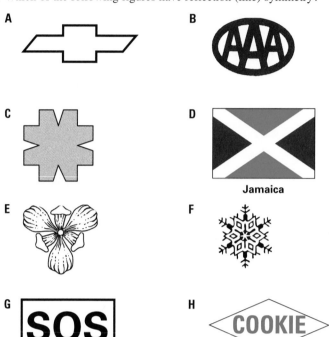

A B

C D
Jamaica

E F

G SOS H COOKIE

d. Which of the figures in Part c have rotational (turn) symmetry? Estimate the angles through which each can be turned to coincide with itself.

e. In Parts c and d, how did you determine which figures had reflection or rotational symmetry?

f. Which of the quadrilaterals that you drew in Activity 3 (page 385) have reflection (line) symmetry? Which have rotational (turn) symmetry?

g. If a figure has reflection symmetry, must it have rotational symmetry? Explain or give a counterexample.

h. If a figure has rotational symmetry, must it have reflection symmetry? Explain or give a counterexample.

6. **c.** Each of the objects B, C, E, F, and H has reflection symmetry. Some students may erroneously think that figure A or G has line symmetry. Figure D has line symmetry if the word "Jamaica" is ignored.

   d. A (180°), C (90°, 180°, 270°), E (120°, 240°), F (60°, 120°, 180°, 240°, 300°), and G (180°). Also, figure D has 180° rotational symmetry if the word "Jamaica" is ignored.

   e. To determine reflection symmetry, most students will draw a line or fold the object in half. To determine rotational symmetry, students probably will physically rotate the objects.

   f.

Reflection Symmetry	**Rotational Symmetry**
square	square (90°)
rectangle	rectangle (180°)
rhombus	rhombus (180°)
kite	parallelogram (180°)

   g. No; a figure such as the Triple A sign in Part c has reflection symmetry but not rotational symmetry.

   h. No; a figure such as figures A or G from Part c has 180° rotational symmetry, but no line symmetry.

Unit 5

CONSTRUCTING A MATH TOOLKIT: Students should summarize the sides-and-angles relationships for polygons, including clarifying diagrams, in their Math Toolkits (Teaching Master 202).

MORE

ASSIGNMENT *pp. 395–401*

Students can now begin Modeling Task 2 or 4, Organizing Task 3, Reflecting Task 3, or Extending Task 5 from the MORE assignment following Investigation 2.

SHARE AND SUMMARIZE full-class discussion

Checkpoint

See Teaching Master 150.

a The logo has four rotational symmetries: 72°, 144°, 216°, and 288°. It also has five lines of symmetry.

b Line symmetry is a property held by a polygon that may be divided in half so that the two halves are mirror images of each other.

c A shape has rotational symmetry if it may be turned around a stationary point a certain number of degrees such that the new figure looks identical to the original figure.

d One procedure is to evaluate the expression $\frac{(n-2) \times 180}{n}$. This yields $\frac{3}{5}(180) = 108°$.

This would be a good time to tie together student statements of characteristics of quadrilaterals and their ideas of symmetries possessed by these quadrilaterals. If you have posted student lists of characteristics with accompanying diagrams, then you could provide a tracing of the shape on an overhead transparency, asking "Can you use reflection symmetry to show why we marked certain angles equal on a kite (rhombus, *etc*.)?" or "Can you use rotation symmetry to confirm angles we marked equal on a square (parallelogram, *etc*.)?"

APPLY individual task

On Your Own

a. Yes. Responses may vary depending on your class definition. One possible response: it is a 2-dimensional closed figure made of line segments which do not cross each other.

b. $Sum = (n-2) \times 180$
$= (8-2) \times 180$
$= 1,080°$

c. $\frac{1,080}{8} = 135°$

d. It has 8 lines of symmetry and rotational or turn symmetries of 45°, 90°, 135°, 180°, 225°, 270°, and 315°.

e. Responses may vary. A yield sign is an equilateral triangle with three symmetry lines and 120° and 240° rotational symmetries. Some students may have seen a square traffic sign.

Checkpoint

Regular polygons have predictable angle measures and symmetry properties.

a Does the logo shown at the right have reflection or rotational symmetry? If so, trace the logo and sketch lines of symmetry or give angles of rotation.

b Describe what is meant by reflection or line symmetry.

c Describe what is meant by rotational or turn symmetry.

d The corner angles of this logo are the same size. Describe how you would determine the measure of any one of these angles without measuring.

Be prepared to share your group's responses with the entire class.

On Your Own

The plane-shape depicted at the right is a drawing of a stop sign (without the word "stop").

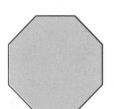

a. Is it a polygon? Explain.

b. What is the *sum* of the measures of its angles?

c. Using what you believe to be true about the shape of stop signs, determine the measure of *each* of its angles.

d. What symmetry, if any, does the shape have?

e. Identify another traffic sign that is in the shape of a regular polygon. Describe the shape and its symmetry.

INVESTIGATION 2 Patterns with Polygons

In a regular polygon, all sides are the same length and all angles are the same size. Because of these characteristics, regular polygons have many useful applications. Prism-like packages are often designed with regular polygons as bases. If you think about tiled walls or floors you have seen, it is likely that the tiles were regular polygons.

1. The figures below show portions of **tilings** of equilateral triangles and squares. The tilings are made of repeated copies of a shape placed edge-to-edge. In this way, the tilings completely cover a region without overlaps or gaps.

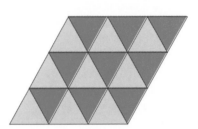 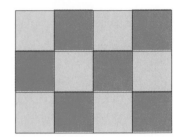

   a. Assume that the tilings are extended indefinitely in all directions to cover the plane. Describe the symmetries of each tiling.

   b. For each tiling:
   - What is the total measure of the angles at a common vertex?
   - What is the measure of each angle at a common vertex?

   c. Using the tiling with equilateral triangles, identify other common polygons formed by two or more triangles. Sketch each and show the equilateral triangles that form the shape.

2. You have seen that equilateral triangular regions tile a plane. In this activity, you will explore other kinds of triangular regions that can be used as tiles.

   a. Each member of your group should cut from poster board a small triangle that is *not* equilateral. Each member's triangle should have a shape different from the other members' triangles. Individually, explore whether a tiling of a plane can be made by using repeated tracings of your triangular region. Draw and compare sketches of the tilings you made.

   b. Can more than one tiling pattern be made by using copies of one triangular shape? If so, illustrate with sketches.

   c. Do you think any triangular shape could be used to tile a plane? Explain your reasoning.

3. You saw above that square regions can tile a plane. In this activity, you will explore other quadrilaterals that can be used to make a tiling.

   a. Each member of your group should cut a non-square quadrilateral from poster board. Again, each of the quadrilaterals should be shaped differently. Individually, investigate whether a tiling of a plane can be made with the different quadrilaterals. Draw sketches of the tilings you made.

INVESTIGATION ▶ 2 Patterns with Polygons

Some regular polygons are used in many everyday activities, because they fit together to make a tessellation, because they are attractive in patterns, and because they can be used to build space-shapes including the Platonic space-shapes (tetrahedron, hexahedron or cube, octahedron, dodecahedron, and icosahedron). In this investigation, students identify regular polygons that tile a plane, and make and interpret nets for space-shapes. Activity 2 Part b, Activity 3, Activity 4 Part b, and Activity 5 are the most challenging. Some additional comments can be found with Activities 2 and 3, and it may be worthwhile to read those sections now.

If your students have access to TI-92 calculators, you may wish to use "Geometric Investigations for the Classrooms" from Texas Instruments as an alternative way to help students understand the tessellation and tiling concepts in this investigation.

1. **a.** Responses will vary as there are many types of symmetry. In the equilateral triangle design, the triangles themselves have rotational and reflectional symmetry. If we consider two strips of the tiling triangles, we see there is a horizontal axis of symmetry mapping one row of triangles onto another. Finally, if we consider the four equilateral triangles that comprise a larger equilateral triangle, we see they have the same reflectional and rotational symmetries as the original triangles.

    In the square design, the squares themselves have rotational and reflectional symmetry. Larger squares may be constructed of the small squares that exhibit analogous rotational and reflectional symmetries.

    b. In the triangle design, the total measure of angles at a vertex is 360° and each angle has a measure of 60°. In the square design, the total measure is also 360°, and each angle has a measure of 90°.

    c. Responses will vary. Three examples are:

    See additional Teaching Notes on page T418S.

Unit 5

Master 151

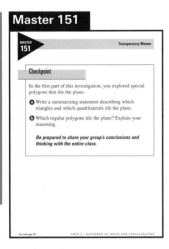

Master 152

EXPLORE *continued*

3. **b.** Squares, rectangles, and kites have a single pattern. Trapezoids, rhombi, and nonrectangular parallelograms have two patterns.

   c. All quadrilaterals will tile the plane.

4. **a.** A regular pentagon does not tile. One argument would relate to the angles at a point: $3 \times 108° = 324°$, which leaves $36°$ unfilled at each vertex.

   b. A regular hexagon tiles the plane. Each interior angle is $120°$ and three fit without a gap or overlap around each point.

   c. The measure of each interior angle of a regular polygon with more than six sides has a measure greater than $120°$. The next largest integer that is both greater than $120°$ and a factor of $360°$ is $180°$. Since the measure of an interior angle of a regular polygon is less than $180°$, there is no regular polygon of more than six sides that tiles the plane.

SHARE AND SUMMARIZE full-class discussion

Checkpoint

See Teaching Master 151.

ⓐ All triangles and all quadrilaterals will tile the plane.

ⓑ Triangles, squares, and hexagons are the only regular polygons that tile the plane because the measure of each interior angle is a factor of $360°$.

CONSTRUCTING A MATH TOOLKIT: Ask all the students to summarize this Checkpoint in their Math Toolkits. They may also wish to add the tiling characteristic to the list of characteristics they entered previously for each of the quadrilaterals.

APPLY individual task

▶On Your Own

See Activity Master 152.

Colored pencils will help students shade the tiling pattern.

Responses will vary, but here is a common choice for a pentagon that tessellates:

See additional Teaching Notes on page T418T.

b. For those quadrilaterals that tile, can more than one tiling pattern be made using the same shape? If so, illustrate and explain.

c. Make a conjecture about which quadrilaterals can be used to tile a plane.

4. You have seen two regular polygons which tile the plane. Now explore other regular polygons that could be used to make a tiling.

a. Can a regular pentagon tile the plane? Explain your reasoning.

b. Can a regular hexagon tile the plane? Explain.

c. Will any regular polygon of more than six sides tile the plane? Provide an argument supporting your view.

Checkpoint

In the first part of this investigation, you explored special polygons that tile the plane.

ⓐ Write a summarizing statement describing which triangles and which quadrilaterals tile the plane.

ⓑ Which regular polygons tile the plane? Explain your reasoning.

Be prepared to share your group's conclusions and thinking with the entire class.

▶ **On Your Own**

Using a copy of the figure at the right, find a pentagon in the figure that will tile the plane. Shade it. Show as many different tiling patterns for your pentagon as you can.

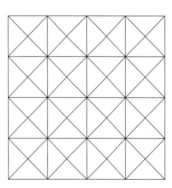

5. Tilings which use only one type of shape are called **pure tessellations**. Those that use more than one type of shape are called **semi-pure tessellations**. Two semi-pure tessellations are shown at the top of the following page. The pattern on the left is from a Persian porcelain painting. The pattern on the right is from the Taj Mahal mausoleum in India.

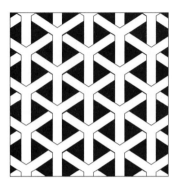

a. Examine carefully each of these patterns. How many different shapes are used in the tessellation on the left? How many different shapes are used in the tessellation on the right?

b. Examine the semi-pure tessellation shown below.

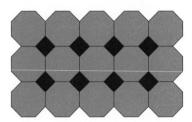

- Use angle measure to explain why the polygons will fit together with no overlaps or gaps.
- At each vertex, is there the same combination and order of polygons?

c. In some semi-pure tessellations of regular polygons, at each vertex there is the same arrangement of polygons. These tilings are called **semi-regular tessellations**. Test whether a regular hexagon, two squares, and an equilateral triangle can be used to make a semi-regular tessellation. If possible, draw a sketch of the tessellation.

d. Semi-regular tessellations are coded by listing the number of sides of the polygons at each vertex. The numbers are arranged in order with the smallest number first. The tessellation in Part b is 4, 8, 8. Use this code to describe:

- the tessellation of equilateral triangles and regular hexagons at the beginning of this lesson (page 383);
- the tessellation you drew in Part c;
- each of the three possible pure edge-to-edge tessellations of regular polygons.

5. **a.** The Persian pattern (on the left) uses two shapes: the black triangle and the white "Y" shape. There are three different shapes used in the pattern on the right: a dodecagon (the star), and a regular and a nonregular hexagon.

    b. ■ Each interior angle in a regular octagon is 135°, and each interior angle in a square is 90°. At each vertex of the first tessellation, there are two octagons and one square, so 135° + 135° + 90° = 360°.

       ■ Yes, at each vertex there are two octagons and one square.

    c. Yes: 120° + 90° + 90° + 60° = 360°.

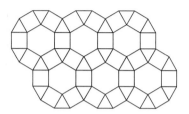

    d. ■ The code is 3, 6, 3, 6.

       ■ The code is 3, 4, 6, 4.

       ■ The code for equilateral triangles is 3, 3, 3, 3, 3, 3.
The code for squares is 4, 4, 4, 4.
The code for hexagons is 6, 6, 6.

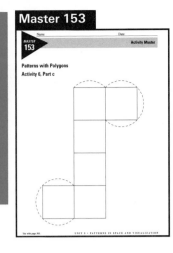

6. a. Nets i and ii can be folded to make a cube.

  b. It is best *not* to distribute Activity Master 153 before students attempt this task. Students should first try to answer the die question by visualization. Another option would be for students to simply sketch a net similar to the one in the text, label and cut out the sketch, and assemble it. Students who still need help can be given a copy of Activity Master 153 to help them.

Responses may vary. Here is one possible net:

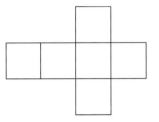

  c. See Activity Master 153.

Die iii is formed by the net on the left.

A **net** is a two-dimensional pattern which can be folded to form a three-dimensional shape. R. Buckminster Fuller, inventor of the geodesic dome (see Extending Task 4 on page 353), created a net for a "globe" of the earth. In the modified version below, each equilateral triangle contains an equal amount of the Earth's surface area.

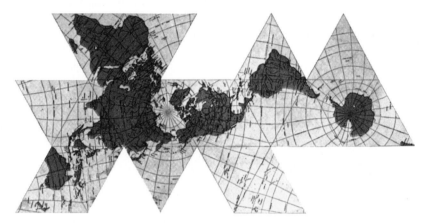

6. To begin your study of nets, consider possible nets for a cube.

   a. Examine the three nets shown below. Which of these nets can be folded to make a cube?

   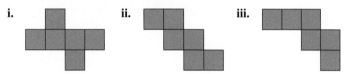

      i.   ii.   iii.

   b. Make a new net of your own that can be folded to make a cube.

   c. Which die could be formed from the net on the left?

   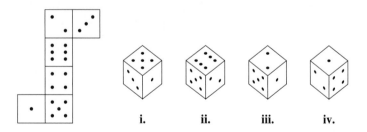

            i.   ii.   iii.   iv.

7. The equilateral triangle is more versatile than the square when it comes to making nets for space-shapes. You can make three different space-shapes using nets of only equilateral triangles attached to each other. Use copies of congruent equilateral triangles to complete this activity.

a. Attach four equilateral triangles edge-to-edge. What space-shapes can you form by folding your pattern? What *complete* (with no open faces) space-shapes can you form? Sketch the net and the complete space-shape formed. Find another pattern of the four triangles that can be folded into the same shape. Sketch your net. You have made a **tetrahedron**.

b. Now try your hand at making a space-shape with eight equilateral triangular faces. Draw a net of eight equilateral triangles that will fold into a space-shape. Sketch the net and the space-shape. You have made an **octahedron**.

c. Examine the net of a "globe" shown on the previous page.

- How many equilateral triangles are in this net?
- When the net is folded to form the "globe," how many triangles are at each vertex?
- Fuller's globe shown at the right is an example of a space-shape called an **icosahedron**. Make an icosahedron model.

Checkpoint

Nets can provide an efficient way of forming space-shapes whose faces are polygons.

ⓐ Sketch a net of squares that can be folded into an open-top box.

ⓑ How could you modify your net in Part a so that it could be folded into a model of a house with a peaked roof?

ⓒ Compare the sum of angle measures at a common vertex of a tiling with those of a net.

Be prepared to share your sketches, findings, and reasoning with the class.

▶ On Your Own

A cereal box is shown at the right. Draw a net for a model of it. Cut out your net and verify that it can be folded into a model of the box.

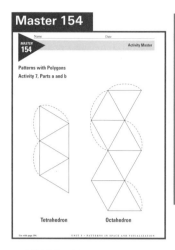

7. **See Activity Master 154 for Parts a and b.**
    a. Tetrahedron
    b. Octahedron
    c. **See Activity Master 155.**
        - There are 20 equilateral triangles in the net.
        - Five triangles meet at each vertex.

SHARE AND SUMMARIZE **full-class discussion**

Checkpoint

See Teaching Master 156.

ⓐ There are a variety of possibilities. Show some on the overhead and see if students can tell (visually) whether they fold to an open top box or not. Use their suggested nets. One possibility is:

ⓑ One possibility is:

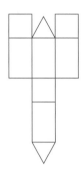

ⓒ The angles sum to 360° at the vertex of a tiling; the sum must be less than 360° at the vertex of a net to allow for folding.

APPLY **individual task**

▶On Your Own

Responses will vary.
One possibility is:

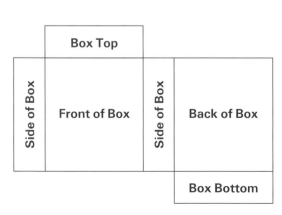

MORE
ASSIGNMENT   *pp. 395–401*

Modeling: 2 or 4, and 5*
Organizing: 1 and 3
Reflecting: Choose one*
Extending: Choose one*

When choice is indicated, it is important to leave the choice to the student.
NOTE: *It is best if Organizing tasks are discussed as a whole class after they have been assigned as homework.*

MORE   **independent assignment**

Modeling

1. **a.** The individual rectangular designs have 180° rotational symmetry. The larger rectangle designs that include two rows of triangles and the rectangles between them also have 180° rotational symmetry.

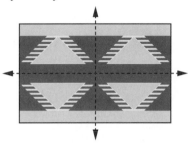

   b. Each rectangle has horizontal and vertical line symmetry. The triangles all have line symmetry; the larger ones have vertical line symmetry while the smaller ones are symmetric through an angle line. The single rows of triangles have vertical line symmetry only through the center triangle. The double rows of triangles have both horizontal and vertical line symmetry. (See the diagram in Part a.)

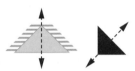

   c. Since both the rectangles and the double rows of triangles have rotational and line symmetry, the center of rotation is at the intersection of the horizontal and vertical symmetry lines.

2. **a.** The center of rotational symmetry of each star is the intersection of the diagonals of the square which contains the star. The magnitudes of the rotation are 45°, 90°, 135°, 180°, 225°, 270°, and 315°.

   b. There is no line symmetry in the stars because the dark and light parts of the stars are not line symmetric.

   c. With color, the whole quilt has 180° rotational symmetry and no line symmetry.

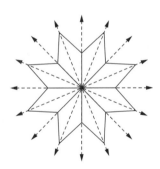

MORE
Modeling • Organizing • Reflecting • Extending

Modeling

1. Examine the picture at the right of a Native American rug.

   a. Are there any designs in this rug that have rotational symmetry? Sketch each design and describe the angles through which it can be turned.

   b. Are there any designs in this rug that have line symmetry? Sketch each design and the lines of symmetry.

   c. Are there any designs which have both rotational and line symmetry? If so, identify them. Where is the center of rotation in relation to the lines of symmetry?

2. Polygons and symmetry are important components of the arts and crafts of many cultures.

   a. The design of the quilt below is called "Star of Bethlehem." What rotational symmetry do you see in the fundamental "stars"? List the degree measure of each turn that will rotate each shape onto itself.

   b. What line symmetry do you see in the "stars"? Sketch to illustrate.

   c. Does the quilt as a whole have rotational or line symmetry? Describe each symmetry you find.

3. Here is a two-person game that can be played on any regular polygon. To play, place a penny on each vertex of the polygon. Take turns removing one or two pennies from adjacent vertices. The player who picks up the last coin is the winner.

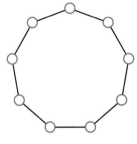

   a. Suppose the game is played on a nine-sided polygon, as shown at the left. Try to find a strategy using symmetry that will permit the second player to win always. Write a description of your strategy.

   b. Will the strategy you found work if the game is played on any polygon with an odd number of vertices? Explain your reasoning.

   c. Suppose the game is played on a polygon with an even number of vertices, say an octagon. Try to find a strategy that will guarantee that the second player still can win always. Write a description of this strategy.

4. Objects in nature are often symmetric in form.

   a. The shapes below are single-celled sea plants called *diatoms*.

   ■ Identify all of the symmetries of these diatoms.

   ■ For those with reflection symmetry, sketch the shape and show the lines of symmetry.

   ■ For those with rotational symmetry, describe the angles of rotation.

A   **B**

C   **D**

   b. Identify all of the symmetries of the two flowers shown below.

   ■ If the flower has line symmetry, sketch the shape and draw the lines of symmetry.

   ■ If the flower has rotational symmetry, describe the angles of rotation.

A 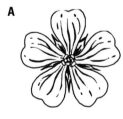   **B**

Geranium   Periwinkle

3. a. If your opponent selects 1 coin, visually draw the line of symmetry which contains the exposed vertex and choose the 2 coins on the opposite side of the 9-sided polygon. Using the same line of reflection, always choose the mirror image of your opponent's play. If your opponent selects 2 coins, draw the symmetry line between the 2 vertices. Then choose the one coin on that symmetry line (see diagram). Proceed as before, choosing the mirror image of your opponent's play.

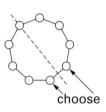

choose

b. Yes, as long as the polygon is regular, it will have a line of symmetry as in the diagram.

c. With an even number of vertices, you again would draw the symmetry line either containing the 1 coin or between the 2 coins your opponent chose. Mirror your opponent's play.

4. a. Diatom A:
reflection symmetry (3 lines)
rotational symmetry (120°, 240°)

Diatom B:
reflection symmetry (2 lines)
rotational symmetry (180°)

Diatom C:
reflection symmetry (4 lines)
rotational symmetry (90°, 180°, 270°)

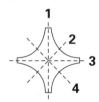

Diatom D:
reflection symmetry (8 lines)
rotational symmetry (45°, 90°, 135°, 180°, 225°, 270°, 315°)

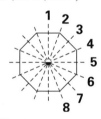

b. Flower A:
line symmetry (5 lines)
rotational symmetry
(72°, 144°, 216°, 288°)

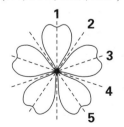

Flower B:
no line symmetry
rotational symmetry
(72°, 144°, 216°, 288°)

4. **c.** ■ The snowflakes all have line symmetry (6 lines) and rotational symmetry (60°, 120°, 180°, 240°, 300°).

■ So, although their designs are different, the snowflakes are exactly alike in symmetry.

5. **a.** The box will be a triangular prism.

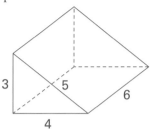

b. Responses will vary. Two examples are given at the right.

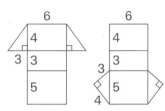

c. $V = Bh = \frac{1}{2}(3 \times 4) \times 6 = 36 \text{ cm}^3$

d. $A = 2\left(\frac{1}{2} \times 3 \times 4\right) + (6 \times 5) + (6 \times 4) + (6 \times 3) = 84 \text{ cm}^2$

e. The box has a plane of symmetry positioned directly between and parallel to the two triangular bases. The faces that are cut by the plane of symmetry (the rectangular faces) are cut on a symmetry line of the face.

Organizing

1. **a.** Ellen's rule is correct. One way of concluding this is to visualize a regular *n*-gon and add edges internally from one vertex until the *n*-gon is a collection of triangles. For example, with the regular hexagon, the transition would look like:

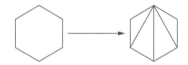

In general, $n - 2$ triangles will be found. Then, using the fact established earlier that the sum of the interior angles of any triangle is 180°, students can reason that the *sum* of the interior angles of an *n*-gon is $(n - 2) \cdot 180°$. Now determining one of the interior angles may be done by simply dividing $(n - 2) \cdot 180°$ by *n*, since each angle of the *n*-gon has the same measure.

b. As the number of sides of a regular polygon increases, the measure of one of its angles increases as well. However, the change is *not* constant, as may be seen from the second column of the table in Part e.

c. 162°. No tiling could be made since multiples of 162° do not fit around a point of rotation.

c. It has been said that no two snowflakes are identical.

■ Identify the symmetries of the snowflakes below.

■ In terms of their symmetry, how are the snowflakes alike?

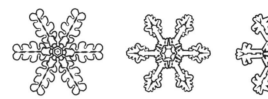

5. Great Lakes Packaging manufactures boxes for many different companies. Shown below is the net for one type of box manufactured for a candy company.

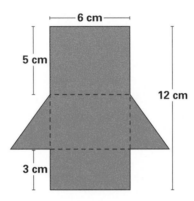

a. Sketch the box.

b. Sketch two other possible nets that could be used to manufacture the same box.

c. Find the volume of the box.

d. Find the surface area of the box.

e. Does the box have any symmetries? If so, explain how the symmetries are related to the symmetries of its faces.

Organizing

1. In Investigation 1 of this lesson, Ellen invented the rule $A = \frac{(n-2)180}{n}$ to predict the measure A of one angle of a regular n-gon.

a. Do you think Ellen's rule is correct? Explain your reasoning.

b. As the number of sides of a regular polygon increases, how does the measure of one of its angles change? Is the rate of change constant? Explain.

c. Use Ellen's rule to predict the measure of one angle of a regular 20-gon. Could a tessellation be made of regular 20-gons? Explain your reasoning.

d. When will the measure of each angle of a regular polygon be a whole number?

e. Use your calculator or computer software to produce a table of values for angle measures of various regular polygons. Use your table to help explain why only regular polygons of 3, 4, or 6 sides will tile a plane.

2. Examine the two histograms below.

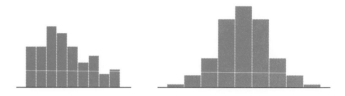

a. Locate any lines of symmetry for the two histograms.

b. On each histogram, estimate the location of the median and mean.

c. If a distribution is symmetric, what can you conclude about its median and mean? Explain your reasoning.

d. If a distribution is symmetric, what, if anything, can you conclude about its mode? Explain your reasoning.

3. Shown below are graphs of various relations between variables *x* and *y*. The scale on the axes is 1.

a. For each graph, locate any line of symmetry. Write the equation of the symmetry line.

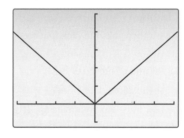 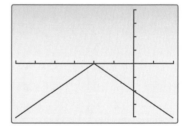

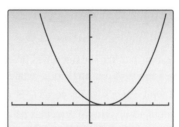 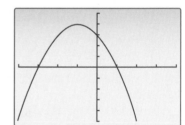

1. **d.** The measure is a whole number when the number of sides is a factor of 360.

   e. The only regular polygons whose interior angles have measures that divide $360°$ (namely $60°$, $90°$, and $120°$) are the 3-gon (triangle), 4-gon (square), and 6-gon (hexagon). Therefore, multiples of each of these three polygons fit evenly around a point.

Number of Sides of Regular Polygon	Measure of Each Interior Angle
3	$60°$
4	$90°$
5	$108°$
6	$120°$
7	$128\frac{4}{7}° \approx 128.6°$
8	$135°$
9	$140°$
10	$144°$
11	$147\frac{3}{11}° \approx 147.3°$
12	$150°$

2. **This task asks students to think again about interpreting displays of data and thus asks them to recall ideas of mean, median, and mode.**

   a.

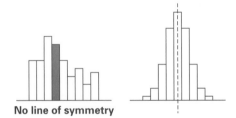

   No line of symmetry

   b. On the first histogram, the median would fall about on the shaded bar (the value corresponding to that bar), whereas the mean might lie between the values corresponding to the 4th and 5th bars.

   On the second histogram, the median and mean equal the value corresponding to the highest bar.

   c. If the distribution is symmetric, the mean and median will be the same.

   d. Nothing can be concluded about the mode. For example the histogram on the right below is symmetric but does not have a mode. The one on the left is symmetric and bimodal.

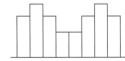

3. Symmetry is a useful description of graphs.

   a. The lines of symmetry are $x = 0$, $x = -2$, $x = 1$, and $x = -1$.

Unit 5

3. **b.** Since the *y*-axis is a line of symmetry, the reflection of the point $(-8, -23)$ over the *y*-axis must be on the graph. This point has coordinates $(8, -23)$.

4. A regular *n*-gon has *n* lines of symmetry (vertex to midpoint of opposite side if *n* is odd, and either vertex to opposite vertex or midpoint to opposite midpoint if *n* is even). A regular *n*-gon has $n - 1$ rotational symmetries (360° is not included).

5. **a.** A circle has an infinite number of symmetry lines, each a diameter of the circle. A circle has an infinite number of rotational symmetries, each with the center of rotation at the center of the circle.

   b. **i.** The only point fixed under a rotation is the center.

   ii. Fold the circle in half, then fold the resulting semicircle in half. The tip of the resulting quarter-circle will be the center.

   iii. Some students may suggest drawing two nonparallel segments whose endpoints are on the circle. Draw the symmetry lines of each (perpendicular bisector). The intersection of these two lines is the center.

   c. Rotationally symmetric figures can be inscribed in a circle whose center is the center of rotation. So, by picturing that circle and using one of the methods in Part b to find the center of it, you can find the center of rotation of the figure.

6. There are four lines of symmetry in the tree curve: horizontal, vertical, and 45° diagonal lines through the center of the diagram. The tree curve has rotational symmetries of 90°, 180°, and 270°. There are no symmetry lines in the dragon curve. It has rotational symmetries of 90°, 180°, and 270°.

Reflecting

1. There are many reasons why logos are symmetric: symmetric figures are more pleasing to the eye; symmetry provides some balance to the figure; and symmetry generally helps us remember the figure.

2. For many, it is easier to find line symmetry in a shape because the figure does not have to be moved (rotated) to identify line symmetry. Also, line symmetry is very familiar to us because the human body is basically line symmetric.

b. Suppose you have a graph and its line of symmetry is the *y*-axis. If one point on the graph has coordinates (–8, –23), what is the *y*-coordinate of the point on the graph with *x*-coordinate 8? Explain your reasoning.

4. In general, how many lines of symmetry does a regular *n*-gon have? How many rotational symmetries?

5. Circles have both line and rotational symmetries.

a. Describe all the line and rotational symmetries of a circle as completely as possible.

b. If you are given a circle, how can you find its center? Describe as many different ways as you can.

c. How can you use a method for finding the center of a circle to help you find the point of rotation for a shape that has rotational symmetry?

6. The following two figures come from a branch of mathematics called *fractal geometry*. Describe all the line and rotational symmetries of each figure as completely as you can.

Tree Curve

Dragon Curve

Reflecting

1. Thumb through the yellow pages of a phone directory noting the shape of company logos. Why do you think so many of the logo designs are symmetric?

2. Do you find it easier to recognize line symmetry or rotational symmetry in a shape? What do you think might explain this fact?

3. Cross-cultural studies suggest that symmetry is a fundamental idea that all people use to help understand, remember, compare, and reproduce forms. However, symmetry preferences have been found across cultures. One study found that symmetry about a vertical line was easier to recognize than symmetry about a horizontal line. The study also found that symmetry about a diagonal line was the most difficult to detect. (Palmer, S.E. and K. Henenway. 1978. Orientation and symmetry: effects of multiple, rotational, and near symmetries. *Journal of Experimental Psychology* 4[4]: 691–702.)

   a. Would the findings of the study apply to the way in which you perceive line symmetry?

   b. Describe a simple experiment that you could conduct to test these findings.

4. Tiling patterns often are found on floors and walls. What tiling patterns are most common in homes, schools, and shopping malls? What might explain this?

5. In Investigation 2 of this lesson, you examined shapes that tessellate a plane—a flat surface. Examine at least three of the following balls: baseball, softball, basketball, tennis ball, volleyball, and soccer ball.

   a. Is it possible to tessellate a sphere?

   b. If so, is the tessellation pure or semipure? Is it semi-regular?

   c. Find a National Geographic magazine with a world map in it. How do the map-makers use the idea of tessellations in their production of world maps reproduced on a flat surface?

   ## Extending

1. Using a computer drawing utility or a straightedge and compass, design a simple quilt pattern. Try to use polygonal shapes which were not used in the designs shown in this lesson. Print or draw your pattern and then indicate all symmetry lines of the design.

2. How could you use a circle to draw a 10-sided polygon with sides of equal length? Try it. Does the polygon have rotational symmetry? If so, through what angles can it be turned? Where is the center?

3. Find as many nets of six squares as you can that will fold to make a cube. Sketch each. (*Hint:* There are more than ten!)

3. **a.** Responses may vary. A sample response could be: The findings of the Palmer and Henenway study would apply to the way in which I perceive line symmetry since the first line symmetry I look for is vertical, the second is horizontal, with "diagonal" last.

   b. A simple experiment to test these findings would be to make copies of a shape with vertical, horizontal, and diagonal lines of symmetry (like the Tree Curve on page 399), pass them out, and ask people to draw any lines of symmetry they see, labeling the lines 1, 2, 3, *etc.*, based on which one they saw first, second, *etc.*

4. It seems the most common tiling patterns involve quadrilaterals; in particular, squares and rectangles. Visually they are not as "busy." They are easier to install. They are probably easier to manufacture.

5. **a.** Yes; see Part b.

   b. A tennis ball, softball, or baseball is pure. All three are made by joining two of the shapes shown at the right.

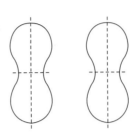

   A volleyball is semi-pure. A volleyball is made by joining six of the shapes shown at the right.

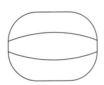

   A soccer ball is semi-pure and semi-regular. A soccer ball is made of 12 pentagons and 30 hexagons.

   c. It cuts the globe in roughly triangular wedges that begin at the poles. These are flattened out to get a less distorted map.

Extending

1. Designs will vary.

See additional Teaching Notes on page T418U.

Unit 5

Patterns with Polygons
Extending Task 4

Dodecahedron

4. **a.** **See Activity Master 157.**

   b. Student work

   c. One possible result is:

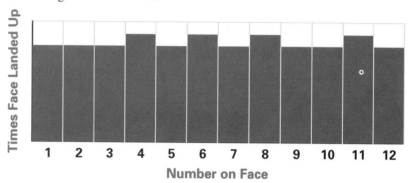

Number on Face	1	2	3	4	5	6	7	8	9	10	11	12
Times Face Landed Up	8	8	8	9	8	9	8	9	8	8	9	8

   d. The histogram is almost flat.

   Times Face Landed Up

   1 2 3 4 5 6 7 8 9 10 11 12

   Number on Face

   e. The resulting histogram should be very similar to the one above.

5. **a.**

Quadrilateral Type	Relationship Between Diagonals and Lines of Symmetry
Square	In a square, the diagonals are the same length and they are perpendicular bisectors of each other. Each is a line of symmetry.
Rhombus	The diagonals are perpendicular bisectors of each other. Each is a line of symmetry.
Parallelogram	Although the diagonals divide the parallelogram into two triangles of equal area, neither is a line of symmetry (unless the parallelogram is also a rhombus).
Rectangle	Again, the diagonals divide the rectangle into two triangles of equal area, but are not lines of symmetry (unless the rectangle is also a square).
Isosceles Trapezoid	Diagonals of an isosceles trapezoid are the same length but are not lines of symmetry.
Kite	Diagonals are perpendicular bisectors of each other. The diagonal that connects the intersections of the congruent sides is a line of symmetry.

   b. Let D_n represent the number of diagonals in an n-gon. (For example, $D_3 = 0$.)
   Then $D_n = \dfrac{n(n-3)}{2}$ for $n = 3, 4, 5, \ldots$. At each vertex you draw a diagonal to all but 3 of the vertices of the polygon. You do not use the two adjacent vertices or the vertex itself. This is represented by $(n-3)$. Doing this for each vertex would give you $n(n-3)$ segments, but you have drawn each diagonal twice (once for each endpoint). So dividing by two will give the number of diagonals.
   A recursive definition would be $NEXT = NOW + (n-2)$, starting at $NOW = 0$ and $n = 4$, or $D_n = D_{n-1} + (n-2)$, starting at $n = 4$ and $D_3 = 0$.

6. Responses will reflect each student's work. The folds are lines of symmetry.
   (For examples and extensions of this project, refer to the April 1991 issue of the *Mathematics Teacher*.)

4. The space-shape shown here is made of 12 regular pentagons. It is called a **dodecahedron**.

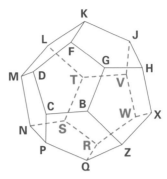

  a. Use a net of pentagons to make a dodecahedron shell.

  b. Make a die by numbering the faces.

  c. Toss the die 100 times. Record the number of times each face lands up.

  d. Make a histogram of your data in Part c. What do you observe?

  e. Repeat Parts a–d for a dodecahedral die for which the opposite faces add to 13. Compare your histograms.

5. The **diagonals** of a polygon are segments connecting pairs of vertices which are not endpoints of the same side.

  a. Examine the diagonals of each type of quadrilateral. For which quadrilaterals are the diagonals lines of symmetry?

  b. Develop a formula for the number of diagonals in any *n*-gon.

6. A *kapa pohopoho* is a Hawaiian quilt made from twelve or more unique designs. The original designs exhibit reflection and rotational symmetry. Each design is cut from one piece of fabric and sewn onto a square piece of background fabric. The following steps illustrate one way to create a Hawaiian quilt design.

"Kualoa" © Helen M. Friend, 1991.

  a. Fold a piece of square paper in half by bringing the bottom side up to meet the top. Fold this half portion into a square. Note which corner of the new square is the center of the original square. Fold along the diagonal that has this corner as one vertex. You now should have a right triangle with one end of the hypotenuse at the center of the original square. The other end is at the point where the four corners of the original square meet. Sketch a design along the leg of the right triangle adjacent to the four corners of the original square. Cut along your design.

  b. Unfold your pattern. If the design has reflection symmetry, sketch in the lines of symmetry. If the design has rotational symmetry, identify the center and angles of rotation.

  c. If you open up the folded square before making any cuts, what lines should your folds represent? (You can repeat Part a to check.)

  d. How does your design compare with those of your classmates?

  e. What would happen if you started with a circle or an equilateral triangle instead of a square? Can you make designs with only one line of symmetry? With two lines? With more than two lines? Explain your reasoning.

INVESTIGATION 3 Symmetry Patterns in Strips

Many plane-shapes and space-shapes have symmetry, either about a line, a point, or a plane. Artists have used these types of symmetry for centuries. For example, from earliest history, space-shapes often have been decorated with *strip patterns*.

1. Imagine slicing the Native American jar at the right by a symmetry plane and then "flattening out" the shape.

   a. Draw what you think would be the strip pattern along the center of the plane-shape.

   b. What is it about the pattern that permitted you to draw the full pattern without seeing the back of the jar?

2. Shown below are some general strip patterns commonly used for decorative art. Imagine that each strip pattern extends indefinitely to the right and to the left.

   a. Examine each pattern and make a sketch of the next two shapes to the right in the pattern.

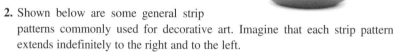
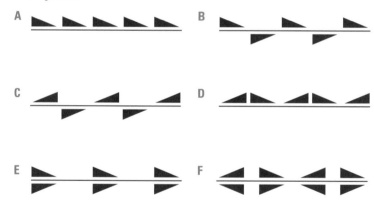

   b. Examine the design symmetries of the two bracelet patterns below. Match each pattern with the strip pattern in Part a which it most resembles.

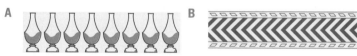

INVESTIGATION ▶ 3 Symmetry Patterns in Strips

During this investigation, students will begin to recognize and create translational and glide reflection symmetries and use isometric (distance preserving) transformations to analyze and create symmetric patterns in the plane. Students will extend the idea of symmetry from rotational and reflection symmetry to situations involving infinite patterns. The symmetry we refer to is *translational symmetry*. This symmetry is best illustrated using linear strips called *strip patterns*. If you can translate a section of the strip along the line of the strip so that it maps onto itself, then the strip has translational symmetry. Note that this is an instance of symmetry because the shape (the strip) maps onto itself. But note also that the strip must be infinite since a translation of magnitude greater than 0 leaves no point fixed.

One way to introduce this investigation is to show the class a strip pattern and ask them to explain how it was created. That is, how would you explain to someone else how to make this strip? The initial introduction in the student material uses a Native American jar to illustrate the idea, but you may wish to use one of the examples in the Modeling tasks or one of your own choosing as a substitute. For example, many buildings and homes have decorative elements that contain strip patterns (stencil patterns, frieze patterns, pictures by Mary Engelbreit) that could be used to introduce this investigation as well.

Students should work in small groups to complete Activities 1–4 and the Checkpoint that follows. As you move from group to group, check to see that students have discovered that the figure being translated does not have to be a single figure like the original examples. The definition they write should not include rotating figures (yet). As always, encourage clear, concise language as they develop their definition for translation.

1. **a.** Responses may vary. One strip pattern on the jar is:

    b. The pattern repeats itself (presumably around the entire jar).

2. **a.**

     A  B C

    D  E  F

    b. The first bracelet matches pattern D (vertical line reflection). The second bracelet matches pattern E (horizontal reflection).

2. c. Each figure in the pattern is the same size, and the pattern repeats itself by sliding over the same distance and direction each time.

   d. Responses may vary. For example, "In a translation, points in the original figure move an identical distance along parallel paths to create the image. The size of the figure does not change."

3. a. Yes, each figure in the pattern is the same size, and the pattern repeats itself by sliding over the same distance and direction each time. You may need to remind students that they are looking for overall symmetry patterns, even though there are slight imperfections in the figures.

   b. Vertical line reflection: Patterns C, F, and G

      Horizontal line reflection: Patterns E and G

      180° Rotation symmetry: Patterns D, F (if the center of rotation is carefully chosen), and G

   c. Yes, the pattern transforms onto itself.

c. Each of the strip patterns in Parts a and b exhibit slide or *translational symmetry*. What are two essential characteristics of the patterns that ensure translational symmetry?

d. Write a definition of translational symmetry for strip patterns. Compare your group's definition with that of other groups. Work out any differences.

3. The portions of the strip patterns below come from artwork on the pottery of San Ildefonso Pueblo, New Mexico.

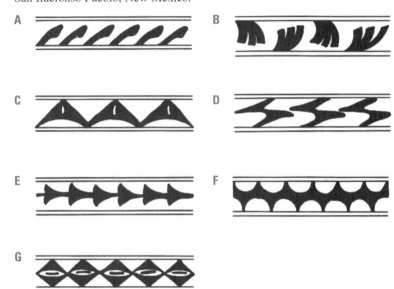

Source: Crowe, D.W. and D.K. Washburn. "Groups and Geometry in the Ceramic Art of San Ildefonso." *Algebras, Groups and Geometries* 2, no. 3 (September 1985): 263–277.

a. Confirm that each pattern has translational symmetry.

b. Examine each strip for reflection and rotational symmetries. If a strip has such a symmetry, it appears the same before and after it is reflected across a line or rotated about a point. Systematically record your results.

c. Look again at strip pattern B. It has neither rotational nor reflection symmetry. However, consider the following *transformation*:

Slide the strip to the right so the first "shape" is above the second "shape." Now reflect the entire strip over the horizontal line through the middle of the strip.

Does the pattern of the strip transform onto itself?

d. Make a sketch of your footprints as they would appear if you walked a straight line in snow or damp sand. How is your footprint strip pattern related to the transformation described in Part c?

e. Using the shape below, draw a strip pattern that has the type of symmetry described in Part c.

The transformation described in Part c of Activity 3 is called a **glide reflection** because you glide (translate) and reflect.

4. Re-examine the seven strip designs of the San Ildefonso Pueblo on page 403. Do any of these patterns have glide reflection symmetry? If so, record it with your other results from Part b of Activity 3.

Checkpoint

Strip patterns by design have translational symmetry. But often they have other symmetries as well.

ⓐ What symmetries, other than translational symmetry, are evident in some strip patterns?

ⓑ Describe how you can test a strip pattern for various symmetries.

Be prepared to share and explain your group's descriptions.

▶On Your Own

Design an interesting strip pattern that has reflection symmetry about a horizontal line and has translational symmetry.

INVESTIGATION ▶4 Symmetry Patterns in Planes

Strip patterns often form a decorative border for other designs that cover part of a plane. Plane tiling patterns are far more numerous than strip designs. They can be found in the floor coverings, ceramic tile work, and textiles of many cultures. The walls and floors of the Alhambra, a thirteenth-century Moorish palace in Granada, Spain, contain some of the finest early examples of this kind of mathematical art. Note the variety of their patterns in the photo at the top of the following page.

3. d. If you could slide the prints of the right foot forward, then reflect them across the horizontal line, they would look like the left foot.

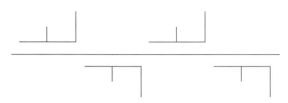

The same motion is true for the left side of the strip.

e.

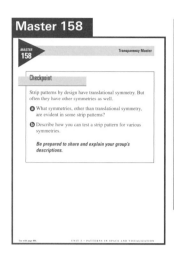

Master 158

MASTER 158   Transparency Master

Checkpoint

Strip patterns by design have translational symmetry. But often they have other symmetries as well.

ⓐ What symmetries, other than translational symmetry, are evident in some strip patterns?

ⓑ Describe how you can test a strip pattern for various symmetries.

Be prepared to share and explain your group's descriptions.

4. The identification of strip patterns can be somewhat subjective. Students should be able to give a clear justification for their choices. The two patterns which are most likely to be labeled "glide reflection" are B and F (move the shape so that the bottom line of humps is directly under the former locations of the upper line of humps; then reflect over the midline). Some students may also label E and G as glide reflections; however, these patterns are usually categorized by their line symmetries since we are looking for the most efficient transforming method. All strip patterns with midline reflection symmetry have glide reflection symmetry by default. Thus, they are excluded.

SHARE AND SUMMARIZE · full-class discussion

Checkpoint

See Teaching Master 158.

ⓐ Strip patterns may have glide reflections, 180° rotations, vertical reflections, or horizontal reflections.

ⓑ A strip pattern has translation symmetry if you slide the pattern along the line of the strip and notice a repeat of the pattern. A strip has line reflection symmetry if it is a mirror image after it is reflected over a horizontal or vertical line. It has rotational symmetry if rotating it about a point maps the strip pattern onto itself. Finally, a strip pattern has glide reflection symmetry if sliding the pattern along the line of the strip and then reflecting it over the horizontal line through the middle of the strip results in mapping the pattern onto itself.

CONSTRUCTING A MATH TOOLKIT: You may wish to have students write their class definition for a glide reflection in their Math Toolkits (Teaching Master 202).

APPLY · individual task

▶On Your Own

Encourage each student to create a unique strip. If you have a graphics utility available, some students may enjoy creating on the computer.

MORE

ASSIGNMENT *pp. 408–415*

Students can now begin Modeling Task 1, 2, or 3; Organizing Task 2 or 3; Reflecting Task 1, 2, or 3; or Extending Task 1 or 2 from the MORE assignment following Investigation 4.

Unit 5

INVESTIGATION 4 ▶ Symmetry Patterns in Planes

In the final investigation of this lesson, students explore tessellation patterns where the translational symmetry may be at a 45 degree or 60 degree angle to the horizontal. The plane patterns, often called wallpaper patterns, are based on tilings of the plane by regular and some nonregular polygons. This investigation concentrates on modifications of the familiar square tessellation. Students will apply their knowledge of symmetries and reflections to analyze tessellations based on polygon tilings of the plane. They will examine some of M.C. Escher's designs and learn how to create their own designs.

1. **a.** The total pattern translates
    - horizontally
    - vertically
    - diagonally up and to the right
    - diagonally up and to the left

    b. If repositioned, the right and left birds are reflections of each other (glide reflections, see Part c), but there are no reflection or rotational symmetries of the entire pattern.

    c. Yes. Slide a dark goose vertically until its bill appears to be the reflection of the bill of a light goose. Reflect in this line. The two motions together make a glide reflection.

    d. It is based on a kite. At this point, this probably will be difficult for students to see, but by the end of the investigation they will have had more experience in spotting the basic polygons. The kite is formed by choosing any goose and connecting the top of its head to the tops of the heads of the three geese whose heads touch the goose.

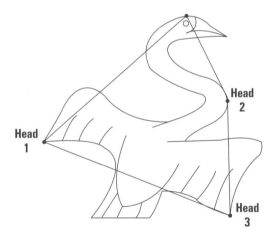

The Alhambra in Granada, Spain

Recently, the tessellation artwork of the Dutch artist, M.C. Escher, has become very popular. Escher was deeply influenced by the work of the ancient Moors. Examine the following Escher pattern.

1. As a class, imagine that this pattern is extended indefinitely to cover the plane.

  a. Describe all translational symmetries that you see.

  b. Does the pattern have reflection or rotational symmetries? If so, describe them.

  c. Does the pattern have glide reflection symmetry? If so, describe it.

  d. On what type of polygon do you think this pattern is based?

Tessellations such as that above are based on polygon tilings of the plane. The polygon is modified carefully so that the new shape will tile the plane when certain transformations are applied. Rotations and translations are two of the most common transformations. Escher was a master at these modifications.

Knowing which polygonal regions tessellate a plane is one important part of understanding Escher-like tilings. Another important aspect is understanding which transformations will take an individual tile into another tile within the entire tiling pattern. Applying these ideas leads to beautiful patterns.

2. A tiling based on squares is shown in the figure below. Adjacent squares have different colors. Think of the square labeled "0" as the beginning tile. How many squares surround square 0?

	1	2	3		
	8	0	4		
	7	6	5		

a. Which transformations (reflection, rotation, translation, or glide reflection) will move square 0 to a surrounding square of the *same* color? Illustrate with diagrams.

b. Which transformations will move square 0 to a surrounding square of the *other* color? Illustrate with diagrams.

c. If *translation* is the only motion permitted, can square 0 be translated to each of squares 1–8? On a copy of the tiling, represent each such translation by drawing an arrow which shows its direction and how far square 0 must be translated.

d. Using only *rotation* about a vertex of square 0, can square 0 be moved onto each of squares 1–8? Describe each such rotation on the copy of the tiling by marking its center and giving its angle. If some squares can be reached in more than one way, describe each way.

Escher used the square tiling and knowledge of the translations that move square 0 to the adjacent positions to help him design some of his art. In the remainder of this investigation, you will explore some of the mathematics behind Escher's art.

2. a. Most students will choose only translation, rotation about a vertex, and glide reflection. Some may choose "diagonal" lines to reflect the square 0 across to a square of the same shading.

   b. Most students will choose translation, reflection, and rotation (about the midpoint of a side).

   c. Yes, square 0 can be translated to each of the other squares.

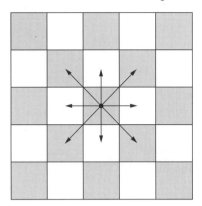

   d. Squares 1, 3, 5, and 7 are rotations of 180° about a corner of the square. Using a corner of the square as the center of rotation, squares 2, 4, 6, and 8 are rotations of 90° or 270°.

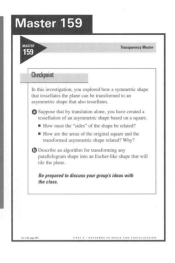

Unit 5

EXPLORE *continued*

3. a. A trapezoidal shape was removed from the left edge of square 0 and replaced on the right edge; this movement can be considered a horizontal translation. On the bottom edge of square 0, a triangle was removed and replaced on the top edge; this is a vertical translation.

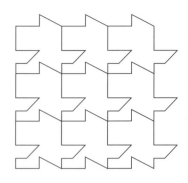

b. The area of square 0 equals the area of the modified (asymmetric) shape.

4. Responses will vary.

SHARE AND SUMMARIZE   full-class discussion

Checkpoint

See Teaching Master 159.

ⓐ ■ Whatever shape is removed from one side must be translated to the opposite side, so one might describe the sides as being "parallel."

■ The area of the asymmetric shape equals the original square, and the two modified sides fit together perfectly. The areas are the same because any part of the shape that is removed is translated and placed on the opposite side.

ⓑ There are several algorithms that will modify a parallelogram to create a new shape that will tessellate a plane:

■ Remove a shape from one side and translate it to the opposite side. Tessellation will occur by translating the parallelogram.

■ Modify each side so that it is half-turn symmetric about its midpoint, as illustrated in the diagram below. Then tessellation will occur by rotating the modified parallelogram by 180° about the midpoints.

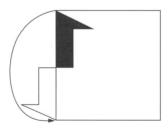

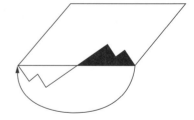

This is a half-turn about the midpoint of a side.

Since a parallelogram has rotation symmetry, it makes sense that a new shape created by altering a side using rotation also will tessellate.

Be sure all student algorithms are discussed. An excellent resource on tessellations is *Introduction to Tessellations* (Dale Seymour and J. Britton. Palo Alto: Dale Seymour Publications, 1989).

See additional Teaching Notes on page T418U.

3. If you were to replace square 0 with the shape at the right, could you make a tiling? If so, sketch the resulting pattern on a sheet of paper.

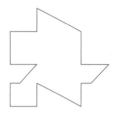

  a. The shape you used is a modification of square 0. Describe as accurately as you can how you think square 0 was modified to obtain this shape.

  b. How do the areas of square 0 and the modified shape compare?

The above shape, like most of Escher's shapes, is an example of an **asymmetric** shape that tiles the plane. It was created by modifying a symmetric shape, the square, that also tiled. This technique can be used to create an unlimited number of interesting tessellations.

4. Working alone, modify the sides of square 0 to create a shape that is asymmetric and that will tile the plane by translation to the eight adjacent positions. Sketch or make a computer-generated nine-square version of your tessellation. Compare your tessellation with those of the other members of your group.

Checkpoint

In this investigation, you explored how a symmetric shape that tessellates the plane can be transformed to an asymmetric shape that also tessellates.

ⓐ Suppose that by translation alone, you have created a tessellation of an asymmetric shape based on a square.

  ■ How must the "sides" of the shape be related?

  ■ How are the areas of the original square and the transformed asymmetric shape related? Why?

ⓑ Describe an algorithm for transforming any parallelogram shape into an Escher-like shape that will tile the plane.

Be prepared to discuss your group's ideas with the class.

▶ On Your Own

Recall that a rhombus is a parallelogram, all of whose sides are the same length. Can a rhombus be made into an Escher-like asymmetrical tile that will tessellate by translation alone? Explain and illustrate your answer.

MORE
Modeling • Organizing • Reflecting • Extending

Modeling

1. Archeologists and anthropologists use symmetry of designs to study human cultures. The table below gives frequency of strip designs on a sampling of pottery from two cultures on two different continents: the Mesa Verde (U.S.A.) and the Begho (Ghana, Africa).

Strip Pattern Symmetry Type	Mesa Verde		Begho	
	Number of Examples	Percentage of Total	Number of Examples	Percentage of Total
Translation Symmetry Only	7		4	
Horizontal Line Symmetry	5		9	
Vertical Line Symmetry	12		22	
180° Rotational Symmetry	93		19	
Glide Reflection Symmetry	11		2	
Glide Reflection and Vertical Line Symmetry	27		9	
Both Horizontal and Vertical Line Symmetry	19		165	
Total	174		230	

Source: Washburn, Dorothy K. and Donald W. Crowe. *Theory and Practice of Plane Pattern Analysis.* Seattle: University of Washington Press, 1988.

a. Copy the chart and fill in the two "Percentage of Total" columns.

b. Which types of symmetry patterns appear to be preferred by the Mesa Verde? By the Begho?

c. Examine the strips shown below. In which place is each strip more likely to have been found? Use the data from the table to explain your answer.

i. 　　ii. 　　iii.

Modeling

MORE
ASSIGNMENT   *pp. 408–415*

Modeling: 4 and choice of
1, 2, or 3*
Organizing: 2, 3, and 4
Reflecting: Choose one*
Extending: Choose one*

*When choice is indicated, it is important
to leave the choice to the student.
NOTE: It is best if Organizing tasks are discussed as a whole class after they have
been assigned as homework.

Unit 5

1. a.

Strip Pattern Symmetry Type	Mesa Verde		Begho	
	Number of Examples	Percentage of Total	Number of Examples	Percentage of Total
Translation Symmetry Only	7	4%	4	2%
Horizontal Line Symmetry	5	3%	9	4%
Vertical Line Symmetry	12	7%	22	10%
180° Rotational Symmetry	93	53%	19	8%
Glide Reflection Symmetry	11	6%	2	1%
Glide Reflection and Vertical Line Symmetry	27	16%	9	4%
Both Horizontal and Vertical Line Symmetry	19	11%	165	72%
TOTALS	174	100%	230	101%

(These percentages have been rounded to the nearest whole number.)

b. The Mesa Verde prefer patterns with 180° rotational symmetry; the Begho prefer patterns with both horizontal and vertical line symmetry.

c.   **i.** Begho
  ii. Mesa Verde
  iii. Mesa Verde

Pattern i is an example of vertical and horizontal line symmetry, whereas patterns ii and iii show 180° rotational symmetry.

2. Responses may vary, depending on whether or not students observe that the design is woven over in some places and under in other places. Answers which are ambiguous are listed with (?) next to them.

Cloths	a. Vertical Line Symmetry	b. Horizontal Line Symmetry	c. Rotational Symmetry	d. Glide Reflection Symmetry
i	no	no	180°	yes
ii	yes (?)	yes (?)	180°	probably
iii	yes	yes	180°	no
iv	no	no	no	yes
v	no	no	180°	no

3. Responses may vary. The response below uses the symmetry types from Modeling Task 1. In many cases, students may want to classify a design in two ways. Encourage them to use only the most descriptive class. For example, figure B has horizontal and vertical line symmetry and must have 180° rotational symmetry, while figure A has rotational symmetry but neither line symmetry. So "Both Horizontal and Vertical" tells us more about figure B than "180° Rotational" would. Using this convention also tells us more about figures in the "180° Rotational" class—it says those figures do not have the line symmetries.

Translation Symmetry Only	E, F
Horizontal Line Symmetry	D, M
Vertical Line Symmetry	L, H
180° Rotational Symmetry	A, I
Glide Reflection Symmetry	G, J
Glide Reflection and Vertical Line Symmetry	C, N
Both Horizontal and Vertical Line Symmetry	B, K

2. Examine the eighteenth-century embroidered-cloth strip patterns of Kuba, Democratic Republic of Congo, shown below.

i.

ii.

iii.

iv.

v.

a. Identify those patterns that exhibit reflection symmetry about a vertical line.

b. Identify those patterns that exhibit reflection symmetry about a horizontal line.

c. Identify those patterns that exhibit rotational symmetry.

d. Identify those patterns that exhibit glide reflection symmetry.

3. The 14 Japanese border designs pictured below seem to have great variability. Sort them into groups. Describe the characteristics used to determine membership in the groups you create.

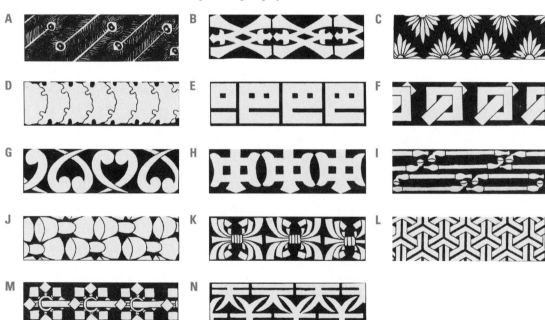

4. Shown here is an example of a common first step used to create a tessellation. This example could become the "flying-horse" tessellation shown on page 406.

a. Trace the modified square. Complete the modification to obtain the horse shape.

b. Test by repeated tracings that the shape will tessellate. If necessary, make further adjustments for a good fit.

c. What kinds of symmetry does your tessellation have?

5. Create an Escher-like tessellation of your own by modifying a square so that it will tessellate the plane by translation alone. Try to construct your shape so that it can be enhanced to look like a common object or animal. (You may use both curved and straight segments.)

Organizing

1. For each of the following descriptions, construct a strip pattern that has translational symmetry and the given symmetry or symmetries. Use a computer drawing utility if it is available.

   a. vertical line symmetry

   b. horizontal line symmetry

   c. 180° rotational symmetry

   d. horizontal and vertical line symmetry

   e. glide reflection symmetry

   f. glide reflection and vertical line symmetry

2. Use the chart below to help organize your thinking about classifying strip patterns.

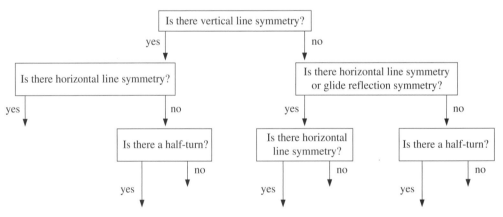

Source: Washburn, D. and D. Crowe. *Symmetries of Culture.* Seattle: University of Washington Press, 1988.

4. **a–b.** The "flying horse" shape is fairly complicated. Encourage students to work in
pencil and make adjustments, as necessary.

 c. Translation symmetry

5. Tessellations will vary.

Organizing

1. See students' strip patterns.

2. **This is an algorithm for classifying strip patterns. Thus, it is another example of "algorithmic" thinking introduced in the discrete math strand of these materials.**

   a.

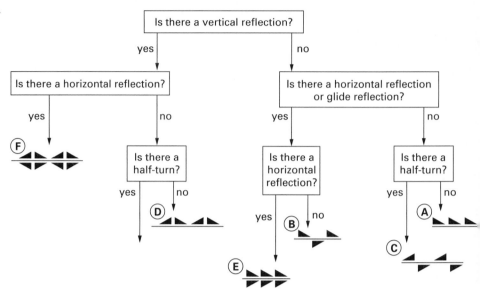

   b. The missing pattern, the second from the left, is one which has a vertical reflection and a half-turn, but no horizontal reflection. One example is:

3. Graphs a and b have translational symmetry. Glide reflection symmetry is exhibited in Graph a. Graphs a and b also have 180° rotational symmetry about the origin. Graph a also has vertical line symmetry. Using the classifications from Modeling Tasks 1 and 3, Graph a could be classified "glide reflection and vertical line symmetry" and Graph b would be classified "180° rotational symmetry."

4. a. A will tessellate because the shape removed from the bottom edge has been translated to the top edge. When the fundamental shape is translated and the area remains unchanged, the two altered edges fit together exactly.

   B will tessellate because the shape removed was rotated through the midpoint of the side. Therefore, the transformed sides will fit together perfectly when the fundamental figure is rotated about that midpoint.

   C will not tessellate because area was removed but not replaced.

   D will tessellate because the four shapes removed were translated to the opposite sides.

   b. A tessellation using shape A will have translational symmetry.

   A tessellation using shape B will have rotational symmetry.

   A tessellation using shape D will have translational symmetry.

   a. Make or obtain an enlarged copy of this chart. For each of the triangle strip patterns in Activity 2 of Investigation 3 (page 402), sketch the pattern at the point on the chart that describes its characteristics.

   b. The chart suggests that there are seven different possible one-color strip patterns. Which pattern was not included in Activity 2? Draw an example of the missing strip pattern at the appropriate place on the chart.

3. Suppose the following graphs extend indefinitely in the pattern illustrated. Which have translational symmetry? For those that do, identify any other symmetries of the graph.

a.

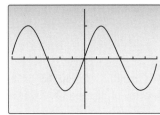

b.

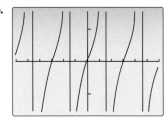

c.

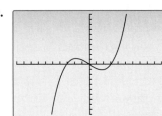

d.

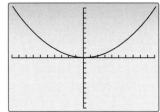

4. Suppose each polygon below is modified as shown.

   a. Explain why you think the shape will or will not tessellate the plane.

   b. If the shape will tessellate, describe the symmetries, if any, of the resulting tessellation.

A

B

C

D

Reflecting

1. Juan has been trying to make a strip pattern which has both horizontal and vertical symmetry, but not 180° rotational symmetry. He asks your advice. What do you suggest and why?

2. The chart in Organizing Task 2 provides a systematic way of analyzing strip patterns. On the basis of the chart, why can you conclude there are exactly seven essentially different strip patterns?

3. In your home or neighborhood, find examples of strip patterns. Investigate why the patterns were chosen or if the patterns have special meaning. Make a sketch of each design. Describe the symmetries evident in the designs.

4. Dorothy Washburn is an archeologist at the University of Rochester. She discovered that the pattern found in Escher's tessellation of lizards is strikingly similar to that found in a Fiji basket lid and an Egyptian wall mosaic. Why do you think patterns of this sort are found in different cultures?

5. In 1970, M.C. Escher wrote: "Although I am absolutely innocent of training or knowledge in the exact sciences, I often seem to have more in common with mathematicians than with my fellow artists." (Escher, M.C. *The Graphic Work of M.C. Escher*, trans. John E. Brigham. New York: Ballantine Books, 1971.)

    a. What is it about mathematics, geometry in particular, that permits people with little mathematical training to discover, on their own, many of its basic principles?

    b. Based on what you have seen of Escher's work, why do you think he felt as he did about himself?

Extending

1. In your previous study of mathematics, you may have observed that decimal representations of numbers often have interesting patterns.

    a. Investigate how the decimal representation of numbers between 0 and 1 might be related to strip patterns. Identify any characteristics of the numbers that make the analogy fail.

    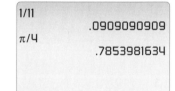

    b. What would be the fundamental unit for the strip pattern for $\frac{2}{11}$? For $\frac{1}{13}$? For $\frac{1}{3}$?

    c. What would you say about the strip pattern representation of $\frac{1}{2}$?

Reflecting

1. Juan cannot make such a strip pattern. If a strip pattern has horizontal and vertical reflection symmetry, then it must have 180° rotational symmetry.
2. From the symmetry built into the chart, you might expect eight rather than seven possible designs. However, on the far left side, it is not necessary to ask "Is there a half-turn?" because patterns with both horizontal and vertical reflections automatically have half-turns.
3. Responses will vary. China patterns often incorporate strip patterns, as do many wallpaper patterns.
4. Responses may vary. Students could conjecture that similar patterns are found worldwide because there are a limited number of polygons which tessellate. Other students may write about the cross-cultural appeal of interesting patterns.
5. **a.** Responses may vary. For example, geometry is built on visual patterns which anyone can discover if they look deeply enough.
    b. His artwork uses symmetry, tessellations, and other geometric principles.

Extending

1. **a.** Rational numbers always can be written as terminating or as repeating decimals. If the rational number is equivalent to a repeating decimal, the pattern of numbers which repeats itself can be seen as the fundamental unit of the strip pattern. The analogy fails when there are numbers which precede the pattern of repeating numbers, as in the case of $\frac{1}{6}$ which equals 0.1666… (with the 6 repeating). If the rational number is equivalent to a terminating decimal, an infinite number of 0s can be placed on the end of the number without changing its value. In this case, 0 is the fundamental unit of the strip pattern.
    b. 18 is the fundamental unit of the strip pattern for $\frac{2}{11}$; 076923 is the fundamental unit of the strip pattern for $\frac{1}{13}$; 3 is the fundamental unit for $\frac{1}{3}$.
    c. The strip pattern representation of $\frac{1}{2}$ is repeated 0s.

MORE ***continued***

2. **a.** San Ildefonso Pueblo

A	111
B	1a1
C	m11
D	112
E	1m1
F	ma2
G	mm2

b. Japanese

A	112	H	m11
B	mm2	I	112
C	ma2	J	1a1
D	1m1	K	mm2
E	111	L	m11
F	111	M	1m1
G	1a1	N	ma2

c. Strips Shown

A	ma2
B	1a1
C	1m1
D	112
E	mm2
F	m11
G	111

2. The strip patterns you have investigated are often identified with several coding schemes. The following one seems useful. It is made up of 3 characters in order. The first character is **m** if there is a vertical reflection and **1** (one) if there is none; the second character is **m** if there is a horizontal reflection, **a** if there is a glide reflection, and **1** if there is neither; the third character is **2** if there is 180° rotational symmetry and **1** otherwise.

a. Assign a symbol to each of the 7 San Ildefonso Pueblo designs studied in Activity 3 of Investigation 3 (page 403).

b. Assign a symbol to each of the Japanese border patterns in Task 3 of the Modeling section.

c. Assign a symbol to each of the strip patterns shown below.

A

B

C

D

E

F

G

3. Shown below are two sketches that M.C. Escher used in his lectures about ways to regularly fill or divide the plane. Each of these patterns is based on a square. Where are the vertices of the squares located?

a. In the sketch at the left, what transformations will move a tile of one color onto a tile of the same color?

b. What transformations will move a tile of one color onto a tile of the other color?

c. Make your own tile with characteristics similar to those found in this sketch. Use it to make a tiling of the plane.

verschuiving en assen.

verschuiving en glijspiegeling.

d. In the sketch at the right above, what transformations will move a tile of one color onto a tile of the same color?

e. What transformations will move a tile of one color onto a tile of the other color?

f. Make a personal tile with characteristics similar to those found in this sketch. Use it to make a tiling of the plane.

3. **a.** Translation
   b. Rotation (centers of rotation are circled), or translation and then rotation
   c. See student work.
   d. Translation
   e. Glide reflection (The reflection is across the dotted diagonal lines.)
   f. See student work.

Unit 5

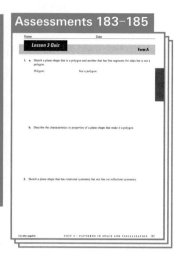

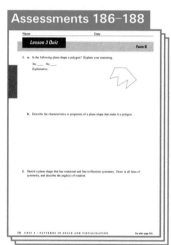

MORE *continued*

4. **a.** The vertices of the hexagon are located at the points where tiles of three different shades meet.

   b. The pieces taken out from one side of the hexagon are rotated and added to an adjacent side.

5. **a.** Square

   b. See student work.

   c. The areas of the polygonal shape and the lizard shape are the same.

   d. ■ Half-turn about a point between their two front or back feet

   ■ 90° clockwise rotation about a point between their two front feet

   ■ 90° counterclockwise rotation about a point between their two front feet (or 270° clockwise)

See Assessment Resources, pages 183–188.

4. The Escher tessellation at the left below is based on a regular hexagon.

   a. What characteristic of the tessellation helps you locate each vertex of the hexagon?

   b. Draw a regular hexagon on poster board. Modify it to make an Escher-like shape. Describe the modifications which you made. Show by repeated tracings of the shape that it will cover the plane.

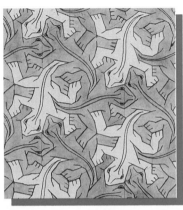 

5. Study the tessellation of light and dark-colored lizards at the right above.

   a. What is the fundamental polygonal shape on which this tessellation is based? Justify your choice and discuss it with a classmate.

   b. Make a poster board model of the polygon on which the tessellation is based. Show the modifications needed to make the shape used in the design.

   c. Compare the areas of the polygon and the lizard tiles.

   d. What transformation will move a light-colored lizard with its head facing upward to:

      ■ a light-colored lizard with its head pointing down?

      ■ a dark-colored lizard with its head toward the right?

      ■ a dark-colored lizard with its head toward the left?

Lesson 4

Looking Back

In this unit, you saw how space-shapes and plane-shapes are related. You also saw how they are constructed and visualized, and how they may be drawn in two dimensions. You learned ways to measure them and what sorts of symmetry they have. You even saw how they may be used in art and design to make our lives more productive and enjoyable, both visually and physically. The landscape architects who designed this mall garden area made extensive and integrated use of these fundamental ideas of geometry.

This final lesson of the unit gives you the opportunity to pull together and apply what you have learned. You will use your visualization skills and knowledge of shapes, symmetry, tessellations, and measurement in new situations.

1. Shown below is a net for a decorative box. Some of its dimensions are given.

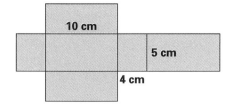

Lesson 4 *Looking Back*

SYNTHESIZE UNIT IDEAS   small-group activity

You might want to begin this lesson by asking students to recall all the important ideas from the unit. As each person offers a word, such as "symmetry," note the word on the board and ask the student to put this in a sentence, or give an example visually. We recommend that students be allowed access to their books and notes during the discussion. As you add each word to the list on the board, ask if the new word relates to any previous word; if so, note it accordingly. This results in a messy version of a concept map, but the discussion should help students see the big picture.

For example:

Perimeter (The perimeter of the desk top is 2 widths and two lengths added.)

Area (We have a formula for the area of a triangle.)

Volume (Volume is how much space a box takes up.)

Symmetry (A hexagonal prism has 6 planes of symmetry.)

Rotation...

Reflection...*etc*.

1. **a.** Rectangular prism

b. Student work

c.

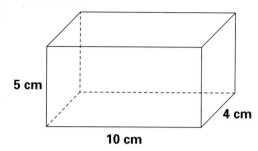

d. There are three planes of symmetry for the above space-shape. Each symmetry plane is parallel to two faces and contains the midpoints of the edges joining those faces.

e–f. All are rectangles with two axes of symmetry and 180° rotational symmetry. Diagrams of the rectangles with their respective axes of symmetry are given below.

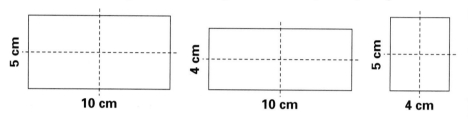

g. Surface Area = $2(10 \times 5) + 2(10 \times 4) + 2(5 \times 4) = 220$ cm²; this *is* the area of the net.

Volume = $10 \times 5 \times 4 = 200$ cm³

h. Using the box as drawn above with the bottom having dimensions 10 cm × 4 cm, the Pythagorean Theorem tells us the length of the diagonal is $\sqrt{10^2 + 4^2}$ or 10.77, so the pencil will not fit in the bottom of the box. If students draw their box so that the bottom has dimensions 10 cm × 5 cm, then the pencil will fit.

i. The longest pencil will fit diagonally in the box as shown. Using the Pythagorean Theorem twice gives a maximum length of $\sqrt{141}$, or approximately 11.87 cm.

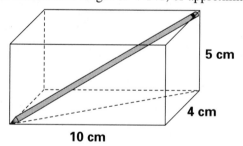

See additional Teaching Notes on page T418V.

a. Name the space-shape for which this is a net.

b. Make a paper model of the space-shape.

c. Sketch the space-shape showing its hidden edges. Give the lengths of each edge.

d. Describe any planes of symmetry for the space-shape.

e. Draw and name each face of the space-shape.

f. Describe all symmetries for each face.

g. Find the surface area and the volume of the space-shape. How is the surface area related to the area of the net?

h. Will a pen 11 cm long fit in the bottom of the box? Explain why or why not in at least two different ways.

i. Estimate the length of the longest pencil that will fit inside the box. Illustrate and explain how you found your answer.

j. Draw a different net for the same space-shape.

2. As an art project, Tmeeka decided to make a decorative baby quilt for her newborn sister Kenya. She chose the quadrilateral below and modified it as shown. Her completed pattern is shown next to the fundamental tile.

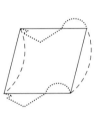
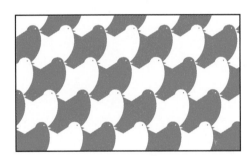

a. Does this quadrilateral have a special name? If so, give it; if not, explain.

b. Describe how Tmeeka modified the sides of the quadrilateral to make the fundamental tile. What transformations did she use?

c. Use the geometric ideas and language developed in this unit to describe how Tmeeka made the quilt pattern.

d. Assuming the pattern continues in all directions, describe all the symmetries you can find.

e. Consider only the bottom row of shapes. Does this row form a strip pattern? If so, describe its symmetries including any centers of rotation and any lines of reflection.

f. Create a strip pattern with both horizontal and vertical line symmetry that could be used as a border for Tmeeka's quilt. Describe all symmetries in your strip pattern.

Checkpoint

In this unit, you have developed ways for making sense of situations involving shapes and spatial relationships.

a Compare and contrast prisms, pyramids, cylinders, and cones.

b Compare and contrast the six special quadrilaterals.

c For each shape in Parts a and b, describe a real-life application of that shape. What properties of the shape contribute to its usefulness?

d Describe a variety of ways you can represent (draw or construct) space-shapes.

e Pose a problem situation which requires use of cubic, square, and linear units of measure. Describe how you would solve it.

f Describe how to make a strip pattern and how to make a tiling of the plane.

Be prepared to share your descriptions with the entire class.

On Your Own

Write, in outline form, a summary of the important mathematical concepts and methods developed in this unit. Organize your summary so that it can be used as a quick reference in future units and courses.

2. e. This row forms a strip pattern with translational symmetry. There is no reflectional or rotational symmetry.

   f. Responses may vary.

SHARE AND SUMMARIZE   full-class discussion

Checkpoint

See Teaching Master 160.

ⓐ Responses will vary. Possible statements to include are given below:
- Pyramids and cones have one base, whereas cylinders and prisms have two identical parallel faces, either of which may be considered a base.
- Cylinders and cones have circles for bases, pyramids and prisms have polygons for bases.
- The volume of a prism or cylinder is found by multiplying the area of the base times the height.
- Faces of pyramids are triangles; faces of prisms are rectangles.
- Cones and cylinders have one lateral face (part of a circle and a rectangle, respectively), whereas prisms and pyramids have many faces.

ⓑ Responses will vary. Suggest that students make a table with columns labeled square, rectangle, parallelogram, rhombus, trapezoid, and kite. Rows could be labeled with properties the quadrilateral may or may not possess, such as rotational symmetry, opposite sides parallel, diagonals bisect one another, and so on.

ⓒ Responses will vary. Examples of applications of space-shapes and plane-shapes can be found in fields from art to engineering. Useful properties may include:
> Triangles and tetrahedron are rigid and often are used because of this property.
> For a quadrilateral, squares enclose the greatest area for a fixed perimeter. For a rectangular prism, cubes enclose the greatest volume for a fixed surface area.
> Cylinders will roll smoothly along a surface, making them useful as wheels.

ⓓ Space-shapes may be drawn from a perspective point of view, with hidden lines showing or not showing, according to which representation is more helpful. Alternatively, space-shapes may be constructed out of all sorts of materials: wood, styrofoam, clay, coffee stirrers, pipe cleaners, and so on.

ⓔ Responses will vary. In general, cubic measure refers to volume, square measure refers to area, and linear measure refers to length.

ⓕ Responses may vary. Look for descriptions that include discussions of symmetry.

APPLY   individual task

▶On Your Own

See Unit 5 Summary Masters

   Responses will vary. Above all, preparation of this unit summary should be something that is useful to the individual student. You may wish to have students use the unit summary masters for "Patterns in Space and Visualization" to help them organize the information.

See Assessment Resources, pages 189–206.

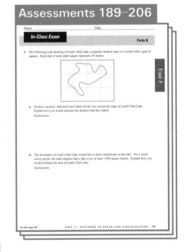

Unit 5

CONSTRUCTING A MATH TOOLKIT: Following a class discussion, students should summarize this Checkpoint in their Toolkits (Teaching Master 202).

Looking Back, Looking Ahead

▶ Reflecting on Mathematical Content

You have just completed the first of several units in the *Contemporary Mathematics in Context* curriculum that are essentially geometric in nature. Your students have begun a substantial geometric journey that will be elaborated on as the geometry strand develops. One fundamental idea that crosses mathematical strands is that of shape.

In geometry, we study a variety of shapes, the properties of those shapes, and the relations among two or more shapes. This trend will be continued throughout the geometry strand. In Course 2, Unit 6, "Geometric Form and Its Function," students will learn how the quadrilateral, the triangle, and the circle are fundamental to much of the mechanical activity of the world around us. Beyond that, more formal reasoning about geometric relations will be encountered in the third year of the curriculum and will emphasize reasoning about common shapes of geometry and writing proofs in order to verify conjectures about shapes and their properties. In Course 4, students will represent shapes with contour lines and cross sections, study conic sections, and use equations to represent three-dimensional surfaces and shapes.

A second way shape is emphasized in the curriculum is in its use in relation to graphs of functions and distributions of data. The graphs of algebraic functions are emphasized throughout the curriculum, and these graphs have distinctive shapes. The same is true of the data distributions: each has a distinctive shape that can be used to identify specific distributions and draw inferences about the underlying data.

Another recurring theme of the geometry strand is the use of transformations in the analysis and description of shape and properties of shapes. We assumed that students would have some informal knowledge of reflections, translations, and rotations, and that they could use these ideas to describe patterns they observed in shapes and strip patterns. In later work, these transformations are revisited and given algebraic descriptions using coordinates and matrices. These transformations are used extensively to describe properties of many everyday natural and manufactured objects in fields such as biology and housing. These transformations also are useful to describe the shape of distributions of transformed data and graphs of families of functions.

The size of an object is an important characteristic of the object, whether it is physical or mathematical. Since transformations, when applied to a shape, may or may not affect the size, the invariance of size under a transformation is an important concept. Many of the transformations that are studied leave size (length, area, and volume) unchanged, but other transformations (such as size transformations) do not. The size transformation is introduced early in Course 2, Unit 2, "Pattern of Location, Shape, and Size," and its characteristic effect on size is studied. It leads to one good way for students to think about similarity and congruence of shapes. In Course 3, congruence is introduced as a special case of similarity in a manner similar to the work of two mathematics education professors, Birkhoff and Beatley, 55 years ago. (For more information on their work, see *Basic Geometry*, Chicago: Scott Foresman, 1941.) In Course 4, transformations are applied to three-dimensional shapes and conic sections.

The representation of shape and motion geometrically is also emphasized in the geometry and trigonometry strand. In this unit, students have seen ideas represented with sketches. The space-shapes are drawn from a number of different perspectives. In Course 2, geometric objects such as lines, points, and polygons are represented algebraically with coordinates and with linear equations, and transformations are represented with coordinate rules and then with matrices. Geometric shapes in relation to their functions (or uses) are studied in Course 2. Representing circular motion leads to the study of trigonometric functions. In Course 3, students provide both synthetic and analytic proofs of geometric relationships. In Course 4, vectors and three-dimensional surfaces are represented pictorially and then algebraically. This idea of multiple representation of geometric ideas is developed throughout the geometry and trigonometry strand.

The next unit, "Exponential Models," shifts the primary focus of the course back to the algebra and functions strand.

Unit 5 Assessment

Lesson Quizzes	Assessment Resources
Lesson 1 *The Shape of Things*	pp. 171–176
Lesson 2 *The Size of Things*	pp. 177–182
Lesson 3 *The Shapes of Plane Figures*	pp. 183–188
In-Class Exams	
Form A	pp. 189–194
Form B	pp. 195–200
Take-Home Assessments	pp. 201–202
Unit 5 Projects	
Geometry, Geometry Everywhere	pp. 203–204
WOW! MOM + DAD	pp. 205–206

Teaching Notes continued

Notes continued from page T326

LAUNCH full-class discussion

Think About This Situation

See Teaching Master 135.

ⓐ Responses may vary. Examples of student observations may include things such as: Space-shapes can be large, small, curved or straight, soft or firm, flat or rounded, narrow, or pointed. After allowing these initial responses, you may wish to provide vocabulary such as "planes," "edges," and "rigid." After doing so, ask if students can add more to their descriptions. The quality of the descriptions will improve remarkably when students have the means to talk about the shapes they see. For example:

> My pencil has 6 plane-shapes connected at the edges, and one other plane-shape, a hexagon, at the non-sharpened end.

> The shapes in the photographs look about the same height, but the one at the right has no straight edges.

ⓑ Students probably will focus on the idea that plane-shapes are connected at the edges and set at various angles.

ⓒ ■ You may wish to have students look back at this sketch after they have completed the unit to notice their improved ability to sketch space-shapes.

■ Student responses probably will focus on length, width, and height.

NOTE: You can use student responses to assess their present knowledge regarding polyhedra and polygons. If it is clear that the class is well-versed in certain aspects of these shapes, you may want to adjust the assignment for the MORE tasks accordingly.

Notes continued from page T327

To make the square columns, fold the paper slightly off center, so that there is a half-inch extra on one end. The extra half-inch then should be folded. Unfold the paper at the center and then fold in the outer sides to the center fold.

Square Columns

Octagonal Columns

To make the octagonal columns, follow the directions for the square pillar and then unfold all but the half-inch overlap. Working from the outer edges to the center, match up adjacent folds and make four additional creases.

In Part c of Activity 2 and in Activity 3, students may need some help setting up a table in which to organize the data they will be collecting. You may want to move from group to group, checking to see that students are able to organize their data in tables and that the reasoning for Activity 3 Part c is complete, well stated, and consistent with student data.

See additional Teaching Notes on page T418D.

Teaching Notes *continued*

Notes continued from page T327

1. Student responses will vary. Their answers and reasons are only conjectures at this point.
2. **a–b.** Students may need some help in building these models. See the instructions given in the introductory material to this investigation.

   c. Responses will vary. Four sample sets of data are shown below; we used medium-sized paperback books. (The base perimeter or circumference is 10.5 inches, the overlap is 0.5 inches, and the column height is 8.5 inches.)

Shape of Base	Trial			
	1	2	3	4
Triangle	3	3	3	3
Square	4	5	4	4
Octagon	6	8	6	6
Circle	10	10	9	11

You may want to have each group add their data to a table displayed on the board. In this way they can see the results of other trials, and can conjecture about what "usually" happens.

Notes continued from page T329

For Activities 3 through 6, have students move into small working groups. As you move from group to group, you have an excellent opportunity to check to see that students are continuing to use the language of bases, edges, and faces discussed in Activities 1 and 2. Teachers probably will need to encourage students to explain their reasoning carefully and completely for each of these activities.

It is important for students to leave this part of the development with clear ideas of prisms and pyramids. When students have completed Activities 3–6, a sharing of group responses among the entire class would be most appropriate. Have students explain their methods for naming prisms and pyramids. It is a good idea to try to show "counterexamples" that fit a student's proposed name but are not intended by the student. By the end of the investigation, all students should understand a standard way to name space-shapes that are either prisms or pyramids and should be able to describe the essential characteristics of each.

Webster's II New Riverside Dictionary defines a prism as "a geometric solid with equal and parallel polygons as ends and parallelograms as sides." A pyramid is defined as "a solid geometric figure having a polygon as its base and triangular faces that meet at a common point." When the students formulate a definition of prism and pyramid for our purposes, they probably will be right prisms and pyramids without being called "right." Students often define prisms as space-shapes that have two equal bases and rectangles for faces, and pyramids as space-shapes that have a polygon base with triangular faces that meet at a point directly above the base. Ask students to record a summary of these ideas in their Math Toolkits. Their preliminary definitions for pyramid and prism may include a sample sketch.

1. **a.** The pen cap and the ice cream cone have circular bases. The disk box and the pencil have some faces that are parallel. The pen cap, disk box, and pencil have two bases the same size. The disk box and the pencil have rectangular faces.

   b. The pen cap, disk box, and pencil have parallel bases. The disk box and pencil have some faces that are parallel, and some edges that are parallel.

Teaching Notes continued

Notes continued from page T333

After the models are completed, perhaps on the following day, you could set up station activities in different parts of the room and have students work simultaneously on different activities that focus on the same mathematical ideas. In the following activities, for example, you also might have Station 2 and Station 3 in two locations so that there are more stations than there are groups of students. This organization allows two different groups to work on the same activity simultaneously and permits groups to continuously cycle through the activities.

The following chart describes possible station activities and lists the necessary materials.

Investigation 2 Activity Stations

Station	Activity	Page	Materials
1	7	333	Transparent cube (filled with colored water or sand) and cubes made of clay or Play-Doh®
2	8, Parts b and c	334	Student-constructed triangular prisms and, if available, transparent triangular prisms
3	8, Parts d and e	334	Student-constructed prisms (excluding triangular prisms) and, if available, transparent prisms
4	9	334	Student-constructed prisms and pyramids
5	Extending Task 1	339	Transparent cube (filled with colored water or sand)

For Activity 7, teachers should check to be sure that the cubes made of clay or Play-Doh® are all right prisms. Activity 8 offers an opportunity to emphasize the use of the term "edge" since each straw represents an edge.

For Activity 9, most students will have an intuitive idea of plane, bilateral, or reflection symmetry. If some groups have difficulty, it may be helpful to interrupt group work briefly for a full-class discussion so that the key ideas can be considered. Every prism will have at least one symmetry plane because we are limiting our attention to right prisms. Thus a plane parallel to the bases and including the midpoint of each lateral edge is a plane of symmetry. This comment applies to Part b of the Checkpoint also.

EXPLORE small-group investigation

7. **a.** Six
   b. There are now 7 faces. The shape of the new face is a triangle.
   c. The shape is a rectangle. The two pieces are identical. Each half is a triangular prism.
   d. Responses may vary. Slicing parallel to a face of the cube gives a new face that is a square shape. Slicing perpendicular to two faces (and not parallel to two other faces) gives a rectangle. A slicing that is not parallel or perpendicular to any faces gives a rectangle, a trapezoid, a pentagon, or a hexagon.
8. **a.** Student work

Teaching Notes continued

Notes continued
from page T334

The regular pentagonal pyramid has five symmetry planes. Each is perpendicular to a base edge and contains both the vertex opposite that edge and the pyramid vertex.

The regular hexagonal pyramid has six symmetry planes. Three are perpendicular to two edges of the base and contain the pyramid vertex. Three contain opposite vertices of the hexagonal base and contain the pyramid vertex.

SHARE AND SUMMARIZE   full-class discussion

Checkpoint

See Teaching Master 138.

ⓐ (1) The plane could be a symmetry plane (parallel to the bases and containing the midpoints of the lateral edges);

(2) the plane could be parallel to the bases without containing the midpoints of the lateral edges; or

(3) the plane could slice at an angle without intersecting the bases.

ⓑ Symmetry planes for pyramids must pass through the vertex of the pyramid and the center of the base. This is similar to the situation for prisms, where the vertical symmetry planes always pass through the midpoints of the base edges.

All symmetry planes for pyramids are perpendicular to the base. Most of the symmetry planes for prisms are also perpendicular to the bases, but right prisms have at least one additional symmetry plane parallel to the two bases. For example, a regular hexagonal prism will have six vertical planes of symmetry and one horizontal plane of symmetry; a pyramid with the same base will have only the six vertical planes of symmetry.

APPLY   individual task

▶On Your Own

It would have three symmetry planes. One plane would be parallel to the rectangular bases and contain the midpoints of the lateral edges. Two others are parallel to two faces and contain the midpoints of opposite sides of each rectangular base.

Teaching Notes continued

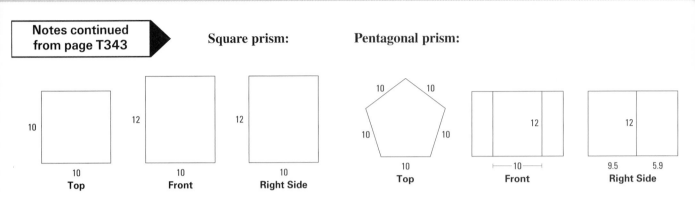

Notes continued from page T343

Square prism:

10 · 10 — Top

12 · 10 — Front

12 · 10 — Right Side

Pentagonal prism:

10 · 10 · 10 · 10 · 10 — Top

12 · 10 — Front

12 · 9.5 · 5.9 — Right Side

Students may consider the "right side" to be the first face to the right, which gives the following:

Hexagonal prism:

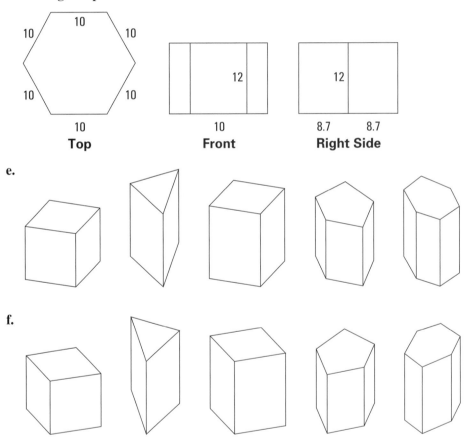

10 · 10 · 10 · 10 · 10 · 10 — **Top**

12 · 10 — **Front**

12 · 8.7 · 8.7 — **Right Side**

e.

f.

g. Sketches will vary. Face views are relatively easy to sketch, but when you are trying to visualize a three-dimensional object from face views, you need to "rebuild" the object in your mind. Isometric drawings are fairly easy to visualize, but some objects can not be represented well on isometric dot paper. Perspective drawings can be difficult to draw and you may not be able to identify all congruent sides, but it is fairly easy to visualize the three-dimensional shape.

Teaching Notes continued

> Notes continued
> from page T344

After all groups have had an opportunity to demonstrate and explain their solutions, you might want to return to the question of the relationships among plane-shapes that make up a three-dimensional model. One way to do this is to provide some proposed views of prisms and pyramids, and ask if the sketches are correct. As examples:

Could these be three views of a triangular prism? (not with the given base)

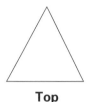  

Top   **Front**   **Side**

Could these be three views of a square prism? (no, front and side views are not the same)

Top   **Front**   **Side**

Could these be three views of a triangular prism? (no, faces are not rectangles)

Top   **Front**   **Side**

It is often easier for students to find flaws in provided drawings than to produce drawings of their own.

CONSTRUCTING A MATH TOOLKIT: At the end of this Checkpoint, you may ask students to select a prism or pyramid space-shape and draw it using each of the three different drawing techniques (*i.e.*, perspective drawings, face views, and isometric drawings). Each drawing could be annotated with the important ideas needed to complete a drawing using that particular technique.

APPLY individual task

▶ On Your Own

This shape could be used for a decorative candy container. It also could be used as an outside gazebo. The pyramid-shaped roof will help to keep rain and snow from collecting.

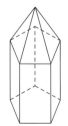    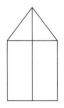

Top   **Front**   **Side**

MORE
ASSIGNMENT   *pp. 347–354*

Students can now begin Modeling Task 1 or 3 or Organizing Task 2 or 5 from the MORE assignment following Investigation 4.

Teaching Notes *continued*

Notes continued from page T347

2. b.

	Top	Front	Right

1 – 15 (diagrams showing Top, Front, Right views)

Some students could benefit by first constructing models using Multilink® cubes.

(cube model diagrams 1–15)

See additional Teaching Notes on page T418J.

◀ **Notes continued from page T347**

2. c. 7 (including motels 8, 9, and 10 on page T418I)

 d. The motel that is four stories high will require the least amount of land. It is not as clear which motel will require the greatest amount of land. If it is assumed that land must be bought in rectangular lots and we don't worry about including any parking areas, then the motels numbered 2, 3, 4, 7, and 15 will require the greatest amount of land (square units).

3. a. 7

 b.

    Top   **Front**   **Right**

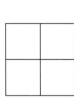  

 c. Many students may find isometric or rectangular dot paper helpful. Constructing a model from interlocking cubes could help students develop spatial thinking and visualization.

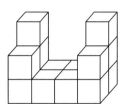

 d. Notice that these face views are not enough to accurately recreate the model.

      Top   **Front**   **Right**

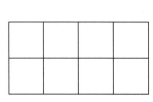 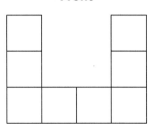 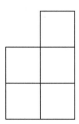

Notes continued from page T355

LAUNCH full-class discussion

Think About This Situation

See Teaching Master 142.

ⓐ The Sears Tower is measured in feet. The Empire State Building is measured in square feet, and the Boeing assembly plant is measured in cubic feet. Thus, linear dimensions were used to describe the size of the Sears Tower, area was used to describe the Empire State Building, and volume was used to describe the Boeing plant. Each of these measures can be applied to space-shapes.

ⓑ You need to think about what aspect of the space-shape you wish to emphasize. If you are a brick layer you may want to know surface area or wall height, while an air conditioning dealer would want to know about volume.

ⓒ The corresponding units of measure are linear, square, and cubic units.

NOTE: As an alternative, or in addition to the discussion on page 355 of the student text, you might want to ask, "Who is bigger, Jane or I?" or "Which is bigger, the carpet or the desk?" You also may want to stir up a reaction by asserting that you are bigger than some tall slender student, or bigger than your desk. These questions or assertions are deliberately ambiguous since the dimension being compared is not stated. Measures of area and volume can not be compared with each other, nor can height and weight. We need to know what we are measuring before we do the calculations and make the comparisons.

Notes continued from page T356

3. a. Responses will depend on the nature of the box, but for rectangular prisms you only need measures of length, width, and height. For circular cylinders, you need only the radius (or diameter) of the base and the height.

   b. Responses will vary. For Part a, students may suggest counting all the edges which are the same length and multiplying those two numbers as a shortcut. This would be repeated with each different edge length. For Part b, students may multiply the appropriate lengths to find the areas of the faces and then add all the areas together.

   c. Possible formulas include:

   $P = 2(l + w)$

   $A = bh$ (rectangle, parallelogram), $A = \frac{1}{2}bh$ (triangle)

   $V = \pi r^2 h$ (cylinder), $V = S^3$ (cube), $V = B \times h$ (prism)

   Students may express total edge length as $TL = 4l + 4w + 4h$ for a rectangular solid or $TL = 2(2\pi r)$ for a cylinder.

Teaching Notes *continued*

▶ **Notes continued from page T358**

5. Students may use several effective methods to estimate area. They may count grid squares, estimating and combining fractions of grid squares as necessary. They may subdivide a shape into more familiar shapes for which they have techniques, such as rectangles or right triangles. They may outline a shape with a rectangle and then subtract the extra area. Or they may have a formula for some common shapes. It is worthwhile having different students demonstrate their methods as a summary for Activity 5.

a. The area of each square is $0.5^2 = 0.25$ square centimeters, since the area of a square can be found by squaring the length of a side of the square. Alternatively, students may outline one square centimeter, that is, a square which has one centimeter for each edge, and then observe that 4 small squares on the grid make one square centimeter. Thus, each grid square is $\frac{1}{4}$ or 0.25 square centimeter. Having students share alternative solutions and strategies helps keep the focus on thinking and problem solving.

b. Student estimates may vary, but should be close to the following:

Figure	Area (cm²)
A	12
B	4
C	9
D	5.25
E	10
F	12.25
G	7
H	6
I	12.5

Procedure for finding area:

A: Students may count squares (remembering each square counts as 0.25 cm²), or they might recall or discover the formula for the area of a rectangle.

B: Again, students will want to consider figure B as a semicircle resting on a rectangle, and use estimation or previous knowledge of area of a circle to determine the total area.

C: Either count squares or multiply the length of one side by itself.

D: This shape can be divided into two triangles and a rectangle. Then students can estimate the area by counting squares and fractions of squares or by using the established formulas for the areas of triangles and rectangles.

E: Students again might determine figure E's area by viewing it as a rectangle surrounded by two triangles, as in figure D. An alternative is to imagine the parallelogram being cut on a vertical line on the grid, then sliding one piece over and around the other so that the slanted edges are matched up. The result is a rectangle whose area may be quickly determined.

See additional Teaching Notes on page T418M.

> **Notes continued from page T358**

5. b. *F*: This area can be found by counting squares and fractions of squares. Once all the whole squares are counted, students might look for ways to combine leftover fractions of squares to form whole ones.

    G: Students could count squares and fractions of squares, or recall the formula for the area of a circle.

    H: Students can simply apply the formula for area of a triangle here, or count squares.

    I: Again, counting whole squares and fractions of squares will yield a good estimate.

  c. The procedure described for figures *F* and *I* are general enough to use for any region. Again, other techniques outlined will not work due to their need for straight lines or alignment with grid paper.

    The general idea of area is the number of unit "pieces of a plane" that are needed to tessellate a plane region; that is, to cover the region with no overlap and no holes. Thus, the counting strategy is the one most closely related to the concept of area. The formulas we develop for some common shapes are "shortcuts" that do the counting for us.

SHARE AND SUMMARIZE   full-class discussion

Checkpoint

See Teaching Master 143.

ⓐ The perimeter is about 25 units. There are several ways of determining the parallelogram's perimeter. Three possibilities are:

  i. to use counting and estimation (since the parallelogram is not perfectly aligned with the grid);

  ii. to use string, a ruler, or transparency grid to measure the sides; or

  iii. to use the Pythagorean Theorem to find the slanted segments and count to find the other lengths.

ⓑ The area is 32 square units. Some possible ways for determining the area are:

  i. identify the base and height, and multiply the two lengths;

  ii. count squares and fractions of squares; or

  iii. use the cut-and-slide method described for figure *E* of Activity 5.

CONSTRUCTING A MATH TOOLKIT: Have students note various methods, with examples, of finding areas and perimeters. Any formulas which they know could be noted at this point in their Math Toolkits, but anything more complicated than the formula for a rectangle, triangle, parallelogram, or circle is not necessary (Teaching Master 202).

Teaching Notes *continued*

▸ Notes continued
from page T362

1. b. The procedure in the text locates a third vertex, in effect giving the lengths of the two adjacent sides. Draw these two sides by connecting the new vertex you just found to the other two (the endpoints of the segment).

There are several ways to locate the fourth vertex. For example, you could place the edge of the extra paper against the longer side of the triangle you just drew. Position a corner at the endpoint of the original segment (the hypotenuse). Draw a line along the edge of the paper at a right angle to the leg of the triangle. (This line should be fairly long.) Repeat this procedure with the other leg and endpoint; if you drew your lines long enough they will meet at the fourth vertex.

Another approach is to use a compass. Draw a circle, centered at one endpoint, with a radius equal to the length of the existing triangle leg that is not touching the chosen endpoint. Repeat with the other endpoint and the other leg. The two circles meet at the fourth vertex.

Yet another method to find the fourth vertex is to mark the extra paper, when you use it to find the third vertex, showing where the segment endpoints touch it. Rotate the paper 180° so that the paper touches the segment in the same places, but on other sides. The corner shows where the vertex is.

c. Responses will vary, but it is very unlikely that any two will be exactly the same.

d. The other sides are about 19.6 inches long. The area is about 78.4 square inches.

e.

Side 1	Side 2	Area	Side 1	Side 2	Area
1	19.97	19.97	11	16.7	183.7
2	19.9	39.8	12	16	192
3	19.8	59.4	13	15.2	197.6
4	19.6	78.4	14	14.3	200.2
5	19.4	97	15	13.2	198
6	19.1	114.6	16	12	192
7	18.7	130.9	17	10.5	178.5
8	18.3	146.4	18	8.7	156.6
9	17.9	161.1	19	6.2	117.8
10	17.3	173			

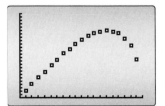
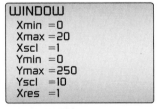

The table and scatterplot suggest the largest area is achieved when the screen is a square with sides approximately 14.14 inches long.

f. Not very well, because there are so many possible rectangular screens with the same diagonal. As we'll see in Organizing Task 2 on page 369, there is a standard ratio (width to height) manufacturers use which reduces the possibilities to one.

Notes continued from page T375 ▶

8. This activity asks students to explore the efficient use of space when shipping canned goods. Below are three different packaging arrangements that could be used to ship the tomatoes.

i. ii. iii.

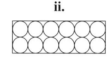

This solution is written considering arrangements of cans oriented like those in diagrams i and ii, not like those in diagram iii. Students interested in a challenge could do this activity using a packaging arrangement such as this last one. Also, you may wish to pose the question of why cans are cylinders, not cubes or other prisms.

a. Boxes are usually rectangular prisms.

b. 12×1, 6×2, or 4×3 arrangements

Notes continued from page T376 ▶

ⓑ *Surface area*: Formulas for prisms are similar to the one developed for the cylinder in that both are the sum of the lateral surface area and the area of the two bases. The formulas are different in that the lateral surface area of a cylinder is not partitioned into n rectangular faces as it is in a regular n-gonal prism.

Volume: In both cylinders and prisms, volume is found by multiplying height times the area of the base.

ⓒ The area of the base is needed in order to calculate the volume or surface area of a prism. In order to compute the area of a triangle using $A = \frac{1}{2}bh$, the height must be known. In an equilateral triangle, the Pythagorean Theorem can be used to compute height since the altitude divides the triangle into two right triangles and it bisects the base. If the length of a side is x, then the height can be found by solving the equation $x^2 = h^2 + \left(\frac{1}{2}x\right)^2$ for h. If the base is a regular hexagon, it can be divided into six equilateral triangles and the Pythagorean Theorem can be used to find the area of one triangle. The area of the base is six times the area of one of these triangles.

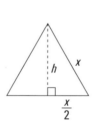   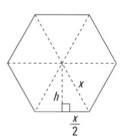

Teaching Notes *continued*

Notes continued
from page T376

APPLY individual task

▶**On Your Own**

a. Responses may vary between these three arrangements:

In the first arrangement, space is available for cushioning materials to be placed around the tins, as shown below.

In the second arrangement, 5 tins will fit tightly along the 20-cm length, as shown below.

In the third arrangement, 6 tins will fit tightly in the box, as shown below.

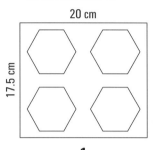

1

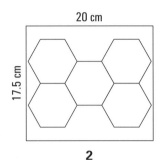

2

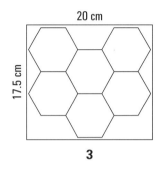

3

b. *H* represents height.

Volume of one tin $= 6(0.5 \times 4 \times 3.46) \times H$
$= 41.52 \times H$ cm^3

Volume of box $= 20 \times 17.5 \times H$
$= 350 \times H$

Arrangement 1: $\dfrac{4 \times 41.52H}{350H} \approx 47\%$

Arrangement 2: $\dfrac{5 \times 41.52H}{350H} \approx 59\%$

Arrangement 3: $\dfrac{6 \times 41.52H}{350H} \approx 71\%$

---

3. This task relates data, rates of change, and volumes of space-shapes.

Notes continued
from page T379

a.

Square Prism **Triangular Prism**

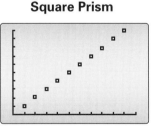

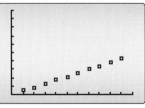

```
WINDOW
  Xmin =0
  Xmax =22
  Xscl =2
  Ymin =0
  Ymax =500
  Yscl =50
  Xres =1
```

b. Linear models would fit both of these scatterplots. The linear regression equations for the square prism and the triangular prism are $y = 24.977x + 0.136$ and $y = 10.827x - 0.182$, respectively.

c. For the square prism, the volume increases by about 25 cubic centimeters for each increase of 1 centimeter in the height.

For the triangular prism, the volume increases by about 10.8 cubic centimeters for each increase of 1 centimeter in the height.

d. The rate of change in each case is equal to the area of the base of the prism.

Notes continued from page T380

2. If the diameter is doubled, then the diameter is $2d$. *Volume* $= \pi \times \left(\frac{2d}{2}\right)^2 \times h = \pi d^2 h$. Therefore, doubling the height doubles the volume while doubling the diameter quadruples the volume.

Students may need to approach this initially using dimensions of specific cylinders. Try to get them to generalize the patterns they find and to work with the algebraic formulas. The algebraic formulas will prove that the patterns they find in specific cases will always hold.

3. Responses may vary. It is not reasonable to calculate volumes of pyramids and cones by multiplying the area of the base by the height because the area of a cross section of the figure is not constant. Some students may make models to discover that, for a given base and height, the volume of 3 pyramids equals the volume of the prism. Since a formula for the volume of a prism is $V = Bh$, it follows that the volume of a pyramid is $\frac{1}{3}Bh$.

4. Responses will vary. An algorithm is a step-by-step procedure to attain a result. A formula also implies that a procedure will be applied, but perhaps not in a specific order. Where a formula is different from an algorithm is in its compactness. The user must interpret the formula to get a procedure out of it.

Notes continued from page T383

LAUNCH full-class discussion

Think About This Situation

See Teaching Master 147.

ⓐ Responses will vary. The precision of the meeting of the shapes is striking, as is the color contrast.

ⓑ Regular hexagons and equilateral triangles comprise the pattern.

ⓒ Much symmetry is evident in the pattern. The hexagons have six axes of symmetry and six rotational symmetries. The six-pointed stars have the same properties. The equilateral triangles have three axes of symmetry and three rotational symmetries.

ⓓ Some seams *are* parallel. This is because they are determined by the shape and placement of the regular hexagons, whose opposite edges are parallel.

ⓔ There do not seem to be any gaps or overlaps in the tiling. The pieces appear to fit together like a puzzle.

EXPLORE small-group investigation

INVESTIGATION 1 ▶ Polygons and Their Properties

Investigation 1 reintroduces students to polygons, the main class of shapes in the plane. If your students have a firm grasp of polygons, you may wish to reduce the amount of time spent on the investigation. However, both line and rotational symmetry of polygons in general, and of quadrilaterals in particular, should be well understood by students when they complete Investigation 1.

Teaching Notes *continued*

◀ **Notes continued from page T385**

Trapezoid:

 ■ One pair of parallel opposite sides

Kite:

 ■ Two pairs of congruent adjacent sides
 ■ One pair of congruent opposite angles
 ■ Diagonals are perpendicular

c. The square has the greatest number of special properties. The trapezoid has the least.

d. As groups work together to resolve differences, encourage them to informally test conjectures with examples and disprove incorrect conjectures with counterexamples. Students may modify their lists as they continue through the investigations.

SHARE AND SUMMARIZE full-class discussion

Checkpoint

See Teaching Master 148.

ⓐ Writing a definition is a good exercise in mathematical communication. The definitions students give may be awkward and wordy. A whole-class discussion is useful to clarify and improve offered definitions. This definition should be entered in each student's Math Toolkit along with some examples and non-examples.

ⓑ Press students to provide minimum criteria to use that would ensure the shape was the special quadrilateral in question. Discuss these different criteria to see if they are defining—that is, that they always uniquely give only the shape specified. This could be a lively discussion. Encourage students to use language such as:

 Two pairs of opposite sides parallel guarantees a parallelogram.

 Four equal sides forces a rhombus.

This helps them get away from simply listing things which are true but redundant. You might want to ask if the same conditions that guarantee a square also will guarantee a rhombus, and so on. Reflect student responses back to the class:

 Dave says you need more conditions to guarantee a square than to guarantee a rhombus. Is he right?

The usual minimal criteria are listed below, but students can make other logical lists.

Kite: Two distinct pairs of congruent adjacent sides
Trapezoid: Exactly one pair of parallel sides
Rhombus: A parallelogram with one pair of equal adjacent sides
Parallelogram: Two pairs of parallel opposite sides
Rectangle: A parallelogram with one right angle
Square: A rectangle and a rhombus

NOTE: Sometimes a trapezoid is defined as having at *least* one pair of parallel sides. This is a good way for students to realize that definitions can vary.

Teaching Notes continued

Notes continued
from page T390

2. **The intent of this investigation is for students to focus on the characteristics they have discovered about triangles, parallelograms, and so on. In Part c, to avoid the students simply saying that "every triangle they tried makes a tessellation, therefore all triangles make tessellations," you might ask them:**

> **What *features* of your patterns encourage you to think that a tessellation will work for any other triangle?**

They might observe, for example, that you can always make a parallelogram by rotating any triangle, and that the parallel sides of the parallelogram guide the placement of the adjoining parallelogram. Or, you might ask them to mark, with symbols or colors, the angles of the basic triangle.

> **How do these angles appear at the vertices where the edges come together? (Two of each color at each vertex.)**

If students seem to be trying to place their shapes at random, point out pieces of sides which do not match, and remark that it will be difficult to repeat exactly that measurement elsewhere in the pattern. Trying to match edges and vertices will be more productive in terms of repeating the plan forever.

   a. Every triangle will tile the plane.

   b. Two patterns are possible:
   - When a triangle is reflected over any one of its sides, the resulting quadrilateral will tile the plane. This quadrilateral is a kite.
   - A parallelogram is formed when a triangle is rotated about the midpoint of one of its sides, and that parallelogram will tile the plane.

   c. Any triangular shape can be used to tile the plane because the sum of the interior angles is 180°. At any vertex of a tiling, two of each of the angles of the triangle will fit exactly; that is, without overlapping or having a gap.

3. **You may want to encourage students to try quadrilaterals of very different types, including concave. As you circulate, ask them what their strategies are. This reminds them to think in geometric terms about the moves their hands are making. For parallelograms, simple sliding works. However, other irregular concave or convex quadrilaterals are more instructive. Suggest they keep track of the placement by coloring or coding the corners. You might ask:**

> **How many quadrilaterals come together at a vertex? What do you have to do when you move your shape to a new position? How do you know these moves could be repeated forever with this quadrilateral? How do you know it could be done with another quadrilateral?**

   a. All quadrilaterals will tile the plane, since the sum of the angle measures is 360°. The plane is tessellated by rotating the quadrilateral through the midpoints of each of the sides.

Teaching Notes *continued*

Notes continued
from page T391

There is more than one tiling pattern for this pentagon. For example, students may note that if they consider the top point of the "house" as a point of rotation, then by rotating the shape 90°, 180°, and 270°, a cross is formed. Then the problem is to create a tiling pattern with crosses, as shown below.

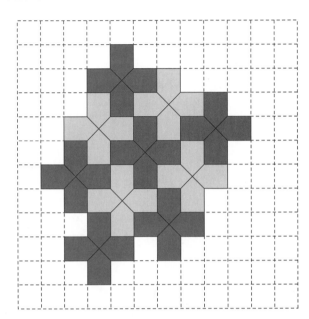

Alternatively, students may simply ignore the given grid and line up several "houses," then flip the resulting row for a pattern that clearly tessellates, as shown below.

Notes continued from page T400

2. At first, students may randomly place 10 points on a circle and connect them to form a non-regular decagon. However, if you wish to create a regular 10-sided polygon, you should draw a circle and a radius of the circle. From the center of the circle, measure 36° from this radius and draw another radius. Continue drawing radii of the circle 36° apart until you return to the first radius. Connect the points on the circle and you have a 10-sided regular polygon. The 10-sided regular polygon is rotationally symmetric; the center of rotation is the center of the circle and the magnitudes of rotation are multiples of 36°.

3.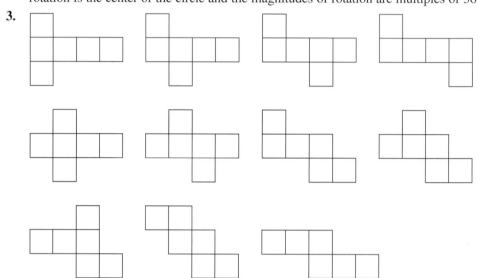

Notes continued from page T407

APPLY individual task

▶**On Your Own**

Yes, an asymmetrical tile that will tessellate by translation alone can be made from a rhombus. The tile is created in the same manner as those that are created from a square. Illustrations will vary.

Teaching Notes *continued*

Notes continued
from page T417

1. **j.** Responses may vary. One possibility is given below:

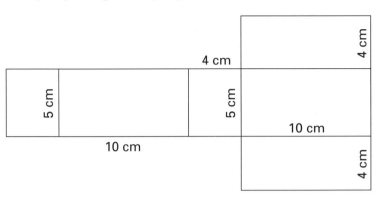

2. **a.** Yes, it is a rhombus.

  b. She performed two translations; one translation was left to right and one was top to bottom.

  c. Tmeeka began with a rhombus, a figure she knew would tessellate, because it is a quadrilateral. She then performed two translations on the rhombus, each of which preserved the area. Finally, she sewed together many copies of her resulting figure. She was able to do this with no holes or overlapping because her new figure tiles the plane.

  d. Although the baby chick itself is not symmetric, the quilt exhibits translational symmetry. For example, a chick may be moved by a translation up, right, left, or diagonally. A chick may be moved to another of the same color by any of four diagonal translations.

Unit 6 ▶ Exponential Models

UNIT OVERVIEW In many quantitative problems, key variables are related in patterns that are described well by linear models. But there are many other important situations in which variables are related by nonlinear patterns. Among the most important nonlinear patterns of change are those that can be modeled well by rules of the form $y = a(b^x)$. Since the independent or manipulated variable occurs in such rules as an exponent, those relations are called exponential models. Exponential models often are useful in solving problems involving change in populations, pollution, temperature, bank savings, drugs in the bloodstream, and radioactive materials. In fact, it is the widespread usefulness of exponential models that has led us to introduce them in the algebra and functions strand ahead of the more familiar, but less applicable, power and polynomial models. These models will be addressed in Course 2.

Another very strong reason for introducing exponential models at this relatively early stage of the curriculum is the fact that the difference equation for exponential growth, which is $NEXT = NOW \times b$, is a natural counterpoint to the difference equation for linear change, which is $NEXT = NOW + b$. Capitalizing on these connections and comparisons as you and your students work through this unit will help students begin to develop recursive (or sequential) thinking.

Unit 6 Objectives

- To recognize and give examples of situations in which exponential models are likely to match the patterns of change that are observed or expected. This model-recognition skill should apply to information given in data tables, graphs, or verbal descriptions of related changing variables.
- To find exponential rules to match patterns of change in exponential model situations. This should include rules in the "$y = \ldots$" and "*NOW-NEXT*" forms.
- To use exponential rules and graphing calculators or computer software to produce tables and graphs to answer questions about exponential change of variables
- To interpret an exponential function rule in order to sketch or predict the shape of its graph and the pattern of change in tables of values
- To describe major similarities and differences between linear and exponential patterns of change

Exponential Models

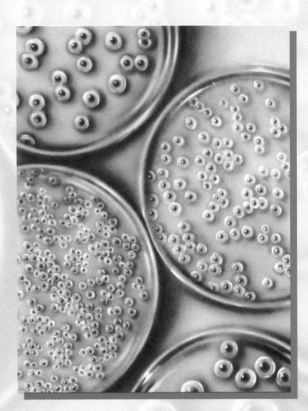

419

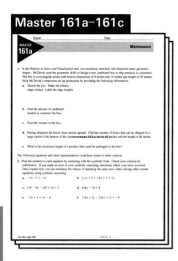

A Variety of Models and Situations

This unit covers a rich sample of the problems that are modeled by exponential growth and decay and extensive analysis of the mathematical properties of those models. However, not all students need to master (or even encounter) all of those applications and properties in their first exposure. For successful progress in the algebra strand, all students should study the core material in Lessons 1, 2, 4, and 5. More ambitious and interested students will find important applications and mathematical insights in the material of Lesson 3 on compound growth, but coverage is not essential to progress through the future units.

The individual lessons are designed to engage students in exploration of a rich variety of situations in which variables change exponentially over time. Following the instructional model, it is important that the context-specific investigations of each lesson be summarized and analyzed in class discussions that articulate the key mathematical ideas embedded in each context so that students come away from the investigations with some broad generalizable ideas, not simply memories of specific problems.

In Lesson 1, "Exponential Growth," students investigate and model exponential growth. This introductory lesson asks students to describe and draw conclusions about several different situations in which exponential models are the best fit to patterns of change. The goal is to get students sensitive to the existence of patterns different from linear, constant additive rates of change and to begin developing skill in writing rules of the form $NEXT = NOW \times b$ and $y = a(b^x)$ based on analysis of the given situation.

Lesson 2, "Exponential Decay," presents a variety of problem situations in which some quantity is decreasing by a constant factor over each unit of time. The students will see how this behavior translates into exponential rules with $0 < b < 1$ and the related table and graph patterns.

In Lesson 3, "Compound Growth," two fundamental types of exponential growth are introduced. These are growth in populations and in investments, where the growth rates are commonly given as percentages.

Lesson 4, "Modeling Exponential Patterns in Data," involves students in finding exponential models for patterns in experimental data, where the exponential pattern is not exact. Students do some data collection and study the pattern in the data. Then they analyze several other sets of data from contexts where exponential patterns of change might be expected, and they use the regression capabilities of calculators or software to find reasonable models.

See Teaching Masters 161a–161c for Maintenance tasks that students can work after Lesson 1.

▶A New Approach to Exponential Models

The focus on exponential functions in this unit represents a new approach to this topic in algebra. For many years, elementary algebra courses in high school have included practice in evaluating exponential expressions like 5^2 or 2^3 and in using properties of exponents to simplify exponential expressions like $(x^2)(x^3)$ or $(x^2)^3$. More recently, algebra curricula have begun to emphasize the patterns of change that are implied by those variable exponential expressions.

Using graphing calculators as tools, students have less need for the rules of formal symbol manipulation when solving practical applications of exponential relations. For this reason, this early algebra unit develops only a few simple properties of exponents. Those properties appear near the end of the unit, at a point when students' rich prior encounters with exponential change and expressions should make using the familiar formal rules quite natural.

Knowledge of formal properties for exponents and ability to use them in reasoning by symbol manipulations will be developed further at several subsequent points in the curriculum. Exponents occur again in the "Power Models" unit of Course 2. At that point the familiar list of rules for operating with symbolic exponential expressions (including negative and fractional exponents) is examined. In that unit and in other geometry and probability units, students will encounter a variety of examples illustrating exponential patterns of change.

Extensive symbolic manipulation skills will be learned in Courses 3 and 4 of the *Contemporary Mathematics in Context* (*CMIC*) curriculum. Practice of skills is available in the *Teaching Resources* and the *Reference and Practice* books for Courses 1-3.

▶Comparing Linear and Exponential Models

Exponential models have several key properties that make them useful for describing and reasoning about common patterns of change. While linear models match patterns of change at a constant additive rate with graphs that are straight lines, exponential models match patterns of change at a constant multiplicative rate with graphs that are curves. For instance, consider the following comparisons of two basic linear and exponential models:

Linear Model									**Exponential Model**								

Rules: $y = 3 + 2x$; $NEXT = NOW + 2$ | $y = 3(2^x)$; $NEXT = NOW \times 2$

Tables:	**x**	0	1	2	3	4	5	6	7	8
	y	3	5	7	9	11	13	15	17	19

x	0	1	2	3	4	5	6	7
y	3	6	12	24	48	96	192	384

Graphs:

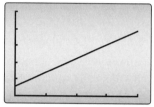   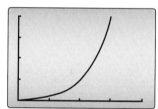

To match patterns of decrease by a constant multiplicative factor, the rules for exponential change would be $y = a(b^x)$ or $NEXT = NOW \times b$ with values of b between 0 and 1. (Exponential decay is the focus of Lesson 2.) The graphs of exponential decay decrease in a pattern that is asymptotic to the x-axis as the following example shows:

Linear Model									**Exponential Model**								

Rules: $y = 16 - 2x$; $NEXT = NOW - 2$ | $y = 16(0.5^x)$; $NEXT = NOW \times 0.5$

Tables:	**x**	0	1	2	3	4	5	6	7	8
	y	16	14	12	10	8	6	4	2	0

x	0	1	2	3	4	5	6	7
y	16	8	4	2	1	0.5	0.25	0.125

Graphs:

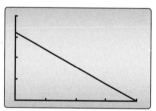   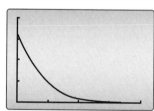

Exponential models of growth or decay are useful when the change in a quantity over time occurs at a pace that is proportional to the size of the quantity. For instance, the population of China is nearly 1.4 billion and the population of the United States is only about 0.29 billion. Both countries have population growth of about 1% per year, but that 1 percent converts into 14 million people per year in China and only 2.9 million people in the United States. Similarly, two bank deposits of $1,000 and $5,000 earning the same 4% interest will increase in one year by $40 and $200, respectively.

Unit 6 Planning Guide

Lesson Objectives	MORE Assignments	Suggested Pacing	Materials
Lesson 1 *Exponential Growth* • To explore simple exponential growth models of the form $y = a(2^x)$ and $y = a(3^x)$ through tables, graphs, and symbolic rules • To compare exponential models of the form $y = a(2^x)$ and $y = a(3^x)$ to linear models • To compare the patterns found in the table and graph of $y = a(2^x)$ to those found in the table and graph of $y = a(3^x)$	**after page 424** Students can begin Modeling Task 4 or Reflecting Task 2 or 4 from page 432 **after page 427** Students can begin Modeling Task 2 or 3, Organizing Task 1 or 3, or Reflecting Task 1 or 5 from page 432 **page 432** **Modeling:** 1 and choice of one* **Organizing:** 1, and 3 or 4* **Reflecting:** 3 and choice of one* **Extending:** Choose one*	7 days	• *Optional*: Tableplot software • Teaching Resources 162–165 • Assessment Resources 207–212 • *Optional*: RAP Book Exercise Set 16, Practice Set 8
Lesson 2 *Exponential Decay* • To determine and explore the exponential decay model, $y = a(b^x)$, where $0 < b < 1$, through tables, graphs, and algebraic rules • To compare exponential decay models with exponential growth models • To compare exponential models of the form $y = a(b^x)$, where $0 < b < 1$, to linear models	**after page 443** Students can begin Modeling Task 1 or Organizing Task 1 from page 448 **after page 445** Students can begin Modeling Task 2 or Reflecting Task 4 from page 448 **page 448** **Modeling:** 6 and choice of one* **Organizing:** 1 and 4 **Reflecting:** 4 and 5 **Extending:** 1	5 days	• 20 black checkers • 160 red checkers • Teaching Resources 161a–161c, 166–169 • Assessment Resources 213–218 • *Optional*: Tableplot software • *Optional*: RAP Book Practice Set 9
Lesson 3 *Compound Growth* • To recognize that if an initial quantity Q is growing at $r\%$ per year, then it can be modeled by the exponential form $y = Q\left(1 + \frac{r}{100}\right)^n$, and to apply this model when solving real-world applications	**page 457** **Modeling:** 1, and 2 or 3* **Organizing:** 1, 2, and 4 **Reflecting:** 1 **Extending:** Choose one*	3 days	• *Optional*: Book of car values • Teaching Resources 170–171 • Assessment Resources 219–224 • *Optional*: RAP Book Exercise Set 17
Lesson 4 *Modeling Exponential Patterns in Data* • To experience exponential change in a visual and tactile manner by completing investigations that result in exponential models • To use the graphing calculator or computer software to determine exponential models for real-world data, modeling both increasing and decreasing exponential situations • To collect a data set, create a scatterplot, and determine an exponential model using the characteristics of the scatterplot and data, or using the graphing calculator or computer software • To appreciate the importance of exponential models in a world where change often occurs at an ever increasing rate	**after page 465** Students can begin Modeling Task 1, 2, 3, or 4 or Organizing Task 1 or 4 from page 468 **page 468** **Modeling:** Choose one of 1–4, and 5 or 6* **Organizing:** 1, 3, and 4 **Reflecting:** Choose one* **Extending:** 2, and 3 or 4*	6 days	• Popcorn kernels • Thumbtacks • Paper plates • *Optional*: 200 plastic spoons • Teaching Resources 172–174 • Assessment Resources 225–230 • *Optional*: RAP Book Exercise Set 18
Lesson 5 *Looking Back* • To review the major objectives of the unit		2–3 days (includes testing)	• Teaching Resources 175a–175b • Unit Summary Master • Assessment Resources 231–248 • *Optional*: RAP Book Practice Set 10

* *When choice is indicated, it is important to leave the choice to the student.*
Note: *It is best if Organizing tasks are discussed as a whole class after they have been assigned as homework.*

Lesson 1

Exponential Growth

News stories spread rapidly in modern society. With broadcasts over television and radio, millions of people hear about important events within hours. The major television and radio news networks try hard to report only stories that they know are true. But quite often, rumors get started and spread around a community by word of mouth alone.

Suppose that to study the spread of information through rumors, two students started this rumor at 5 PM one evening:

Because of the threat of a huge snowstorm, there will be no school tomorrow and probably for the rest of the week.

The next day, they surveyed students at the school to find out how many heard the rumor and when they heard it. How fast do you think this rumor would spread?

Think About This Situation

The graphs below show three possible patterns in the rate at which the school-closing rumor could spread.

a How would you describe the rate of rumor-spread in the case of each graph?

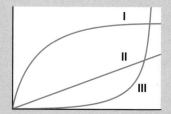

b Which pattern of spread is most likely if the students plant the story on the 5 o'clock television or radio news? Explain your reasoning.

c Which pattern of spread is most likely if the rumor spreads only by word of mouth around the community? Why?

Lesson 1 *Exponential Growth*

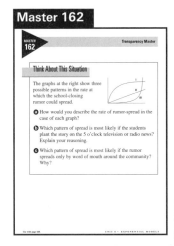

LESSON OVERVIEW The first investigation of this lesson presents students with several different situations to think about, all involving patterns of growth by doubling, tripling, and so on from one time period to the next. The aim is for students to produce tables and graphs for the patterns of change dictated by different problem conditions, to notice that those patterns are different from the simple linear models that have been the focus of earlier algebra units, and to begin developing skill and understanding in writing rules for the exponential growth patterns.

The first situations involve simple doubling or tripling and rules in the form $y = 2^x$ or $y = 3^x$. The third investigation introduces the variation that occurs when one starts with some quantity other than 1. Students discover how this changes the table, graph, and algebraic rule for the relation. In writing this unit, the developers assumed that students have some prior exposure to use of exponents as a shortcut for writing repeated factors. However, it is important that this prior knowledge be articulated, clarified, and refreshed in class discussions of results from the several problems.

NOTE: You may wish to use the Tableplot software in Lessons 1 and 2. This software is available on the disk that accompanies the *CMIC Calculator Software Guide* for Course 1.

Lesson Objectives

■ To explore simple exponential growth models of the form $y = a(2^x)$ and $y = a(3^x)$ through tables, graphs, and symbolic rules

■ To compare exponential models of the form $y = a(2^x)$ and $y = a(3^x)$ to linear models

■ To compare the patterns found in the table and graph of $y = a(2^x)$ to those found in the table and graph of $y = a(3^x)$

LAUNCH   full-class discussion

If your students have difficulty thinking about the questions in the text, it may help to ask different questions, such as, "What variable is represented by the *x*-axis? By the *y*-axis? Which pattern shows the most people learning the rumor over the course of the time period shown in the graph?" This will help students interpret the graph carefully. Students then should focus on the *rates of change* implied by the graphs so that they can answer the original questions.

See additional Teaching Notes on page T481C.

Unit 6

INVESTIGATION 1 Have You Heard About ...?

In this investigation, students explore the pattern of growth associated with two calling trees. The patterns are expressed by a *NOW-NEXT* relationship and compared to linear patterns of change.

1. The vertices represent families and the edges represent phone calls.

2. **a.** Be sure students realize that they need to find the number of *new* families being informed at each stage. To help them correct their thinking you may wish to ask them questions such as "After the second call, how many families, including the president, have been notified?" As you circulate, ask students to explain how they are getting the answers for the table. They will very likely give a description of a recursive process: "You double the last answer." Ask if there is any way to check that you have done enough doubling steps when you get to a particular point in the table; for example, Stage 8 $(2 \times 2 \times 2 \times 2 \times 2 \times 2 \times 2 \times 2)$. This idea gets formalized in Investigation 2.

You might also want to ask students if the numbers are growing more quickly or less quickly than they thought they would grow. The pattern of exponential growth should surprise students; the numbers seem to get quite large, very quickly.

Stage of Calling Tree	0	1	2	3	4	5	6	7	8	9	10
Families Informed	1	2	4	8	16	32	64	128	256	512	1,024

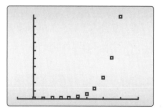
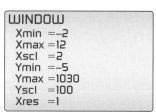

```
WINDOW
 Xmin =-2
 Xmax =12
 Xscl =2
 Ymin =-5
 Ymax =1030
 Yscl =100
 Xres =1
```

In many problems, key variables are related by linear models. But there are many other important situations in which variables are related by nonlinear patterns. Some examples include the spread of information and disease, changes in populations, pollution, temperature, bank savings, drugs in the bloodstream, and radioactivity. These situations often require mathematical models with graphs that are curves. Equations for the models use forms other than the familiar $y = a + bx$. In this unit, you will learn to use the family of nonlinear models that describes *exponential* patterns of change.

INVESTIGATION 1 ▶ Have You Heard About ... ?

Some organizations need to spread accurate information to many people quickly. One way to do this efficiently is to use a telephone calling tree. For example:

The Silver Spring Soccer Club has boys and girls from about 750 families who play soccer each Saturday in the fall. When it is rainy, everyone wants to know if the games are canceled. The club president makes a decision and then calls two families. Each of them calls two more families. Each of those families calls two more families, and so on.

This calling pattern can be represented by a **tree graph** that starts like this:

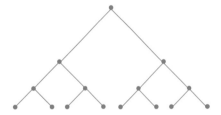

1. What do the vertices of this tree graph represent? What do the edges represent?

2. At the start of the calling process, only the president knows whether the games are on or not. In the first stage of calling, two new families get the word. In the next stage, four others hear the decision, and so on.

   a. Make a table showing the number of families who will hear the decision at each of the next eight stages of the calling process. Then plot the data.

Stage of Calling Tree	0	1	2	3	4	5	6	7	8	9	10
Families Informed	1	2	4								

b. How does the number of families hearing the message grow as the calling tree progresses in stages? How is that pattern of change shown in the plot of the data?

c. How many stages of the tree will be needed before all 750 families know the decision? How many telephone calls will be required?

3. How will word pass through the club if each person in the tree calls three other families, instead of just two?

a. Make a tree graph for several stages of this calling plan.

b. Make a table showing the number of families who will hear the decision at each of the first ten stages of the calling process. Then plot the data.

Stage of Calling Tree	0	1	2	3	4	5	6	7	8	9	10
Families Informed	1	3									

c. How does the number of families hearing the message increase as the calling tree progresses in stages? How is that pattern of change shown in the plot of the data?

d. How many stages of the tree will be needed before all 750 families know the decision? How many telephone calls will be required?

4. In each of the two calling trees, you can use the number of phone calls at any stage to calculate the number of calls at the next stage.

a. Use the words *NOW* and *NEXT* to write equations showing the two patterns.

b. Explain how the equations match the patterns of change in the tables of (*stage, number of families informed*) data.

c. Describe how the equations can be used with your calculator or computer to produce the tables you made in Activities 2 and 3.

d. Write an equation relating *NOW* and *NEXT* that could be used to model a telephone calling tree in which each family calls four other families.

2. b. The number of members hearing the message doubles as the calling tree progresses in stages. This pattern is shown in the plot of the data since the vertical distance between any two consecutive ordered pairs is twice that of the vertical distance between the previous two.

c. To figure the number of people that have been informed at any given stage in the tree, you must add up the number of people informed at each previous stage. After the 8th stage, 511 know the decision. Since $750 > 511$, that means 9 stages are required. (Not everyone will have to participate in the 9th stage, however.) Since everyone except the club president must receive a telephone call, 749 calls are required.

3. a.

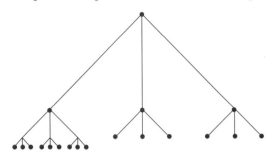

b.

Stage of Calling Tree	0	1	2	3	4	5	6	7	8	9	10
Families Informed	1	3	9	27	81	243	729	2,187	6,561	19,683	59,049

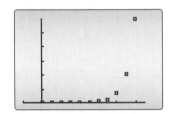 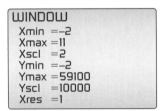

```
WINDOW
Xmin =-2
Xmax =11
Xscl =2
Ymin =-2
Ymax =59100
Yscl =10000
Xres =1
```

c. The number of members hearing the message triples as the calling tree progresses in stages. This pattern is shown in the plot of the data since the vertical distance between any two consecutive ordered pairs is three times that of the vertical distance between the previous two.

d. Seven stages of the tree are required but, as before, not everyone will have to participate in the 7th stage. 749 phone calls are needed.

4. a. First tree: $NEXT = NOW \times 2$ (starting at 1)
Second tree: $NEXT = NOW \times 3$ (starting at 1)

b. First tree: Twice as many people find out about the decision from one stage to the next.
Second tree: Three times as many people find out about the decision from one stage to the next.

c. In the case where $NEXT = NOW \times 3$, for example, the 2nd row of the table may be obtained by beginning with $NOW = 1$ (press 1, then press [ENTER]). Press [×] 3 [ENTER] to obtain the second table entry. Continue by pressing [ENTER] for all the entries needed. The sequence is 1, 3, 9, 27, ..., 59,049.

d. $NEXT = NOW \times 4$ (starting at 1)
Four times as many people find out about the decision from one stage to the next.

NOTE: There is not an item asking students to find a pattern that will quickly enable them to know the sum of the members who hear at any stage. If groups do observe that this sum is always one less than the next table entry, they can share their discovery with the entire class.

Unit 6

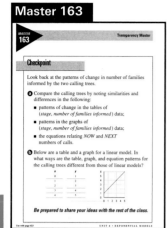

MASTER
163
Transparency Master

Checkpoint

Look back at the patterns of change in number of families informed by the two calling trees.

ⓐ Compare the calling trees by noting similarities and differences in the following:
■ patterns of change in the tables of (*stage, number of families informed*) data;
■ patterns in the graphs of (*stage, number of families informed*) data;
■ the equations relating *NOW* and *NEXT* numbers of calls.

ⓑ Below are a table and a graph for a linear model. In what ways are the table, graph, and equation patterns for the calling trees different from those of linear models?

Be prepared to share your ideas with the rest of the class.

Use with page 423   UNIT 6 · EXPONENTIAL MODELS

SHARE AND SUMMARIZE   full-class discussion

Checkpoint

See Teaching Master 163.

ⓐ ■ In each table, at the zero stage, one person (the club president) knows the decision. In the first stage, the number of people who are called by one person know the decision. In the second stage, this number is squared. (Make sure students know that multiplying a number by itself is called squaring the number.) Successive stages result in an increase in the number of members who hear the decision by a factor of the number of people called by one person.

■ The shapes of both graphs are similar, but the more people that are called at each stage, the bigger the change in vertical distance between successive ordered pairs. Try to get students to use vocabulary such as "steeper" or "rising faster" and to connect this with the difference in change between successive ordered pairs in the two models.

■ The equations relating *NOW* and *NEXT* are very similar; all are of the form *NEXT* = *NOW* × (*number of people called by each person at each stage*), starting at 1.

ⓑ In linear models, y increases or decreases by a constant amount as x increases. The graph of a linear model is a line. The equations relating *NOW* and *NEXT* look like *NEXT* = *NOW* ± *n*, where *n* is some number.

In the nonlinear models explored thus far, y increases by a constant *factor* as x increases. The graph is an upward curve. The equations relating *NOW* and *NEXT* look like *NEXT* = *NOW* × *n*, where *n* is the factor by which y increases at each successive stage.

JOURNAL ENTRY: Think about *NEXT* = *NOW* + 2, *NEXT* = *NOW* × 2, *NEXT* = *NOW* + 20, all starting at 1. Make a table for each and say which is growing fastest. Can you explain why the vertical jumps in the y values are not constant for one of these?

APPLY   individual task

▶On Your Own

You may need to help students focus on the fact that they are only recording the bacterial count every 20 minutes and that they are counting 20-minute time periods.

Checkpoint

Look back at the patterns of change in number of families informed by the two calling trees.

ⓐ Compare the calling trees by noting similarities and differences in the following:

- patterns of change in the tables of (*stage, number of families informed*) data;
- patterns in the graphs of (*stage, number of families informed*) data;
- the equations relating *NOW* and *NEXT* numbers of calls.

ⓑ Below are a table and a graph for a linear model. In what ways are the table, graph, and equation patterns for the calling trees different from those of linear models?

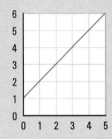

x	y
0	1
1	2
2	3
3	4
4	5

Be prepared to share your group's ideas with the rest of the class.

On Your Own

The patterns of change in information spread by calling trees occur in many other situations. For example, when bacteria infect some part of your body, they grow and split into two genetically equivalent cells again and again.

a. Suppose a single bacterium lands in a cut on your hand. It begins spreading an infection by growing and splitting into two bacteria every 20 minutes.

- Make a table showing the number of bacteria after each 20-minute period in the first three hours. (Assume none of the bacteria are killed by white blood cells.)

- Plot the (*number of 20-minute time periods, bacteria count*) data.
- Describe the pattern of growth of bacteria causing the infection.

b. Use *NOW* and *NEXT* to write an equation relating the number of bacteria at one time to the number 20 minutes later. Then use the equation to find the number of bacteria after fifteen 20-minute periods.

c. How are the table, graph, and equation of bacteria growth similar to, and different from, the calling tree examples? How are they similar to, and different from, typical patterns of linear models?

INVESTIGATION 2 Shortcut Calculations

Everyone knows that mathematics is useful in solving business, engineering, or science problems. It is also used to design works of music and art. Sometimes it even plays a role in the plots of stories and books. For example, an old Persian legend illustrates the speed of exponential growth.

A wealthy king was rescued from danger by the quick thinking and brave action of one of his soldiers. The king wanted to honor the poor soldier, so he offered a very generous reward: a beautiful chessboard made of ivory and ebony and a set of gold chess pieces.

While the chess set was beautiful and valuable, the young man asked for a different reward. To help the poor people in his country, he asked the king to distribute rice from his storehouse—two grains for the first square of the chessboard, four grains for the second square, eight grains for the third square, sixteen grains for the fourth square, and so on. The king was pleased that he could keep his beautiful chessboard and repay the brave soldier with such a simple grant of rice to the poor. But he soon discovered that the request was not as simple as he thought.

a. **Number of 20-min**

Time Periods	0	1	2	3	4	5	6	7	8	9
Number of Bacteria	1	2	4	8	16	32	64	128	256	512

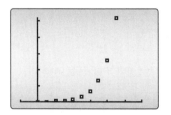 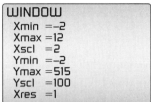

The number of bacteria doubles every twenty minutes, or increases by a factor of 8 each hour.

b. *NEXT = NOW* × 2, starting at 1.

After fifteen twenty-minute periods there will be 32,768 bacteria.

c. Responses should be similar to those given in Checkpoint, Parts a and b. Since we are increasing by a factor of 2, students should be able to recognize this is the exact same pattern as the calling tree pattern where one person called two people.

MORE

ASSIGNMENT   *pp. 432–438*

Students can now begin Modeling Task 4 or Reflecting Task 2 or 4 from the MORE assignment following Investigation 3.

Unit 6

EXPLORE   small-group investigation

INVESTIGATION 2 Shortcut Calculations

Students, even apparently very sophisticated students, really enjoy this story. After students read it together, a useful introductory activity is to ask them to predict (no calculator help) whether the king will have room on the 8th square (end of one row) for all the rice he owes. This will give you an idea of how they are thinking about doubling an initial 1 grain of rice 8 times. You can follow by asking about the 16th square: Will there still be room for all the rice? After listening to the conjectures without commenting on them, you may want to offer the information that there are 256 grains of rice on the 8th square, and ask how many we can expect (again, no calculators) on the 16th. Do not expect correct answers at this stage. However, you may find that the level of disagreement about the correct answers (from estimates of simply twice 256 to millions) lends an interest factor to the number-crunching process.

As you circulate around the room, you may have to supply facts, such as there are 3 feet in a yard. You may also have to remind students that a cubic yard is 3 feet by 3 feet by 3 feet; that is, it forms a prism with a base area of 9 square feet and a height of 3 feet. Some students already will have met exponential notation, such as 2^4 for $2 \times 2 \times 2 \times 2$. You might invite them to wonder why this notation ever was invented: who thought of writing the number of factors (the exponent) higher than the factor itself (the base), and why might this have been useful. Students need to see notation as a human construct intended to be helpful, not a barrier to understanding.

1.

Square Number	10	20	30	40
Number of Grains of Rice	1,024	1,048,576	1,073,741,824	1.1×10^{12}*

Square Number	50	60	64
Number of Grains of Rice	1.1×10^{15}*	1.2×10^{18}*	1.8×10^{19}*

* These values are approximate.

2. The number representing the national debt is smaller than the number of grains of rice on the 64th square by a factor of about 3.2 million.

3. Students may draw pictures to help them with the units of measure in this activity.

   a. $2^{64} \div 2,000 \approx 9.22 \times 10^{15}$ in.^{3}

   b. $2^{64} \div 2,000 \div 1,728 \approx 5.34 \times 10^{12}$ ft^3

   c. $2^{64} \div 2,000 \div 1,728 \div 27 \approx 1.98 \times 10^{11}$ yd^3

   d. $2^{64} \div 2,000 \div 1,728 \div 27 \div 1,760^3 \approx 36.26$ mi^3 or
   $2^{64} \div 2,000 \div 1,728 \div 5,280^3 \approx 36.26$ mi^3

4. The value would be about 4.6×10^{14} dollars.

5. a. The third square has twice as many grains as the second square, which has twice as many grains as the first square, which has 2 grains.

   b. Simply multiplying 2s together, we get the following:

   ■ $2 \times 2 \times 2 \times 2 \times 2$

   ■ $2 \times 2 \times 2 \times 2 \times 2 \times 2 \times 2 \times 2 \times 2 \times 2$

   ■ $2 \times 2 \times 2 \times 2 \times 2 \times 2 \times 2 \times 2 \times 2 \times 2 \times 2 \times 2 \times 2 \times 2 \times 2 \times 2 \times 2 \times 2 \times 2 \times 2$

   c. $2^5, 2^{10}, 2^{20}$

   d. $2^{64}, 2^x$

   e. Be sure that each group has Parts c and d done correctly.

6. The calculator program *Tableplot* will be useful in this activity.

   a.

Square	1	2	3	4	5	6	7	8	9	10
Number of Grains of Rice	2	4	8	16	32	64	128	256	512	1,024

1. Use your calculator to find the number of grains of rice for each of the squares 10, 20, 30, 40, 50, 60, and 64.

2. The national debt of the United States in 2000 was about $5,600,000,000,000. How does this number compare to the number of grains of rice for square 64 of the king's chessboard?

3. For some kinds of rice it takes about 2,000 grains to fill one cubic inch of space. Consider the number of grains that the king owed for the 64th square alone.

   a. How many cubic inches would that rice occupy?

   b. How many cubic feet?

   c. How many cubic yards?

   d. How many cubic miles? (There are 5,280 feet in 1 mile.)

4. A cubic inch of rice costs about $0.05. What would this mean for the present-day value of the rice on square 64 alone?

5. To calculate the number of grains of rice for each square of the king's chessboard, you could use the equation $NEXT = NOW \times 2$, beginning at 2 grains for the first square. So the number of grains of rice for square 2 could be represented as 2×2.

   a. Why can the number of grains of rice for square 3 be expressed as $(2 \times 2) \times 2$?

   b. Write expressions for the number of grains of rice for squares 5, 10, and 20.

   c. What is the shorthand way of writing the calculations in Part b using *exponents*?

   d. Write an exponential expression for the number of grains of rice for square 64. For any square x.

   e. Compare your exponential expressions in Parts c and d with those of another group. Resolve any differences.

6. You can use your graphing calculator or computer software and the exponential rule for any square x to make tables and graphs of the pattern formed by counting rice grains. Enter the rule in the "Y=" list of your calculator or computer, using the ⌒ key before the exponent. (With some tools, you may need to use the y^x or a^b key or a different symbol instead.)

   a. Make a table showing the number of grains of rice for squares 1 through 10. You may use the calculator program *Tableplot* (TBLPLOT), if available. The program allows you to switch easily between the table and a scatterplot of the table's values.

LESSON 1 • EXPONENTIAL GROWTH   425

b. Use TBLPLOT or similar software to plot the (*square number*, *number of grains of rice*) data.

c. Explain why the table and plot produced using your exponential rule are the same as those produced using the equation $NEXT = NOW \times 2$, starting at 2.

7. Suppose the wealthy Persian king offered his soldier a more generous deal: 3 grains of rice for the first square, 9 for the second, 27 for the third, 81 for the fourth, and so on.

a. Use an equation relating *NOW* and *NEXT* and your calculator or computer software to find the number of grains of rice for each of the first 10 squares of the chessboard in this case.

b. Write a rule using exponents that could be used to calculate the number of grains of rice for any square, without knowing the amount on the previous square.

c. Enter your rule for Part b in the "Y=" list of your graphing calculator or computer software. Find the number of grains of rice for squares 15, 25, and 35.

d. For which square will the number of grains of rice first exceed 1 billion?

Checkpoint

Look back at the patterns of change in the situation involving the king's chessboard and those in the bacterial growth and telephone calling tree situations in Investigation 1.

ⓐ How are the patterns of change in the tables for the king's chessboard similar to, and different from, those in the telephone trees and bacterial growth problems?

ⓑ How are the graphs of those relations similar to each other and how are they different?

ⓒ Compare the equations modeling the three situations.

  ■ How are the rules using *NOW* and *NEXT* similar and how are they different?

  ■ Write exponential rules ($y = …$) that model the telephone trees. Write a rule that models the bacterial growth problem.

  ■ How are these rules similar and how are they different?

Be prepared to share your ideas with the entire class.

The patterns of change in the situations involving the king's chessboard, bacterial growth, and telephone calling trees are called **exponential growth**. Exponential growth patterns of change can be modeled using rules involving exponents.

6. b.

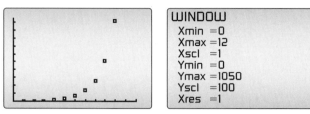

```
WINDOW
Xmin =0
Xmax =12
Xscl =1
Ymin =0
Ymax =1050
Yscl =100
Xres =1
```

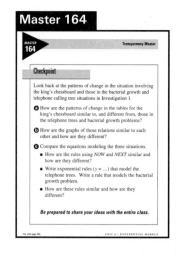

c. 2^x can be thought of as the *NOW* value with $2^{(x + 1)}$ as the *NEXT* value. In other words, $2^{x + 1} = 2^x \times 2$ or *NEXT* = *NOW* $\times$ 2, both starting at 2.

7. a.

Square	1	2	3	4	5	6	7	8	9	10
Number of Grains of Rice	3	9	27	81	243	729	2,187	6,561	19,683	59,049

b. Let y be the number of grains of rice on square x. Then $y = 3^x$.

c. The number of grains of rice for square 15 is 14,348,907.
The number of grains of rice for square 25 is approximately 8.47×10^{11}.
The number of grains of rice for square 35 is approximately 5.00×10^{16}.

d. On the nineteenth square there will be 1,162,261,467 grains of rice.

SHARE AND SUMMARIZE   full-class discussion

Checkpoint

See Teaching Master 164.

ⓐ Responses will vary. In each problem, as the top-row (or x) values increase by 1 unit, the bottom (or y) values increase by a factor n. They are different because the factor n is sometimes different.

ⓑ The graphs are all nonlinear, curving upward as x becomes larger. They have different rates of increase if the factor is different.

ⓒ Responses will vary.

■ Rules involving *NOW* and *NEXT* are of the form *NEXT* = *NOW* $\times$ n, where n varies according to the problem situation. For most of the situations in this lesson the factor was 2.

■ Exponential rules will be of the form $y = n^x$, where x refers to the stage of growth (time period, stage of calling tree, square on chessboard) and n varies according to the problem. All three of these are modeled by $y = 2^x$. One telephone tree problem was modeled by $y = 3^x$.

■ They are similar because they are of the form $y = n^x$. In one telephone tree problem, n is 3. For the other situations, n is 2.

See additional Teaching Notes on page T481D.

► **On Your Own**

a.

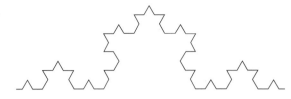

At each stage, the fractal is symmetric about a vertical line through the uppermost peak.

b.

Stage of Growth	0	1	2	3	4	5	6	7
Segments in Design	1	4	16	64	256	1,024	4,096	16,384

c. $NEXT = NOW \times 4$, starting at 1.

d. $y = 4^x$

e.

Stage of Growth	8	9	10	20
Segments in Design	65,536	262,144	1,048,576	1.1×10^{12}*

* approximate

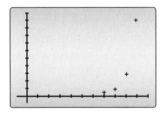 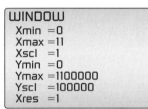

```
WINDOW
Xmin =0
Xmax =11
Xscl =1
Ymin =0
Ymax =1100000
Yscl =100000
Xres =1
```

This graph shows the first 10 stages of growth.

f. The number of small segments first reaches 1 million at the 10th stage.

NOTE: You may want to discuss fractals with the class and tell interested students about Extending Tasks 1–4. For more information on fractals consult the following.

1. *Fractals For The Classroom*. Peitgen, Jurgens, and Saupe. New York: Springer-Verlag, in cooperation with the National Council of Teachers of Mathematics, 1992.

2. *An Eye For Fractals*. McGuire. Boston: Addison-Wesley, 1991.

3. *Fractals, Chaos, Power Laws*. Schroeder. New York: WH Freeman, 1991.

4. *Fractal Geometry of Nature*. Mandelbrot. New York: WH Freeman, 1983.

5. Internet Sources
   http://archives.math.utk.edu/software.html
   http://fractalus.com
   http://www.calweb.com/~bjohnson/fract.html

Unit 6

MORE
ASSIGNMENT   *pp. 432–438*

Students can now begin Modeling Task 2 or 3, Organizing Task 1 or 3, or Reflecting Task 1 or 5 from the MORE assignment following Investigation 3.

On Your Own

The sketch below shows the first stages in the formation of a geometric figure. This figure is an example of a *fractal*. At each stage in the growth of the figure, the middle of every segment is replaced by a triangular tent. The new figure is made up of more, but shorter, segments.

Start

Stage 0   Stage 1   Stage 2

a. Make a sketch showing at least one more stage in the growth of this fractal. Describe any symmetries that the fractal has at *each* stage.

b. Continue the pattern begun in this table:

Stage of Growth	0	1	2	3	4	5	6	7
Segments in Design	1	4						

c. Write an equation showing how the number of segments at any stage of the fractal can be used to find the number of segments at the next stage.

d. Write an exponential rule that can be used to find the number of segments in the pattern at any stage *x*, without finding the numbers at each stage along the way. Begin your rule, "$y = \dots$."

e. Use the rule from Part d to produce a table and a graph showing the number of segments in the fractal pattern at each of the first 10 stages of growth. Do the same for the first 20 stages. (The calculator program TBLPLOT is helpful here.)

f. At what stage will the number of small segments first reach 1 million?

INVESTIGATION ▶ 3 Getting Started

Bacterial infections seldom start with a single bacterium. Suppose that you cut yourself on a rusty nail that puts 25 bacteria cells into the wound. Suppose also that those bacteria divide in two after every quarter of an hour.

Unit 6

1. Use *NOW* and *NEXT* to write an equation showing how the number of bacteria changes from one quarter-hour to the next.

2. Make a table showing the number of bacteria in the cut for each quarter-hour over the first three hours. Then plot a graph of the (*number of quarter-hours*, *bacteria count*) data.

3. In what ways are the table, graph, and equation of bacteria counts in this case similar to, and different from, the simple case (pages 423–424) that started from a single one-celled bacterium?

You could use the equation from Activity 1 to find the number of bacteria after 8 hours. (That would assume your body did not fight off the infection and you did not apply any medication.) Activity 4 will help you find a way to get that answer directly, without finding the bacteria count at each quarter-hour along the way.

4. Begin by making an estimate of the number of bacteria after 8 hours.

   a. What arithmetic operations are required to calculate the bacteria count after 8 hours (32 quarter-hours) if the equation relating *NOW* and *NEXT* is used?

   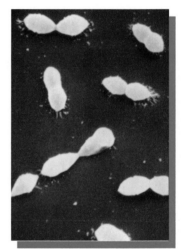

   - How can those operations be written in short form using exponents?

   - What set of calculator keystrokes will give the result quickly?

   - What is the number of bacteria after 8 hours? How close was your estimate?

   b. Write a rule using exponents that could help calculate the bacteria count. Then use your rule to calculate the number of bacteria after 8 hours and compare your answer to that in Part a.

5. Investigate the number of bacteria expected after 8 hours if the starting number of bacteria is 30, 40, 60, or 100, instead of 25. For each starting number, do the following. (Divide the work among your group members.)

   a. Find the number of bacteria after 8 hours.

   b. Write two equations that model the bacterial growth. One should use *NOW* and *NEXT*. The other should begin "y = … ."

   c. Make a table and plot of (*number of quarter-hours*, *bacteria count*) data.

INVESTIGATION 3 Getting Started

In this investigation, students explore patterns of exponential growth where the initial value varies.

1. $NEXT = NOW \times 2$, starting at 25.

2. Students usually find the making of the table complicated. If they are accustomed to writing tables with no labels or sloppily worded labels, they will find this table confusing. To make sense of it you have to know that the variable is "time in quarter-hour units." Encourage students to write "Number of Quarter-Hour Units" for their table heading, not simply "Time."

Number of Quarter-Hour Units	0	1	2	3	4	5	6	7	8	9	10	11	12
Number of Bacteria in Cut	25	50	100	200	400	800	1,600	3,200	6,400	12,800	25,600	51,200	102,400

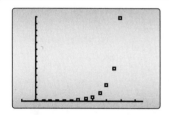
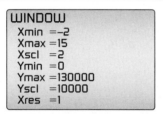

```
WINDOW
 Xmin =-2
 Xmax =15
 Xscl =2
 Ymin =0
 Ymax =130000
 Yscl =10000
 Xres =1
```

3. The table of the simple case and the case beginning with 25 bacteria differ in that the entries in the simple case are smaller by a factor of 25 than their corresponding counterparts in the 25-bacteria case. However, the tables are similar in that progressive entries increase by a factor of two. Similarly, the graphs are the same overall shape, but in the simple case, the y-coordinates are smaller by a factor of 25. The simple case graph must be stretched vertically by a factor of 25 to get the graph corresponding to the case beginning with 25 bacteria.

4. Student estimates probably will not be high enough.
   a. Multiplication is used.
      ■ In short form, the operations are written 25×2^{32}.
      ■ The keystrokes are 25 ⊠ 2 ⊼ 32.
      ■ The number of bacteria is 107,374,182,400, or approximately 107 billion. Student estimates probably were much lower.
   b. $y = 25(2^x)$ or $y = 25 \times 2^x$; results should match those found in Part a.

5. a. $30 \times 2^{32} \approx 1.29 \times 10^{11}$
      $40 \times 2^{32} \approx 1.72 \times 10^{11}$
      $60 \times 2^{32} \approx 2.58 \times 10^{11}$
      $100 \times 2^{32} \approx 4.29 \times 10^{11}$
   b. Each problem setting implies a different starting point; namely the starting number of bacteria, so the equations will be of the form $NEXT = NOW \times 2$ (starting at a) and $y = a \cdot 2^x$, where a represents the starting number of bacteria.

See additional Teaching Notes on page T481D.

Unit 6

5. **d.** Comparing results should help students identify errors in their work.

   ■ The 2^{32} was multiplied by different factors: 30, 40, 60, and 100.

   ■ The *NOW-NEXT* equations have different starting values but the same factor, and the equations of the form $y = a(2^x)$ vary as $a = 30, 40, 60,$ and 100

   ■ The "0" entry in each table will be the starting number of bacteria; call this number a. The first entry will be $2a$, the second entry $4a$, and so on. The nth entry will be $a \times 2^n$. Therefore, the pattern of change in all tables will be the same, but the numbers themselves will depend on a. The *shapes* of the graphs will be the same, but as usual, the y-coordinates will differ according to a.

6. **a.** Students will need several stages of the tree to help them see the patterns.

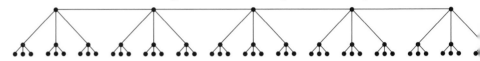

   b. *NEXT = NOW* $\times 3$, starting at 15. (The *number of calls* starts a 5×3 or 15.

   c.

Stage	1	2	3	4	5	6
Number of Calls	15	45	135	405	1,215	3,645

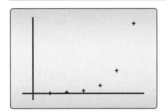

   d. Multiplication is used.

   ■ The short form is 5×3^8 or 15×3^7.

   ■ The calculator keystrokes are 5 ⊠ 3 ⌃ 8 or 15 ⊠ 3 ⌃ 7.

   ■ The number of calls at stage 8 is 32,805.

   e. $y = 5(3^x)$ or $y = 15(3^{x-1})$

7. **a.** The 5s should be replaced with 4s, and the 3s should be replaced with 5s.

   b. If everyone makes 5 phone calls instead of 3, the number of families notified grows much more quickly: by a factor of 5 rather than 3. So the second tree will reach all the families in less time.

d. Compare your results.

- How were your calculations of the number of bacteria after 8 hours similar and how were they different?

- How are the equations relating *NOW* and *NEXT* and the equations beginning "$y = \ldots$" for bacteria counts similar and how are they different?

- How are the tables and graphs of (*number of quarter-hours, bacteria count*) data similar and how are they different?

Just as bacterial growth won't always start with a single cell, other exponential growth processes can start with different initial numbers. Think again about the telephone calling tree for the Silver Spring Soccer Club in Investigation 1.

6. Suppose that before deciding to call off play because of bad weather, the president must talk with the club's four-member board of directors. When the calling tree is started, there are already five people who know the news to be spread. The president and each member of the board begin the calling tree by calling three other families apiece. Each family then calls three other families, and so on.

a. Draw a tree graph illustrating this pattern of calling.

b. Write an equation showing how the number of calls at any stage of the calling process can be used to find the number of calls at the next stage.

c. Use the equation from Part b to make a table and a plot showing how the number of calls increases as the process moves to further stages.

d. What arithmetic operations are required to find the number of calls at the 8th stage of the tree, using the equation relating *NOW* and *NEXT*?

- How can those operations be written in short form using exponents?

- What set of calculator keystrokes will give the result quickly?

- What is the number of calls at Stage 8?

e. What rule using exponents could help with the number of call calculations?

7. Suppose the board of directors had only three members (so four people know the news at the start), and each caller in the tree is expected to call five other families.

a. How would your answers to Activity 6 change?

b. Which phone tree should reach all families in the least amount of time? Why?

In studying exponential growth, it is common to refer to the *starting point* of the pattern as **Stage 0** or the **initial value**.

8. Use your calculator and the ◻^ key to find each of the following values: 2^0, 3^0, 5^0, 23^0.

  a. What seems to be the calculator value for b^0, for any positive value of b?

  b. Recall the examples of exponential patterns in bacterial growth and telephone calling trees. How is your conclusion for Part a supported by these examples?

9. Now use your calculator to make tables of (x, y) values for each of the following equations. Use values for x from 0 to 10. Share the work among members of your group.

  i. $y = 5(2^x)$ **ii.** $y = 4(3^x)$

  iii. $y = 3(5^x)$ **iv.** $y = 7(23^x)$

  a. What patterns do you see in your tables that show how to model exponential growth from any starting point?

  b. If you see an equation of the form $y = a(b^x)$ relating two variables x and y, what will the values of a and b tell you about the relation?

Checkpoint

The tables that follow show variables changing in a pattern of exponential growth.

I.

x	0	1	2	3	4	5	6
y	1	2	4	8	16	32	64

II.

x	0	1	2	3	4	5	6
y	3	6	12	24	48	96	192

ⓐ What equation relating *NOW* and *NEXT* shows the common pattern of growth in the tables?

ⓑ How are the patterns of change in the tables different? How will that difference show up in plots of the tables?

ⓒ What equations ($y = \ldots$) will give rules for the patterns in the tables?

ⓓ How do the numbers used in writing those rules relate to the patterns of entries in the table? How could someone who knows about exponential growth examine the equation and predict the pattern in a table of (x, y) data?

Be prepared to share your equations and observations with the entire class.

8. a. Obtaining the following results, $2^0 = 1$, $3^0 = 1$, $5^0 = 1$, $23^0 = 1$, implies $b^0 = 1$ for any positive value of b.

b. In Stage 0, there is only 1 person who hears the message. In Stage 0, there is only 1 bacterium.

9. i.

X	Y₁
0	5
1	10
2	20
3	40
4	80
5	160
6	320

$Y_1 = 5(2\verb|^|X)$

X	Y₁
7	640
8	1280
9	2560
10	5120
11	10240
12	20480
13	40960

$Y_1 = 5(2\verb|^|X)$

ii.

X	Y₁
0	4
1	12
2	36
3	108
4	324
5	972
6	2916

$Y_1 = 4(3\verb|^|X)$

X	Y₁
7	8748
8	26244
9	78732
10	236196
11	708588
12	2.13E6
13	6.38E6

$Y_1 = 4(3\verb|^|X)$

iii.

X	Y₁
0	3
1	15
2	75
3	375
4	1875
5	9375
6	46875

$Y_1 = 3(5\verb|^|X)$

X	Y₁
7	234375
8	1.17E6
9	5.86E6
10	2.93E7
11	1.46E8
12	7.32E8
13	3.66E9

$Y_1 = 3(5\verb|^|X)$

iv.

X	Y₁
0	7
1	161
2	3703
3	85169
4	1.96E6
5	4.51E7
6	1.04E9

$Y_1 = 7(23\verb|^|X)$

X	Y₁
7	2.4E10
8	5.5E11
9	1.3E13
10	2.9E14
11	6.7E15
12	1.5E17
13	3.5E18

$Y_1 = 7(23\verb|^|X)$

a. The y value when $x = 0$ (the y-intercept) is the starting value. The ratio $\frac{\text{2nd } y \text{ value}}{\text{1st } y \text{ value}}$ will give the growth rate b.

b. Using the model $y = a(b^x)$, the starting point is a and the growth rate is b.

SHARE AND SUMMARIZE full-class discussion

Vocabulary can be important, so you may want to have several students answer Part b. If "stretched" is not used, you may want to tell the students it is a commonly used term and they may want to say "stretched vertically" since it is in the direction of the *y*-axis. They have used "stretched" in Unit 1, "Patterns in Data," to describe data with a skewed distribution.

Checkpoint

See Teaching Master 165.

ⓐ *NEXT = NOW* × 2; however, the first starts at 1 while the second starts at 3.

ⓑ Each y entry in II is 3 times that of its counterpart in I. Therefore, the plots of the two tables will have the same shape but the plot of II will be "stretched" by a factor of 3.

See additional Teaching Notes on page T481E.

Master 165

Checkpoint

The tables that follow show variables changing in a pattern of exponential growth.

I.	x	0	1	2	3	4	5	6
	y	1	2	4	8	16	32	64
II.	x	0	1	2	3	4	5	6
	y	3	6	12	24	48	96	192

ⓐ What equation relating *NOW* and *NEXT* shows the common pattern of growth in the tables?

ⓑ How are the patterns of change in the tables different? How will that difference show up in plots of the tables?

ⓒ What equations (y = ...) will give rules for the patterns in the tables?

ⓓ How do the numbers used in writing those rules relate to the patterns of entries in the table? How could someone who knows about exponential growth examine the equation and predict the pattern in a table of (*x*, *y*) data?

Be prepared to share your equations and observations with the entire class.

CONSTRUCTING A MATH TOOLKIT: After completing the Checkpoint, have students write a paragraph describing the patterns found in the tables, graphs, and equations of situations that involve exponential growth (Teaching Master 200).

On Your Own

You may wish to remind students that they will have to read carefully how long each time period is. As you circulate, ask students what pairs of entries mean. For example: "What does (7, 3,200) mean?" (At the 7th stage there are 3,200 bacteria.) Then you can ask, "Why is this not just 2 × 2 × 2 × 2 × 2 × 2 × 2?"

a. ■ Let x be the number of 5-minute periods. Let y be the number of copies of DNA after x 5-minute periods. Then $y = 7(2^x)$. Alternatively, the equation *NEXT = NOW × 2* (starting at 7) may be used.

■ In 2 hours, there are 24 5-minute periods. Therefore x is 24 and $y = 7(2^{24}) = 117,440,512$.

■ The value is $7(2^{28}) = 1,879,048,192$ (28 five-minute time periods are required).

b. ■ Let n be the starting number of copies. Then, $y = n(2^x)$ and *NEXT = NOW × 2*, starting at n.

■ $n = 1$: 16,777,216
$n = 2$: 33,554,432
$n = 3$: 50,331,648

■ $n = 1$: 30 time periods
$n = 2$: 29 time periods
$n = 3$: 29 time periods

c. ■ It will take about 250 ÷ 55, or about 4.5 hours.

■ $y = 55x$ or *NEXT = NOW + 55*, starting at 0. In the "$y = \ldots$" equation given here, x is multiplied, whereas in "$y = \ldots$" equations dealing with exponential growth, x is an exponent. *NOW-NEXT* equations representing exponential growth involve multiplication; those representing linear growth involve addition.

■ The table giving (*time, distance*) data for this car will have y values that increase by 55 miles whenever x increases by 1 hour. With exponential growth, the difference between successive y values is either increasing or decreasing. The graph of the car data will be a line; the graph of exponential data will be a curve.

▶ On Your Own

Jurassic Park is a book and a movie about a dinosaur theme park. It is based on the idea that dinosaur DNA might be recovered from fossils and copied in laboratories until the genetic material for dinosaurs is available. The possibility of actually "recreating" dinosaurs is remote. But chemists *have* invented processes for copying genetic materials. The 1993 Nobel Prize for chemistry was shared by two scientists who developed such processes. In the PCR (polymer chain reaction) process invented by Kary Mullis, a sample of DNA is doubled. The process takes about 5 minutes.

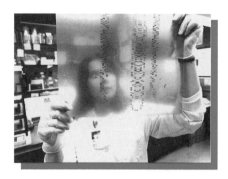

a. Suppose a chemist starts the PCR process with a sample that holds only 7 copies of a special piece of DNA.

- ■ Write two different equations that can be used for calculating the number of copies of the DNA on hand after any number of 5-minute periods.

- ■ Use your equations from above to find the number of copies of the DNA produced after 2 hours.

- ■ Use your equations to find the number of 5-minute periods required to first produce 1 billion copies of the DNA.

b. How would your answers to Part a change if the starting DNA sample held 1, 2, or 3 copies of the DNA to be copied?

c. From your earlier study of linear models, you know that the exponential growth pattern common in living organisms is not the way all things change. For example, think about a car that accelerates quickly to the speed limit of 55 mph on a highway and keeps going at that speed for some time.

- ■ How long will it take the car to cover a distance of 250 miles?

- ■ What equations allow you to calculate the distance traveled by this car for any time? How are those equations different from what you expect to find with exponential growth?

- ■ What patterns do you expect to find in tables and graphs of (*time, distance*) data for this car? How are those patterns different from what you find with exponential growth?

MORE
Modeling • Organizing • Reflecting • Extending

Modeling

1. Suppose a single bacterium lands in an open cut on your leg and begins doubling every 15 minutes.

   a. How many bacteria will there be after 15, 30, 45, 60, and 75 minutes have elapsed (if no bacteria die)?

   b. Write rules that can be used to calculate the number of bacteria in the cut after any number of 15-minute periods.

   ■ Make the first an equation relating *NOW* and *NEXT*.

   ■ Make the second a rule using exponents, beginning "$y = \ldots$."

   c. Use your rules from Part b to make a table showing the number of bacteria in the cut at the end of each 15-minute period over 3 hours. Then describe the pattern of change in number of bacteria from each quarter hour to the next.

   d. Use the rules from Part b to find the predicted number of bacteria after 5, 6, and 7 hours. (**Hint:** How many 15-minute periods will that be?)

2. Suppose the wealthy Persian king in Investigation 2 offered his soldier an even more generous deal. The king will distribute 5 grains of rice for the first square, 25 for the second, 125 for the third, 625 for the fourth, and so on.

   a. Use an equation relating *NOW* and *NEXT* rice grain counts to find the number of grains of rice for each of the first 5 squares of the chessboard.

   b. Write a rule using exponents that could be used to calculate the number of grains of rice for any square, without starting from the first square.

   c. Use the rule in Part b to make a table showing the number of grains of rice for each of the first 10 squares. Describe the pattern of change in this table, from one square to the next.

   d. How would your answers to Parts a–c change if the king offered 5 grains for square 1, 10 grains for square 2, 15 grains for square 3, 20 grains for square 4, and so on?

3. The following sketches show several stages in the growth of a *fractal tree*.

Stage 1   Stage 2   Stage 3   Stage 4   Stage 5

Modeling

MORE
ASSIGNMENT   *pp. 432–438*

Modeling: 1 and choice of one*
Organizing: 1, and 3 or 4*
Reflecting: 3 and choice of one*
Extending: Choose one*

When choice is indicated, it is important to leave the choice to the student.
NOTE: *It is best if Organizing tasks are discussed as a whole class after they have been assigned as homework.*

1. a.

Time Elapsed (in minutes)	15	30	45	60	75
Number of Bacteria		2	4	8	16	32

b. ■ *NEXT = NOW* × 2, starting at 1 (indicating the first 15-minute time period).
■ $y = 2^x$, where x is the number of 15-minute periods elapsed.

c. **Number of 15-min.**

Time Periods	0	1	2	3	4	5	6	7	8	9	10	11	12
Number of Bacteria	1	2	4	8	16	32	64	128	256	512	1,024	2,048	4,096

The number of bacteria will double every 15-minute period.

d. In 5 hours, there will be 1,048,576 bacteria.
In 6 hours, there will be 16,777,216 bacteria.
In 7 hours, there will be 268,435,456 bacteria.

2. a. *NEXT = NOW* × 5, starting with 5

```
5
                    5
Ans*5
                   25
                  125
                  625
                 3125
```

b. $y = 5^x$

c.

X	Y1	
0	1	
1	5	
2	25	
3	125	
4	625	
5	3125	
6	15625	
Y1 ▊5^X		

X	Y1	
7	78125	
8	390625	
9	1.95E6	
10	9.77E6	
11	4.88E7	
12	2.44E8	
13	1.22E9	
Y1 ▊5^X		

As you move from one chessboard square to the next, the number of grains of rice is multiplied by 5.

d. ■ *NEXT = NOW* + 5, starting with 5

```
5
                    5
Ans+5
                   10
                   15
                   20
                   25
```

■ You could not write a rule using exponents. The rule would be $y = 5x$.
■ The rule is $y = 5x$, where x is the number of the square. For each successive square, instead of multiplying by 5, the change is that 5 more grains are added.

X	Y1	
1	5	
2	10	
3	15	
4	20	
5	25	
6	30	
7	35	
Y1 ▊5X		

X	Y1	
8	40	
9	45	
10	50	
11	55	
12	60	
13	65	
14	70	
Y1 ▊5X		

Unit 6

3. a.

Year	0	1	2	3	4	5	6	7	8	9	10
Number of New Branches		1	2	4	8	16	32	64	128	256	512	1,024

   b. $2^{20} = 1,048,576$

   c. In year 30, there will be over 1 billion new branches.

   d. For Part a:
   - You could use the equation $NEXT = NOW \times 2$, starting with 2. Enter 2, multiply by 2, and then hit ENTER for each successive year.
   - You could enter the function $y = 2^x$ in the functions list of a graphing calculator or computer software. Then go to the table feature to determine a table of values for this function, or use a single value calculation (such as through Y-VARS) to evaluate $y = 2^x$.
   - You could use the calculation feature of the calculator or computer software and calculate 2^3, 2^4, *etc.*

   For Part b:
   - You could calculate 2^{20}.
   - You could evaluate Y(20) (for example, using the Y-VARS menu on a TI-82 or TI-83).
   - You could use the last answer function to get to year 20. (Note: On a TI-82 or TI-83, the table cannot be used because it rounds the answer.)

   For Part c:
   - You could guess and check the various years.
   - You could check the table for the year that the y value is greater than 1 billion.
   - You could use the last answer function until you get a result larger than 1 billion.
   - You could use the graph and trace to find the smallest integer x when y is over 1 billion.

   e. There is line reflection symmetry about the line containing the "trunk" of the tree. Once you have drawn one half (left or right), you can copy that half onto the other half.

4. One day later it covers $\frac{1}{4}$ of the dish surface. Two days later it covers $\frac{1}{2}$ of the dish surface. Three days later it covers all of the dish surface.

Organizing

1. a. 5^4 b. 3^8
   c. $(1.5)^6$ d. $(-10)^8$
   e. 6^n f. a^n

2. a. Students will need to use repeated multiplication. This can be done using the last answer feature.
   - i. 625   ii. 49   iii. 1
   - iv. −512   v. 256   vi. 1,024

   b. Using a calculator:
   - Enter b [^] x then press ENTER.
   - Enter b then press ENTER. Next, press [×] and enter b again. Then press ENTER repeatedly, counting each ENTER until you have x of them (including the first one).
   - Enter b [^] X in the functions list and evaluate Y(x) using the Y-VARS menu or the table.

a. Suppose at Stage 0 there is one branch. Each year the tree grows exactly two new branches at the end of each branch. Make a table showing the number of new branches in each year from 0 to 10.

b. How many new branches will there be on this tree in year 20?

c. At what age will this sort of tree first produce at least 1 billion new branches?

d. Explain how you could find the answers to Parts a–c in three different ways using your calculator or computer.

e. Describe any symmetries that the fractal tree has at each stage. How could this information be used in drawing the next stage of the tree?

4. The drug penicillin was discovered by observation of mold growing on biology laboratory dishes. Suppose a mold begins growing on a lab dish. When first observed, the mold covers only $\frac{1}{8}$ of the dish surface, but it appears to double in size every day. When will the mold cover the entire dish?

Alexander Fleming, discoverer of penicillin

Organizing

1. Write each of the following calculations in shorter form using exponents.

a. $5 \times 5 \times 5 \times 5$

b. $3 \times 3 \times 3 \times 3 \times 3 \times 3 \times 3 \times 3$

c. $1.5 \times 1.5 \times 1.5 \times 1.5 \times 1.5 \times 1.5$

d. $(-10) \times (-10) \times (-10) \times (-10) \times (-10) \times (-10) \times (-10) \times (-10)$

e. $\underbrace{6 \times 6 \times \ldots \times 6}_{n \text{ factors}}$

f. $\underbrace{a \times a \times \ldots \times a}_{n \text{ factors}}$

2. Think about the meaning of an exponent as you complete the following tasks.

a. Do each of the following calculations without use of the exponent key ($\boxed{\wedge}$ or $\boxed{y^x}$) on your calculator.

  i. 5^4 **ii.** $(-7)^2$ **iii.** 10^0

  iv. $(-8)^3$ **v.** 2^8 **vi.** 2^{10}

b. Suppose b is any number and x is some positive whole number. Describe two ways in which you can calculate the value of b^x.

3. Exponential growth models, like linear models, can be expressed by an equation relating x and y values and an equation relating *NOW* and *NEXT* y values.

  a. Compare the patterns of (x, y) values produced by these two rules: $y = 2(3^x)$ and $y = 2 + 3x$.

  ■ For each rule, make a table of (x, y) values for x from 0 to 10 in steps of 1.

  ■ For each rule, plot the data obtained. The program TBLPLOT would be helpful here.

  ■ For each rule, write an equation using *NOW* and *NEXT* that could be used to produce the same pattern of (x, y) data.

  ■ For each rule, describe the way that y changes as x increases. Explain how that pattern shows up in the table and the graph.

  b. Now think about any two relations with rules $y = a(b^x)$ and $y = a + bx$ where $b > 1$.

  ■ What patterns are you sure to find in any table of (x, y) values in each case? What will the values of a and b tell about those patterns?

  ■ What patterns are you sure to find in graphs of the two relations? What will the values of a and b tell about those patterns?

  ■ What equations relating *NOW* and *NEXT* will give the same patterns of (x, y) values as the equations $y = a(b^x)$ and $y = a + bx$?

4. Shown below are partially completed tables for four relations between variables. In each case, decide if the table shows an exponential or a linear pattern of change. Based on that decision, complete the table as the pattern suggests. Then write equations for the patterns in two ways: using rules relating *NOW* and *NEXT* y values and using rules beginning "$y = ...$" for any given x value.

a.

x	0	1	2	3	4	5	6	7	8
y				8	16	32			

b.

x	0	1	2	3	4	5	6	7	8
y				40	80	160			

c.

x	0	1	2	3	4	5	6	7	8
y				48	56	64			

d.

x	0	1	2	3	4	5	6	7	8
y				125	625	3,125			

3. a. ■

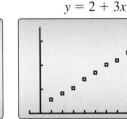

X	Y₁	Y₂
0	2	2
1	6	5
2	18	8
3	54	11
4	162	14
5	486	17
6	1458	20

Y₁ ■2*3^X

$$y = 2(3^x)$$

X	Y₁	Y₂
6	1458	20
7	4374	23
8	13122	26
9	39366	29
10	118098	32

Y₂ ■2+3X

$$y = 2 + 3x$$

NOTE: These are shown in different windows.

■ For $y = 2(3^x)$: $NEXT = NOW \times 3$, starting at 2.
For $y = 2 + 3x$: $NEXT = NOW + 3$, starting at 2.

■ In $y = 2(3^x)$, y is tripled as x increases by 1. The graph increases slowly at first, but then it increases more rapidly. In $y = 2 + 3x$, y increases by 3 as x increases by 1. This is shown in the graph as a linear scatterplot with the constant slope of 3.

b. ■ The table of $y = a(b^x)$ will have increasing y values. When the x values increase by 1, each successive y value will be b times the previous value. When $x = 0$, the value of y will be a. The table of $y = a + bx$ also will have increasing y values. When the x values increase by 1, each y value will be b more than the previous one. When $x = 0$, the value of y will be a.

■ For both $y = a(b^x)$ and $y = a + bx$, the graphs rise from left to right when $b > 1$. The graph of $y = a(b^x)$ is a curve, and the graph of $y = a + bx$ is a straight line. For $y = a(b^x)$, the greater b is, the more quickly the rate of change (and the vertical distance between points at regular intervals) increases; a is the y-intercept. For $y = a + bx$, the value of a is the y-intercept of the graph and b is the slope of the graph.

■ $NEXT = NOW \times b$ (starting at a), for $y = a(b^x)$.
$NEXT = NOW + b$ (starting at a), for $y = a + bx$.

4. a. Exponential; $NEXT = NOW \times 2$ (starting at 1), $y = 2^x$

x	0	1	2	3	4	5	6	7	8
y	1	2	4	8	16	32	64	128	256

b. Exponential; $NEXT = NOW \times 2$ (starting at 5), $y = 5(2)^x$

x	0	1	2	3	4	5	6	7	8
y	5	10	20	40	80	160	320	640	1,280

c. Linear; $NEXT = NOW + 8$ (starting at 24), $y = 24 + 8x$

x	0	1	2	3	4	5	6	7	8
y	24	32	40	48	56	64	72	80	88

d. Exponential; $NEXT = NOW \times 5$ (starting at 1), $y = 5^x$

x	0	1	2	3	4	5	6	7	8
y	1	5	25	125	625	3,125	15,625	78,125	390,625

Unit 6

5. a.

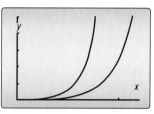 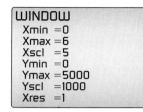

In both the table and the graphs, you can see that the rates of change are continually increasing. The values change faster for the $NEXT = NOW \times 5$ equation than for $NEXT = NOW \times 3$.

b.

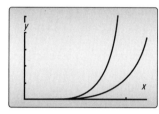 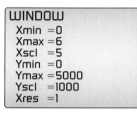

The table and the graphs show that both equations are increasing. The different initial values make very little difference in the overall pattern. Just as before, the model with the greater base changes at a faster rate.

c.

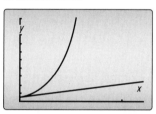 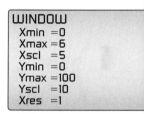

The initial values for these rules are the same. The table and the graphs show this too. The rates of change for the two rules are different. For the rule $NEXT = NOW \times 3$, the rate of change is continually increasing, whereas for $NEXT = NOW + 3$, the rate of change is constant.

d.

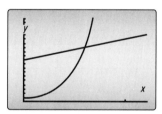 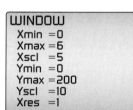

The initial value for the rule $NEXT = NOW + 10$ (starting at 100) is much greater than the initial value for $NEXT = NOW \times 3$ (starting at 5). The rate of change for $NEXT = NOW + 10$ is constant and therefore the values do not increase nearly as quickly as they do with the rule $NEXT = NOW \times 3$, which increases at a continually increasing rate.

See additional Teaching Notes on page T481E.

5. For each pair of equations relating *NOW* and *NEXT y* values, produce tables and scatterplots of data. Then compare the patterns of growth by describing similarities and differences in the tables and graphs produced and in the rates of change.

   a. Compare change patterns produced by the equations *NEXT* = *NOW* × 3 and *NEXT* = *NOW* × 5, starting at 10 in each case.

   b. Compare change patterns produced by *NEXT* = *NOW* × 3 (starting at 5) and *NEXT* = *NOW* × 5 (starting at 3).

   c. Compare change patterns produced by *NEXT* = *NOW* × 3 (starting at 5) and *NEXT* = *NOW* + 3 (starting at 5).

   d. Compare change patterns produced by *NEXT* = *NOW* × 3 (starting at 5) and *NEXT* = *NOW* + 10 (starting at 100).

Reflecting

1. One common illness in young people is *strep throat*. This bacterial infection can cause painful sore throats. Have you or anyone you know ever had strep throat? How does what you have learned about exponential growth explain the way strep throat seems to develop very quickly?

2. Suppose you are asked to design a telephone calling tree for a school chorus that has 30 members. The purpose of the tree will be to help the director reach families of all chorus members as quickly and reliably as possible with information about trips, performances, and practices.

   a. Sketch diagrams of several different possible calling trees.

   b. Explain the advantages and disadvantages of each design.

3. You've now worked on many different problems involving exponential growth patterns.

   a. What are the key features of a relation between variables that are hints that exponential growth will be involved?

   b. How are the patterns of exponential growth models different from those of linear models?

4. Which of the two models for growth by doubling do you prefer: *NEXT* = *NOW* × 2 or $y = 2^x$? Give reasons for your preference and explain how the two models are related to each other.

Unit 6

5. The population of our world is now about six billion. At the present rate of growth, that population will double approximately every 50 years.

  a. If this rate continues, what will the population be 50, 100, 150, and 200 years from now?

  b. How would that growth pattern compare to a pattern that simply added six billion people every 50 years?

  c. Do you think the population is likely to continue growing in the "doubling every 50 years" pattern? Explain your reasoning.

  d. What do you think the effect of rapid population growth will be on your life in the 21st century?

Extending

1. Here are five stages in growth of another fractal design called the *dragon fractal.*

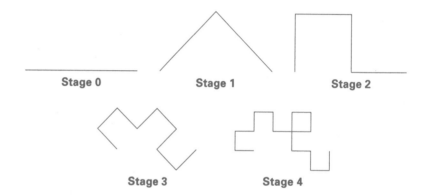

Stage 0   Stage 1   Stage 2

Stage 3   Stage 4

  a. Draw the next stage of growth in the dragon fractal.

  b. What pattern of change do you see in the number of segments of the growing fractal?

  c. Make a table and a plot of the data showing that pattern of change.

  d. Write an equation relating *NOW* and *NEXT* and an equation beginning "*y* = …" for finding the number of segments in the figure at each Stage of growth.

  e. How many segments will there be in the fractal design at Stage 16?

  f. At what stage will the fractal design have more than 1,000 segments?

5. a. 12, 24, 48, and 96 billion

b. This linear pattern of growth would produce populations of 12, 18, 24, and 30 billion, resulting in a final difference of 66 billion.

c. Responses will vary. Some students may feel that as the world becomes more crowded, better education on population control will be put in place and growth will slow. Others may simply feel that there is no reason to suggest that the current trend will not continue.

d. Responses will vary. Rapid population growth means heavy demands on the natural resources of this world. It also means an expansion of the problems of crime, education, health care, *etc.*

Extending

1. a.

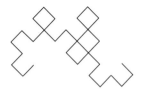

b. Each stage has twice the number of line segments as the previous stage.

c.

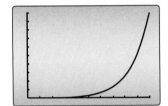

WINDOW
Xmin =0
Xmax =10
Xscl =1
Ymin =0
Ymax =1000
Yscl =100
Xres =1

X	Y₁
0	1
1	2
2	4
3	8
4	16
5	32
6	64

Y₁ = 2^X

d. $NEXT = NOW \times 2$, starting at 1; $y = 2^x$

e. 65,536

f. $2^{10} = 1,024$, so stage 10 has more than 1,000 segments.

Unit 6

2. a.

| Stage 0 | Stage 1 | Stage 2 |

b.

X	Y₁	Y₂
0	3	1
1	12	.33333
2	48	.11111
3	192	.03704
4	768	.01235
5	3072	.00412
6	12288	.00137

$Y_1 = 3*4^X$

X	Y₂	Y₃
0	1	3
1	.33333	4
2	.11111	5.3333
3	.03704	7.1111
4	.01235	9.4815
5	.00412	12.642
6	.00137	16.856

$Y_2 = (1/3)^X$

X: stage
Y_1:   number of sides
Y_2:   side length
Y_3:   perimeter

c. (*stage, number of sides*)
$NEXT = NOW \times 4$, starting at 3.
$y = 3(4)^x$

(*stage, side length*)
$NEXT = NOW \times \frac{1}{3}$, starting at 1.
$y = \left(\frac{1}{3}\right)^x$

(*stage, perimeter*)
$NEXT = NOW \times \frac{4}{3}$, starting at 3.
$y = 3\left(\frac{4}{3}\right)^x$

d. The number of sides increases very rapidly, while the length of the sides decreases very rapidly. In spite of the fact that the length of the sides become very, very small, the perimeter always continues to increase. This snowflake has a finite area and an infinite perimeter.

3. Responses will vary. The fractal should demonstrate exponential growth, which will be reflected in both the equation forms and the graph.

4. a. $\frac{1}{3}$ inch

b. $\frac{1}{9}$ inch

Unit 6

2. One of the most famous fractal forms is the *Koch snowflake*. It grows in much the same way as the tent-like fractal you explored in the "On Your Own" on page 427, except it starts with an equilateral triangle. In the first growing step, divide each segment into three equal pieces. Raise a "tent" over the center section with segments equal in length to the two remaining pieces on each side of the center section. Then the next stage repeats that process on each segment of the pattern at stage one, and so on.

   a. Draw Stages 0–2 of the Koch snowflake.

   b. Make a table showing the number of segments, the length of each segment, and the perimeter of the total figure at each stage through stage 6. Assume the length at Stage 0 is 1.

   c. Write equations in two ways for each of the following relations: (*stage, number of segments*); (*stage, segment length*); (*stage, perimeter*).

   d. Study the pattern in each variable (*number of segments, segment length,* and *perimeter*) as the number of growth stages increases to a very large number. Write a report describing your observations, making sure to comment especially on any surprising patterns.

3. Create a fanciful fractal of your own. Use color, or simply create it in black and white. Draw at least five stages of your fractal. Analyze it mathematically. Be sure to include a table, a graph, an equation relating *NOW* and *NEXT*, and an equation beginning "*y* = … ."

4. In this task, you will examine more closely the tent-like fractal from page 427.

Stage 0	**Stage 1**	**Stage 2**

   Recall that in moving from one stage to the next, each segment is divided into three equal-length parts. A tent is raised over the middle section with sides equal in length to the parts on each side.

   a. If the original line segment is one inch long, how long is each segment of the pattern in Stage 1?

   b. How long is each segment of the pattern in Stage 2?

Unit 6

c. Complete the following table showing the length of segments in the first ten stages.

Stage	0	1	2	3	4	5	6	7	8	9
Length	1	$\frac{1}{3}$	$\frac{1}{9}$							

d. Look back to Parts c and d of the "On Your Own" on page 427 where you wrote equations giving the number of short segments at each stage of the pattern. Then use that information and the results of Part c to complete the following table giving the length of the total pattern at each stage.

Stage	0	1	2	3	4	5	6	7	8	9
Length	1	$\frac{4}{3}$	$\frac{16}{9}$							

e. What appears to be happening to the length of the total pattern as the number of segments in the pattern increases?

5. In the king's chessboard problem described in Investigation 2, it was easy to calculate the number of grains of rice for any given square. In this task, you will investigate the total number of grains for all squares taken together.

   a. Find these sums:
   $$1 + 2 + 4 + 8$$
   $$1 + 2 + 4 + 8 + 16$$
   $$1 + 2 + 4 + 8 + 16 + 32$$
   $$1 + 2 + 4 + 8 + 16 + 32 + 64$$

   b. What pattern do you see in the results of Part a that would allow you to predict the sum of any number of terms of this sequence? Test your conjecture on the sum: $1 + 2 + 4 + 8 + 16 + 32 + 64 + 128 + 256 + 512 + 1{,}024$. Revise your conjecture and test again if necessary.

   c. Plan and carry out an investigation that would allow you to quickly calculate the sum of terms in a tripling sequence: $1 + 3 + 9 + 27 + 81 + 243 + \ldots + N$.

   d. Try to find a pattern in your work in Parts b and c that would allow you to quickly calculate the sum of terms in any exponential sequence: $1 + r + r^2 + r^3 + r^4 + \ldots + r^n$.

MORE *continued*

4. **c.**

Stage	0	1	2	3	4	5	6	7	8	9
Length	1	$\frac{1}{3}$	$\frac{1}{9}$	$\frac{1}{27}$	$\frac{1}{81}$	$\frac{1}{243}$	$\frac{1}{729}$	$\frac{1}{2{,}187}$	$\frac{1}{6{,}561}$	$\frac{1}{19{,}683}$

d.

Stage	0	1	2	3	4	5	6	7	8	9
Length	1	$\frac{4}{3}$	$\frac{16}{9}$	$\frac{64}{27}$	$\frac{256}{81}$	$\frac{1{,}024}{243}$	$\frac{4{,}096}{729}$	$\frac{16{,}384}{2{,}187}$	$\frac{65{,}536}{6{,}561}$	$\frac{262{,}144}{19{,}683}$

  e. It is getting longer and longer without limit, each time increasing by a factor of $\frac{4}{3}$.

5. **a.** $1 + 2 + 4 + 8 = 15$

  $1 + 2 + 4 + 8 + 16 = 31$

  $1 + 2 + 4 + 8 + 16 + 32 = 63$

  $1 + 2 + 4 + 8 + 16 + 32 + 64 = 127$

  b. $Sum = 2^n - 1$

  $Sum = 2^{11} - 1 = 2{,}047$

  c.

n	1	2	3	4	$\cdots$	n
Sum	1	4	13	40	$\cdots$	$\frac{3^n - 1}{2}$

  d. $Sum = \dfrac{r^n - 1}{r - 1}$

See Assessment Resources, pages 207–212.

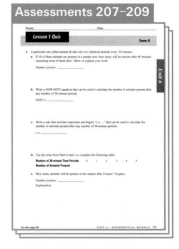

Unit 6

Lesson 2 *Exponential Decay*

LESSON OVERVIEW This lesson engages students in analysis of situations where some quantity of interest decreases by some constant factor as each unit of time passes. Since the factor change for a function that decreases is a fraction between 0 and 1, exponential decay is likely to be a bit more challenging for students than the previous lesson on exponential growth.

The experiment at the beginning of the lesson is designed to illustrate visually one of the common settings for exponential decay—removal or diffusion of some pollutant. You could derive a mathematical model for the pollution remaining after n days, or the change from one day to the next, but since there is an element of randomness involved in this process, it is probably better to begin looking for an algebraic rule with the other, more well-behaved, examples that follow.

If you actually *do* this experiment you will get better results using large numbers of beans of two colors, removing two small cups at a time. Students do not actually have to count the beans which are removed. It is enough for students to understand that, if there are two cups of brown beans (the pollution) mixed with eight cups of white, then the two cups removed will subtract some but not all of the original brown beans. As you add two more small cups of white beans to compensate for the runoff, students can see that the proportion of brown beans *looks* less, so fewer will be removed with the next runoff. (If you actually count the brown beans removed each time, be sure to count the initial number first. In this way, you can track the pollution *remaining* in the container. These data are good to come back to after students know how to use exponential regression on the calculator.)

To begin developing the arithmetic and algebraic rules that match exponential decay, we have chosen a simple example—the height of a bouncing ball after each rebound. The idea is that if a ball always rebounds to some fraction r ($0 < r < 1$) of its drop height, then the height of each succeeding bounce will be related to the prior bounce height by the equation *NEXT* $= r \times NOW$. Repeated application of this relation leads to the exponential pattern that on bounce number n the ball will rebound to r^n of its original height. Students might need some help to find this pattern, and especially to find a way to express it with algebraic rules.

The example of drug decay illustrates a significant setting for exponential decay. Although we provide students with the rule in this case, it is important for them to see why the shape of that rule implies decay by repeated multiplication with the factor 0.95.

By the end of this lesson, students should realize that there are decay analogs for the repeated multiplication models of Lesson 1 and that the rules take the same general form (with rate factors between zero and one). They also should have a sense of the shape of graphs that arise from rules of the form $y = a(b^x)$ when $0 < b < 1$.

Lesson Objectives

- To determine and explore the exponential decay model, $y = a(b^x)$, where $0 < b < 1$, through tables, graphs, and algebraic rules
- To compare exponential decay models with exponential growth models
- To compare exponential models of the form $y = a(b^x)$, where $0 < b < 1$, to linear models

Lesson 2 Exponential Decay

In 1989, the oil tanker Exxon Valdez ran aground in waters near the Kenai peninsula of Alaska. Over 10 million gallons of oil spread on the waters and shoreline of the area, endangering wildlife. That oil spill was eventually cleaned up—some of the oil evaporated, some was picked up by specially equipped boats, and some sank to the ocean floor as sludge.

For scientists planning environmental cleanups, it is important to be able to predict the pattern of dispersion in such contaminating spills. *Think about* the following experiment that simulates pollution of a lake or river by some poison and the cleanup.

- Mix 20 black checkers (the pollution) with 80 red checkers (the clean water).
- On the first "day" after the spill, remove 20 checkers from the mixture (without looking at the colors) and replace them with 20 red checkers (clean water). Count the number of black checkers remaining. Then shake the new mixture. This simulates a river draining off some of the polluted water and a spring or rain adding clean water to a lake.
- On the second "day" after the spill, remove 20 checkers from the new mixture (without looking at the colors) and replace them with 20 red checkers (more clean water). Count the number of black checkers remaining. Then stir the new mixture.
- Repeat the remove/replace/mix process for several more "days."

Think About This Situation

The graphs below show two possible outcomes of the pollution and cleanup simulation.

a What pattern of change is shown by each graph?

b Which graph shows the pattern of change that you would expect for this situation? Test your idea by running the experiment several times and plotting the (*time, pollutant remaining*) data.

c What sort of equation relating pollution *P* and time *t* would you expect to match your plot of data? Test your idea using a graphing calculator or computer.

The pollution cleanup experiment gives data in a pattern that occurs in many familiar and important problem situations. That pattern is called **exponential decay**.

INVESTIGATION 1 ▶ More Bounce to the Ounce

Most popular American sports involve balls of some sort. In playing with those balls, one of the most important factors is the bounciness or *elasticity* of the ball. For example, if a new golf ball is dropped onto a hard surface, it should rebound to about $\frac{2}{3}$ of its drop height.

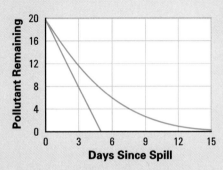

Suppose a new golf ball drops downward from a height of 27 feet onto a paved parking lot and keeps bouncing up and down, again and again.

Think About This Situation

See Teaching Master 166.

ⓐ The straight line shows a constant decrease in the pollutant remaining as the time increases. The curve shows large decreases initially, but the rate of decrease slows as time increases.

ⓑ The curve is the pattern that would be expected. Repeat the experiment until the class sees that the curve is the correct graph.

ⓒ The models for these graphs are $y = -4x + 20$ and $y = 20(0.8)^x$. Students may not have a good equation to model the cleanup situation, but you should leave the response open for now. You may wish to come back to it later in the unit. Students should realize that the graph should not be linear.

EXPLORE small-group investigation

INVESTIGATION 1 ▶ More Bounce to the Ounce

Many students are uncomfortable with fractions. As you circulate you may need to help them get started. $27 \times \frac{2}{3} = 18$, $18 \times \frac{2}{3} = \ldots$. Some will want to use their calculators to enter 27×0.66. Discourage this by pointing out that the factor 0.66 is rounded off. They could enter on their calculators $27 \times 2 \div 3 = 18$, or $18 \times 2 \div 3 = \ldots$, but recording answers in fraction form makes it a lot easier to see the familiar powers of two in some numerators and powers of three in the denominator. Of course, starting with 15 or some other whole number will result in the same pattern, but there may not be any powers of 2 readily apparent in the numerator. For some students, it may be appropriate to ask if we always will see the powers of 3 in the denominator.

1.

Bounce Number	0	1	2	3	4	5	6	7	8	9	10
Rebound Height	27	18	12	8	$\frac{16}{3}$	$\frac{32}{9}$	$\frac{64}{27}$	$\frac{128}{81}$	$\frac{256}{243}$	$\frac{512}{729}$	$\frac{1,024}{2,187}$

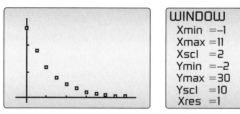

```
WINDOW
Xmin =-1
Xmax =11
Xscl =2
Ymin =-2
Ymax =30
Yscl =10
Xres =1
```

    a. It decreases by one-third on each bounce. The scatterplot is decreasing, but by a smaller amount each time. Students may not see the $\frac{1}{3}$. Adding a row "Change in Rebound Height" to the table may help.

    b. *NEXT* $= \frac{2}{3}$(*NOW*), starting at 27.

    c. $y = 27\left(\frac{2}{3}\right)^x$

    d. The table values will be smaller; the plot will have the same shape but will not be as high, and the coefficient in the equation will be 15 instead of 27.

2.   **a–c.** Responses will vary but should be close to a 0.67 rebound factor.

NOTE: You may wish to use the Texas Instruments CBL or a similar piece of technology to measure the height and graph the relationship. Give the students plenty of time to practice how to measure the height with the technology.

---

3. A sample response using a tennis ball follows.

    a.

Bounce Number	0	1	2	3
Rebound Height	50	30	18	10

    b. *NEXT* $=$ *NOW* $\times 0.6$, starting at 50.

        $y = 50(0.6)^x$

1. Make a table and plot of the data showing expected heights of the first ten bounces.

Bounce Number	0	1	2	3	4	5	6	7	8	9	10
Rebound Height	27										

   a. How does the rebound height change from one bounce to the next? How is that pattern shown by the shape of the data plot?

   b. What equation relating *NOW* and *NEXT* shows how to calculate the rebound height for any bounce from the height of the preceding bounce?

   c. Write an equation beginning "$y = \ldots$" to model the rebound height after any number of bounces.

   d. How will the data table, plot, and equations for calculating rebound height change if the ball drops first from only 15 feet?

As is the case with all mathematical models, data from actual tests of golf-ball bouncing will not match exactly the predictions from equations of ideal bounces. You can simulate the kind of quality control testing that factories do by running some experiments in your classroom.

2. Get a golf ball and a tape measure or meter stick for your group. Decide on a method for measuring the height of successive rebounds after the ball is dropped from a height of at least 8 feet. Collect data on the rebound height for successive bounces of the ball.

   a. Compare the pattern of your data to that of the model that predicts rebounds which are $\frac{2}{3}$ of the drop height. Would a rebound height factor other than $\frac{2}{3}$ give a better model? Explain your reasoning.

   b. Write an equation using *NOW* and *NEXT* that relates the rebound height of any bounce of your tested ball to the height of the preceding bounce.

   c. Write an equation beginning "$y = \ldots$" to predict the rebound height after any number of bounces.

3. Repeat the experiment of Activity 2 with some other ball such as a tennis ball or a basketball.

   a. Study the data to find a reasonable estimate of the rebound height factor for your ball.

   b. Write an equation using *NOW* and *NEXT* and an equation beginning "$y = \ldots$" that model the rebound height of your ball on successive bounces.

Unit 6

Checkpoint

Different groups might have used different balls and dropped the balls from different initial heights. However, the patterns of (*bounce number*, *rebound height*) data should have some similar features.

ⓐ Look back at the data from your two experiments.

- How do the rebound heights change from one bounce to the next in each case?
- How is the pattern of change in rebound height shown by the shape of the data plots in each case?

ⓑ List the equations relating *NOW* and *NEXT* and the rules ($y = ...$) you found for predicting the rebound heights of each ball on successive bounces.

- What do the equations relating *NOW* and *NEXT* bounce heights have in common in each case? How, if at all, are those equations different and what might be causing the differences?
- What do the rules beginning "$y = ...$" have in common in each case? How, if at all, are those equations different and what might be causing the differences?

ⓒ What do the tables, graphs, and equations in these examples have in common with those of the exponential growth examples in the beginning of this unit? How, if at all, are they different?

Be prepared to share and compare your data, models, and ideas with the rest of the class.

On Your Own

When dropped onto a hard surface, a brand new softball should rebound to about $\frac{2}{5}$ the height from which it is dropped. If a foul-tip drops straight down onto concrete after achieving a height of 25 feet, what pattern of rebound heights can be expected?

a. Make a table and plot of predicted rebound data for 5 bounces.

b. What equation relating *NOW* and *NEXT* and what rule ($y = ...$) giving height after any bounce match the pattern of rebound heights?

Checkpoint

Master 167

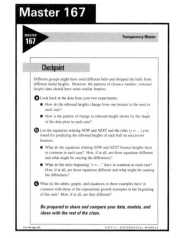

When you are listening to students share their answers for the Checkpoint, you may want to remind them that the rumor grew much faster when the tree grew by a factor of 3 at each stage than when the factor was 2. Ask which will make the bounce heights *decline* faster, a bounce factor of $\frac{2}{3}$ or a bounce factor of $\frac{2}{5}$ (as in the upcoming "On Your Own"). Students will have to think about the results of multiplying by $\frac{2}{3}$ or $\frac{2}{5}$: Which gives the smaller result? How can this be seen on the graph?

See Teaching Master 167.

ⓐ ■ The rebound heights are always less by some constant factor.
  ■ The change is shown by a gradual decline in the height of the data points.

ⓑ ■ The equations relating *NOW* and *NEXT* all have the same form: $NEXT = b \cdot NOW$, starting at a. They are different because a and b may be different. This differences are probably due to the different materials from which the balls are made.

  ■ All of the equations have the form $y = a(b^x)$, where a is equal to the original height of the ball, and the exponent (x) represents the number of bounces the ball has taken. The equations have different coefficients (a) because of the different initial heights. They also have different rates of rebounding (b) due to the type of ball.

ⓒ The form is the same: $NEXT = b \cdot NOW$ starting at a, or $y = a(b^x)$. The patterns in this investigation are different only because b is a rational number less than 1 rather than an integer. When $b < 1$, the curve is decreasing. The examples from Lesson 1 were all increasing curves.

On Your Own

a.

Bounce Number	0	1	2	3	4	5
Rebound Height	25	10	4	$\frac{8}{5}$	$\frac{16}{25}$	$\frac{32}{125}$

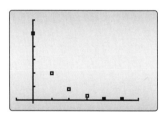

```
WINDOW
 Xmin = -1
 Xmax = 6
 Xscl = 1
 Ymin = -1
 Ymax = 30
 Yscl = 5
 Xres = 1
```

b. $NEXT = \frac{2}{5}(NOW)$, starting at 25.

$y = 25\left(\frac{2}{5}\right)^x$

c. ■ The rebound height of the softball is consistently less than what would be expected from a new softball. Furthermore, the ratio of the rebound height from one drop to the next is not consistent. So the data may indicate that this softball is not top quality.

■ Responses may vary, depending on what height ratio the student chooses. A sample table of rebound heights for the ball dropped from 20 feet is provided here. For this table, the ratio from one bounce to the next is the same as the ratio for the corresponding bounces in the original table.

Bounce Number	1	2	3	4	5
Rebound Height	7.6	3	1.2	0.4	0.1

d. $y = 20\left(\frac{2}{5}\right)^x$ or $NEXT = \left(\frac{2}{5}\right)(NOW)$, starting at 20.

MORE
ASSIGNMENT   *pp. 448–454*

Students can now begin Modeling Task 1 or Organizing Task 1 from the MORE assignment following Investigation 3.

EXPLORE   small-group investigation

INVESTIGATION 2▸ Sierpinski Carpets

It is apparently not as obvious to students as it is to teachers that if we cut out 1 square in 9 there will be $\frac{8}{9}$ of the original carpet area left. Students may find the large hole in the center distracting. Even those who understand that $\frac{1}{9}$ is removed may have trouble connecting this to $\frac{8}{9}$ remaining. Perhaps it is the question "$\frac{8}{9}$ of what?" that needs to be stated clearly. Expect to see more counting than seems necessary, until students convince themselves of the pattern. If students spend too much time coloring and counting, you might want to do this as a large group, though this still will leave some students unconvinced.

1.

c. Here are some data from bounce tests of a softball dropped from a height of 10 feet.

Bounce Number	1	2	3	4	5
Rebound Height	3.8	1.5	0.6	0.2	0.05

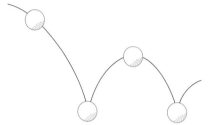

- What do these data tell you about the quality of the tested softball?

- What bounce heights would you expect from this ball if it were dropped from 20 feet instead of 10 feet?

d. What equation would model rebound height of an ideal softball if the drop were from 20 feet?

INVESTIGATION 2 Sierpinski Carpets

One of the most interesting and famous fractal patterns is named after the Polish mathematician Waclaw Sierpinski. The first two stages in forming that fractal are shown here.

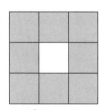
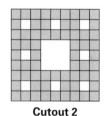

| **Start** | **Cutout 1** | **Cutout 2** |

Starting with a solid square "carpet" one meter on a side, smaller and smaller squares are cut out of the original in a sequence of steps. Notice how, in typical fractal style, small pieces of the design are similar to the design as a whole.

At the start of a Sierpinski carpet there is one square meter of carpet. But as cutting proceeds, there seems to be less and less carpet, and more and more hole.

1. Make a sketch showing the new holes that will appear in the third cutout from the carpet.

Unit 6

2. The carpet begins with an area of 1 square meter.

    a. How much of the original carpet is left after the first cutout?

    b. What fraction of the carpet left by the first cutout remains after the second cutout? How much of the original 1 square meter of carpet remains after the second cutout?

    c. What fraction of the carpet left by the second cutout remains after the third cutout? How much of the original 1 square meter of carpet remains after the third cutout?

    d. Following the pattern in the first three stages, how much of the original 1 square meter of carpet will remain after cutout 4? After cutout 5?

3. Write an equation showing the relation between the area of the remaining carpet at any stage and the next stage.

    a. What area would you predict for the carpet left after cutout 10?

    b. Find the area of the carpet left after cutout 20. After cutout 30.

4. Write an exponential equation that would allow you to calculate the area of the remaining carpet after any number of cutouts x, without going through all the cutouts from 1 to x.

    a. Make a table giving the area of the Sierpinski carpet from the start through cutout 10. Use TBLPLOT or similar software to make a plot of this data.

    b. How many cutouts are needed to get a Sierpinski carpet in which there is more hole than carpet remaining?

Checkpoint

Summarize the ways in which the table, graph, and equations for the Sierpinski carpet pattern are similar to, and different from, those for the following patterns:

ⓐ the bouncing ball patterns of Investigation 1;

ⓑ the calling tree, king's chessboard, and bacteria growth patterns of Lesson 1.

Be prepared to share your summaries of similarities and differences with the entire class.

2. a. $\frac{8}{9}$

  b. $\frac{64}{72} = \frac{8}{9}$

   This is $\frac{8}{9}$ of $\frac{8}{9}$, which is $\frac{64}{81}$ of the original square meter of carpet.

  c. $\frac{512}{576} = \frac{8}{9}$

   This is $\frac{8}{9}$ of $\frac{8}{9}$ of $\frac{8}{9}$, which is $\frac{512}{729}$ of the original.

  d. After 4 cutouts: $\frac{8}{9} \times \frac{8}{9} \times \frac{8}{9} \times \frac{8}{9} = \frac{4,096}{6,561}$

   After 5 cutouts: $\left(\frac{8}{9}\right)^5 = \frac{32,768}{59,049}$

3. $NEXT = NOW\left(\frac{8}{9}\right)$, starting at 1

  a. After 10: $\left(\frac{8}{9}\right)^{10} = 0.31$ m²

  b. After 20: $\left(\frac{8}{9}\right)^{20} = 0.09$ m²

   After 30: $\left(\frac{8}{9}\right)^{30} = 0.03$ m²

4. $y = \left(\frac{8}{9}\right)^x$

  a.

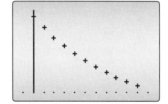

X	Y1
0	1
1	.88889
2	.79012
3	.70233
4	.6243
5	.55493
6	.49327
X=0	

X	Y1
4	.6243
5	.55493
6	.49327
7	.43846
8	.38974
9	.34644
10	.30795
X=4	

  b. 6 cutouts are needed in order to get more hole than carpet.
   $\left(\frac{8}{9}\right)^6 = \left(\frac{262,144}{531,441}\right) \approx 0.49$

NOTE: Some groups may need help understanding that there is more hole than carpet remaining when *y* is less than 50%.

SHARE AND SUMMARIZE full-class discussion

Checkpoint

See Teaching Master 168.

  ⓐ The patterns are the same. Slight differences are due to a larger value for the base in the Sierpinski problem and a smaller value for the coefficient.

  ⓑ The Sierpinski pattern represents an exponential decrease, whereas the problems in Lesson 1 represented an exponential increase. In one case, the base is less than one, and in the other it is greater than one. All of the graphs show a changing rate of change. Be sure students understand that exponential decrease occurs when the base is less than one, and exponential growth or increase occurs when the base is greater than one.

See additional Teaching Notes on page T481F.

Master 168

Checkpoint

Summarize the ways in which the table, graph, and equations for the Sierpinski carpet pattern are similar to, and different from, those for the following patterns:

ⓐ the bouncing ball patterns of Investigation 1;

ⓑ the calling tree, king's chessboard, and bacteria growth patterns of Lesson 1.

Be prepared to share your summaries of similarities and differences with the entire class.

Unit 6

► **On Your Own**

a. The cutout number is in L_1 and the area of the remaining carpet is in L_2.

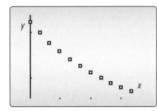

b.

c. $NEXT = NOW \cdot \left(\frac{8}{9}\right)$, starting at 9

d. $y = 9 \cdot \left(\frac{8}{9}\right)^x$

e. Six cuts are needed.

■ In a table of values, you can look for a y value that is less than 4.5.

■ In the plot of the data, you could use the trace function to determine when the value of y is less than 4.5.

f. The data show the same patterns but these answers are all larger because the second carpet was larger. In the *NOW-NEXT* equation, we start at 9 instead of 1; the coefficient in the other equation is 9 instead of 1. The answer to Part e is still 6 cuts.

MORE

ASSIGNMENT   *pp. 448–454*

Students can now begin Modeling Task 2 or Reflecting Task 4 from the MORE assignment following Investigation 3.

Unit 6

On Your Own

Suppose you started working on a very large Sierpinski carpet—a square that is 3 meters long on each side. Its starting area would be 9 square meters.

a. Find the area of the remaining carpet after each of the first 10 cutouts.

b. Make a plot of the (*cutout number*, *area*) data from Part a.

c. Write an equation that shows the change in area from one cutout to the next.

d. Write an exponential equation showing how to calculate the area of the carpet after any number *x* of cutouts.

e. How many cutouts are needed to get a Sierpinski carpet in which there is more hole than carpet remaining?

 ▪ Show how the answer to this question can be found in a table of (*cutout number*, *area*) data.

 ▪ Show how the answer to this question can be found in a plot of (*cutout number*, *area*) data.

f. How do your answers to Parts a–e compare to those for the first Sierpinski carpet with an original area of 1 square meter?

INVESTIGATION ▶ 3 Medicine and Mathematics

Drugs are a very important part of the human health equation. Many drugs are essential in preventing and curing serious physical and mental illnesses.

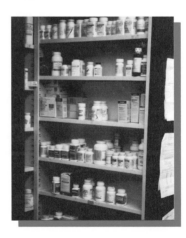

Diabetes, a disorder in which the body cannot metabolize glucose properly, affects people of all ages. In 1998, there were about 10 million diagnosed cases of diabetes in the United States. It was estimated that another 5 million cases remained undiagnosed.

In 5–10% of the diagnosed cases, the diabetic's body is unable to produce insulin, which is needed to process glucose.

To provide this essential hormone, these diabetics must take injections of a medicine containing insulin. The medications used (called insulin delivery systems) are designed to release insulin slowly. The insulin itself breaks down rather quickly. The rate varies greatly between individuals, but the following graph shows a typical pattern of insulin decrease.

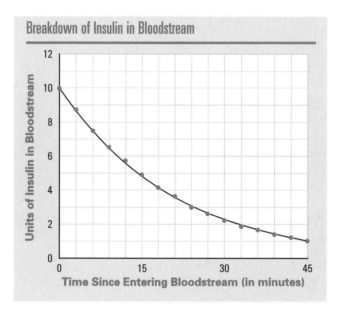

Breakdown of Insulin in Bloodstream

1. Medical scientists usually are interested in the time it takes for a drug to be reduced to one half of the original dose. They call this time the **half-life** of the drug. What appears to be the half-life of insulin in this case?

2. The pattern of decay shown on this graph for insulin can be modeled well by the equation $y = 10(0.95)^x$. Experiment with your calculator or computer to see how well a table of values and graph from this rule fit the pattern in the given graph. Then explain what the values 10 and 0.95 tell about the amount of insulin in the bloodstream.

3. What equation relating *NOW* and *NEXT* shows how the amount of insulin in the blood changes from one minute to the next, once 10 units have entered the bloodstream?

4. The insulin graph shows data points for each minute following the original insulin level. But the curve connecting those points reminds us that the insulin breakdown does not occur in sudden bursts at the end of each minute! It occurs *continuously* as time passes.

INVESTIGATION 3 Medicine and Mathematics

Students often mix up how much insulin is *lost* every minute (5%) with how much is *left* (95%). As you circulate, be sure they are writing carefully what multiplying by 0.95 does. You may wish to ask questions such as the ones below.

What variables are we tracking in the graph? (Amount of insulin remaining against time)

What does the equation say about these variables? (If you get vague answers for this one, such as "It is decreasing by 95%," you may be able to stir up some reaction if you deliberately misinterpret this. "The number of diabetics is decreasing by 95%? The amount of blood is decreasing by 95%? The amount of insulin is decreasing by 95%?" All of these are, of course, incorrect. The amount of insulin in the blood is decreasing by 5%, and the amount remaining is 95% of what it was, for every unit of time.)

You may see a similar problem occurring in contexts which develop the concept of a gain of 5%, resulting in a next value of 105% of whatever the current value is. The implied 100% "start" may be the missing idea.

1. About 14 minutes
2. Approximate values of the data from the graph are in the table below.

x	0	3	6	9	12	15	18	21	24	27
y	10	8.75	7.5	6.5	5.75	4.9	4.2	3.75	3	etc.

The equation fits the data fairly well but generally gives values a little less than those on the graph. 10 is the initial amount of insulin taken and 0.95 is the fraction of the original insulin left after 1 minute.

3. *NEXT = NOW*(0.95), starting at 10.

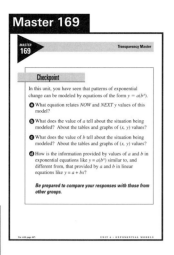

Master 169

EXPLORE *continued*

4. The calculations tell you both the amount left after a particular time, and that the amount left is continuously decaying.

   a. The amount of insulin left after a minute and a half is $10(0.95)^{1.5}$, or about 9.3 units.

   b. The amount left after four and a half minutes is $10(0.95)^{4.5}$, or about 7.9 units.

   c. The amount left after eighteen and three-quarters minutes is $10(0.95)^{18.75}$, or about 3.8 units.

5. **a.**

Time in Minutes	0	1.5	4.5	7.5	10.5	13.5	16.5	19.5
Insulin in Blood	10	9.3	7.9	6.8	5.8	5.0	4.3	3.7

   b. These values are close for the first few minutes but then are slightly lower than the values on the graph.

   c. After approximately 13.5 minutes, the insulin is half gone.

SHARE AND SUMMARIZE   full-class discussion

Checkpoint

See Teaching Master 169.

ⓐ $NEXT = NOW \times b$, starting at a.

ⓑ The value of a tells us the beginning value of y. In the table, it is the value of y when x equals zero, and it is the value of the y-intercept of the graph.

ⓒ The value of b tells us how the values of y are changing. Each successive term can be obtained by multiplying the preceding term by b. Assuming the x values change by one, it is the constant ratio between two consecutive y values in the table. If b is greater than one, the graph and table values will be increasing; if b is less than one and greater than zero, the graph and table values will be decreasing.

ⓓ In both linear and exponential equations, a provides the value of y when x is zero. In both types of equations the value of b will tell us if the values are increasing or decreasing. For linear equations, if b is greater than *zero* the y values will be increasing, but for exponential models the value of b must be greater than *one* for the values to be increasing. Also, linear models change by a constant *amount* (b), whereas exponential models change by a constant *factor* (b).

CONSTRUCTING A MATH TOOLKIT: Students should add a summary of the Checkpoint responses for Parts a–c to their Toolkits (Teaching Master 200).

NOTE: Responses will vary, but students should be able to prove that it would have been difficult, if not impossible, for the toddler to drink enough (256 tsp) antifreeze Sunday morning for two teaspoons of ethylene glycol to be present in the youngster on Monday morning.

JOURNAL ENTRY: Imagine that you are a medical examiner assigned to the following case. A toddler died mysteriously at 12:05 on a Monday afternoon. An autopsy revealed that the youngster's system contained 2 teaspoons of ethylene glycol, the primary ingredient in antifreeze.

When questioned by the police, the parents were certain that the child had not been left alone, except for a short time early the previous morning when the parents were folding the laundry, around 7 or 8 o'clock. After some mathematical calculations, you conclude that it was not likely that the child had drunk antifreeze while unattended. (The metabolic half-life of ethylene glycol is approximately 4 hours.)

Consequently, you continue the investigation. Searching through a medical database, you find references to a rare disease that causes the body to produce a chemical similar to ethylene glycol. Using further tests, you conclude that this disease was indeed the cause of death.

Write a report explaining how you came to the conclusion that it was unlikely that the child had drunk antifreeze. Include in your explanation any calculations you may have made.

What would each of the following calculations tell about the insulin decay situation? Based on the graph on the previous page, what would you expect as reasonable values for those calculations?

a. $10(0.95)^{1.5}$ **b.** $10(0.95)^{4.5}$ **c.** $10(0.95)^{18.75}$

5. Mathematicians have figured out ways to do calculations with fractional or decimal exponents so that the results fit in the pattern for whole number exponents. One of those methods is built into your graphing calculator or computer software.

a. Enter the rule $Y = 10(0.95^X)$ in the "Y=" list of your calculator or computer software. Then complete the following table of values showing the insulin decay pattern at times other than whole minute intervals.

Time in Minutes	0	1.5	4.5	7.5	10.5	13.5	16.5	19.5
Units of Insulin in Blood	10							

b. Compare the entries in this table with data shown by points on the graph on page 446.

c. Use your rule to estimate the half-life of insulin.

Checkpoint

In this unit, you have seen that patterns of exponential change can be modeled by equations of the form $y = a(b^x)$.

a What equation relates *NOW* and *NEXT* y values of this model?

b What does the value of a tell about the situation being modeled? About the tables and graphs of (x, y) values?

c What does the value of b tell about the situation being modeled? About the tables and graphs of (x, y) values?

d How is the information provided by values of a and b in exponential equations like $y = a(b^x)$ similar to, and different from, that provided by a and b in linear equations like $y = a + bx$?

Be prepared to compare your responses with those from other groups.

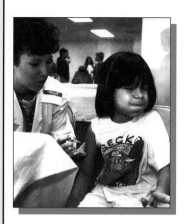

On Your Own

The most famous antibiotic drug is penicillin. After its discovery in 1929, it became known as the first *miracle drug*, because it was so effective in fighting serious bacterial infections.

Drugs act somewhat differently on each person, but on average, a dose of penicillin will be broken down in the blood so that one hour after injection only 60% will remain active. Suppose a patient is given an injection of 300 milligrams of penicillin at noon.

a. Make a table showing the amount of that penicillin that will remain at hour intervals from noon until 5 PM.

b. Make a plot of the data from Part a. Explain what the pattern of that plot shows about the rate at which penicillin decays in the blood.

c. Write an equation of the form $y = a(b^x)$ that can be used to calculate the amount of penicillin remaining after any number of hours x.

d. Use the equation from Part c to produce a table showing the amount of penicillin that will remain at *quarter-hour* intervals from noon to 5 PM. What can you say about the half-life of penicillin?

e. Use the equation from Part c to graph the amount of penicillin in the blood from 0 to 10 hours. Find the time when less than 10 mg remain.

MORE
Modeling • Organizing • Reflecting • Extending

Modeling

1. If a basketball is properly inflated, it should rebound to about $\frac{1}{2}$ the height from which it is dropped.

a. Make a table and plot showing the pattern to be expected in the first ten bounces after a ball is dropped from a height of 10 feet.

b. At which bounce will the ball first rebound less than 1 foot? Show how the answer to this question can be found in the table and on the graph.

c. Write two different forms of equations that can be used to calculate the rebound height after many bounces.

d. How will the data table, plot, and equations change for predicting rebound height if the ball is dropped from a height of 20 feet?

▶On Your Own

a.

Time	12:00	1:00	2:00	3:00	4:00	5:00
Amount left (mg)	300	180	108	64.8	38.88	23.33

b.

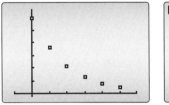

```
WINDOW
Xmin =-1
Xmax =6
Xscl =1
Ymin =0
Ymax =330
Yscl =50
Xres =1
```

The plot shows that penicillin decays at a decreasing rate.

c. $y = 300(0.6)^x$

d.

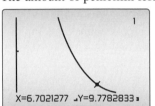 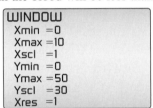 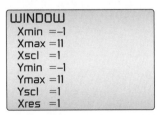

The half-life of penicillin is between 1 hour 15 minutes and 1 and a half hours.

e. The amount of penicillin left in the blood will be less than 10 mg after about 6.7 hours.

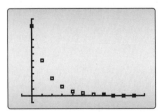

```
WINDOW
Xmin =0
Xmax =10
Xscl =1
Ymin =0
Ymax =50
Yscl =30
Xres =1
```

MORE | **independent assignment**

Modeling

1. a.

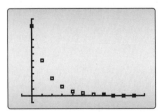

```
WINDOW
Xmin =-1
Xmax =11
Xscl =1
Ymin =-1
Ymax =11
Yscl =1
Xres =1
```

See additional Teaching Notes on page T481F.

MORE
ASSIGNMENT   *pp. 448–454*

Modeling: 6 and choice of one*
Organizing: 1 and 4
Reflecting: 4 and 5
Extending: 1

*When choice is indicated, it is important to leave the choice to the student.
NOTE: It is best if Organizing tasks are discussed as a whole class after they have been assigned as homework.

Unit 6

2. a.

Stage 3

b.

Stage Number	0	1	2	3	4	5
Area Remaining	3	2.25	1.69	1.27	0.95	0.71

c.

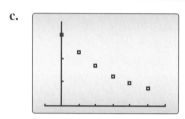 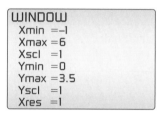

```
WINDOW
Xmin =-1
Xmax =6
Xscl =1
Ymin =0
Ymax =3.5
Yscl =1
Xres =1
```

d. $NEXT = NOW\left(\frac{3}{4}\right)$, starting with 3.
$y = 3\left(\frac{3}{4}\right)^x$ or $y = 3(0.75)^x$

e. ■ After 3 cuts, there will be more hole than carpet.
■ After 44 cuts, less than 0.1 square centimeter of carpet remains.

f. The pattern is similar because you are cutting out a portion of the area each time. For both situations, the values in the table decrease but not at a constant rate. The graphs are similar, but since $\frac{8}{9} > \frac{3}{4}$ the graph of the square carpet declines less rapidly than the graph of the triangular carpet. The equations follow the same form, but the values reflect the specific situations. For the square carpet, the equation is $y = \left(\frac{8}{9}\right)^x$ and for the triangular carpet $y = 3\left(\frac{3}{4}\right)^x$.

g. All three altitudes are lines of symmetry if the triangle is equilateral. If the triangle is assumed to be isosceles, then the altitude to the base is the only line of symmetry.

3. a.

Time Since Use (in days)	0	1	2	3	4	5	6	7
Steroid Present (in mg)	100	90	81	72.9	65.61	59.049	53.144	47.83

2. The sketch below shows the start and two cutout stages in making a triangular Sierpinski carpet. Assume that the area of the original triangle is 3 square meters.

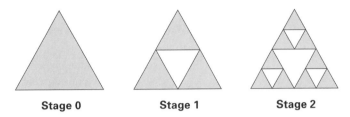

Stage 0   Stage 1   Stage 2

a. Sketch the next stage in the pattern.

b. Make a table showing (*cutout number, area remaining*) data for cutout stages 0 to 5 of this process.

c. Make a plot of the data in Part b.

d. Write two different equations that can be used to calculate the area of the remaining carpet at different stages. One equation should show change from one stage to the next. The other should be in the form "$y = \dots$."

e. How many stages are required to reach the points where there is:

■ more hole than carpet remaining?

■ less than 0.1 square centimeter of carpet remaining?

f. How are the pattern, table, graph, and equations for this triangular carpet similar to, and different from, those of the square carpets in Investigation 2?

g. Describe any symmetries that the triangular carpet has at each stage.

3. You may have heard of athletes being disqualified from competitions because they have used anabolic steroid drugs to increase their weight and strength. These steroids can have very damaging side effects for the user. The danger is compounded by the fact that these drugs leave the human body slowly. With an injection of the steroid *ciprionate*, about 90% of the drug and its by-products will remain in the body one day later. Then 90% of that amount will remain after a second day, and so on. Suppose that an athlete tries steroids and injects a dose of 100 milligrams of ciprionate. Analyze the pattern of that drug in the athlete's body by completing the following tasks.

a. Make a table showing the amount of the drug remaining at various times.

Time Since Use (in days)	0	1	2	3	4	5	6	7
Steroid Present (in mg)	100	90	81					

b. Make a plot of the data in Part a and write a short description of the pattern shown in the table and the plot.

c. Write two equations that describe the pattern of amount of steroid in the blood.

■ Write one equation showing how the amount of steroid present changes from one day to the next.

■ Write a second equation in the form $y = a(b^x)$ that shows how one could calculate the amount of steroid present after any number of days.

d. Use one of the rules in Part c to estimate the amount of steroid left after 0.5 and 8.5 days.

e. Estimate, to the nearest tenth of a day, the half-life of ciprionate.

f. How long will it take the steroid to be reduced to only 1% of its original level in the blood? That is, how many days will it take for only 1 milligram of the original dose to be left in the bloodstream?

4. When people suffer head injuries in accidents, emergency medical personnel sometimes administer a paralytic drug to keep the patient immobile. If the patient is found to need surgery, it's important that the immobilizing drug decay quickly.

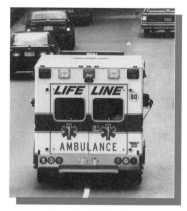

For one typical paralytic drug the standard dose is 50 micrograms. One hour after the injection, half the original dose has decayed into other chemicals. The halving process continues the next hour, and so on.

a. How much of the 50 micrograms will remain in the patient's system after 1 hour? After 2 hours? After 3 hours?

b. Write an equation for calculating the amount of drug that will remain x hours after the initial dose.

c. Use the equation from Part b to make a table showing the amount of drug left at half-hour intervals from 0 to 5 hours.

d. Make a plot of the data from Part c and then a continuous graph using the [Y=] and [GRAPH] commands.

e. How long will it take the 50-microgram dose to decay to less than 0.05 microgram?

3. b.

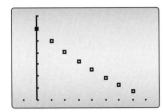

```
WINDOW
Xmin =-1
Xmax =8
Xscl =1
Ymin =40
Ymax =110
Yscl =10
Xres =1
```

In both the table and in the graph, you can see that the values decrease but not at a constant rate.

c. ■ *NEXT = NOW*(0.9), starting at 100.

■ $y = 100(0.9)^x$

d. After 0.5 day there is 94.868 mg of the steroid left. After 8.5 days, 40.838 mg of the steroid is left.

e. The half-life of cipronate is approximately 6.6 days. The table entry for 6.6 days is 49.889 mgs.

f. It will take about 44 days for the amount of steroid in the blood to be reduced to 1% of the original level.

4. a. 25 mg; 12.5 mg; 6.25 mg

b. $y = 50(0.5)^x$

c.

X	Y₁	
0	50	
.5	35.355	
1	25	
1.5	17.678	
2	12.5	
2.5	8.8388	
3	6.25	

Y₁■50(.5)^X

X	Y₁	
3.5	4.4194	
4	3.125	
4.5	2.2097	
5	1.5625	
5.5	1.1049	
6	.78125	
6.5	.55243	

Y₁■50(.5)^X

d.

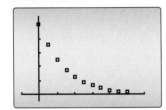

```
WINDOW
Xmin =-1
Xmax =6
Xscl =1
Ymin =-5
Ymax =55
Yscl =10
Xres =1
```

e. It will take approximately 10 hours for the amount of drug to decrease to 0.05 microgram.

X	Y₁	
9.5	.06905	
9.6	.06443	
9.7	.06011	
9.8	.05609	
9.9	.05233	
10	.04833	
10.1	.04556	

Y₁■50 (.5)^X

(An alternate situation that can be used for this problem follows. Because of the controversial and sensitive nature of the subject, professional discretion is required.

Although cocaine is a dangerous, illegal, and addictive drug, it does have some legal applications in the medical profession. Doctors sometimes use cocaine to provide local anesthesia to the nose, mouth, or throat to allow some types of surgery or examinations without pain. It is applied by spray or cotton swab directly to the area immediately before surgery, and it metabolizes in the blood rapidly. One hour after being introduced into the bloodstream, half the original amount has decayed into other chemicals. The halving process continues the next hour, and so on.)

5. **a.** *NEXT* = *NOW*(0.7), starting at 10.

$y = 10(0.7)^x$

b. It will take about 13 days.

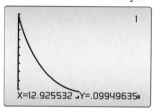

c. Its half-life is about 2 days.

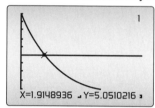

d. Using the equation $y = 5(0.7)^x$ and either the graph or table, you can find that the half-life is still about 2 days.

(An alternate situation that can be used for this problem follows. Because of the controversial and sensitive nature of the subject, professional discretion is required.

Although marijuana is a dangerous and illegal drug, some doctors have provided legal prescriptions to reduce eye pressure in glaucoma patients, or to ease pain and nausea in chronically ill cancer patients. A key ingredient in the drug is the chemical Delta-9-THC. If 10 milligrams of Delta-9-THC are introduced to the bloodstream of a typical adult, 70% of that chemical still will be present one day later. After another day, 70% of that amount will remain, and so on.)

6. **a.** After 1 year, 98% or 98 grams will be left.

After 2 years, 96.04% or 96.04 grams will be left.

After 3 years, 94.12% or 94.12 grams will be left.

b. *NEXT* = *NOW*(0.98), starting at 100.

$y = 100(0.98)^x$

c.

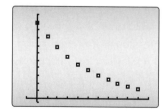

d. 73.115 grams will be left after 15.5 years.

5. In Unit 1, "Patterns in Data," you studied growth charts as you learned about percentiles. For children who fall under the 5th percentile level on these charts, a growth hormone may be used to help them grow at a more normal rate. If 10 milligrams of one particular growth hormone is introduced to the bloodstream, as much as 70% will still be present the next day. After another day, 70% of that amount will remain, and so on.

   a. Write two different equations that can be used to calculate the amount of a 10-milligram dose of growth hormone remaining after any number of days.

   b. How long will it take for the original 10-milligram dose to be reduced to 0.1 milligram? Show how the answer to this question can be found in a table of (*time, drug amount*) data and in a graph of that data.

   c. What is the half-life of this growth hormone?

   d. Suppose half the amount (5 milligrams) of the drug is introduced to the bloodstream. Compare the half-life of this dosage with that in Part c.

6. Radioactive materials have many important uses in the modern world, from fuel for power plants to medical x-rays and cancer treatments. But the radioactivity that produces energy and tools for "seeing" inside our bodies has some dangerous effects too; for example, it can cause cancer in humans.

   The radioactive chemical strontium-90 is produced in many nuclear reactions. Extreme care must be taken in transportation and disposal of this substance. It decays rather slowly—if any amount is stored at the beginning of a year, 98% of that amount will still be present at the end of that year.

   a. If 100 grams (about 0.22 pound) of strontium-90 are released due to an accident, how much of that radioactive substance will still be around after 1 year? After 2 years? After 3 years?

   b. Write two different equations that can be used to calculate the amount of strontium-90 remaining from an initial 100 grams at any year in the future.

   c. Make a table and a scatterplot showing the amount of strontium-90 that will remain from an initial amount of 100 grams at the end of every 10-year period during a century.

Limerick Generating Station, Montgomery County, PA. Owned and operated by PECO Energy Company.

Years Elapsed	0	10	20	30	40	50	. . .
Amount Left (in g)	100						

   d. Use one of the equations in Part b to find the amount of strontium-90 left from an initial amount of 100 grams after 15.5 years.

e. Use one of the equations from Part b to find the number of years that must pass until only 10 grams remain.

f. Estimate to the nearest tenth of a year, the half-life of strontium-90.

Organizing

1. The following graphs, tables, and equations model four exponential growth and decay situations. For each graph, there is a matching table and a matching equation. Use what you know about the patterns of exponential relations to pair each graph with its corresponding table and equation. In each case, explain the clues that can be used to match the items without any use of a graphing calculator or computer.

Graphs

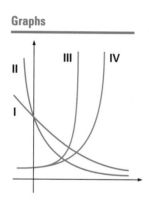

Tables

A.

x	1	2	3	4
y	40	16	6.4	2.56

B.

x	1	2	3	4
y	30	90	270	810

C.

x	1	2	3	4
y	60	36	21.6	12.96

D.

x	1	2	3	4
y	20	40	80	160

Equations

a. $y = 100(0.6^x)$

b. $y = 100(0.4^x)$

c. $y = 10(2^x)$

d. $y = 10(3^x)$

2. This task will help you develop a better understanding of fractional or decimal exponents.

a. Use your calculator or computer software to produce a table of values for $y = 4^x$. Use values of x from 0 to 3 in steps of 0.1.

b. Use your calculator or computer software to produce a table of values for $y = (0.36)^x$. Use values of x from 0 to 4 in steps of 0.25.

c. Suppose you have an exponential model of the form $y = b^x$ where $b > 0$ and $b \neq 1$. If x is a decimal number between two numbers s and t, how is b^x related to b^s and b^t? Test your conjecture using exponential models different from those in Parts a and b.

d. Without using your calculator, estimate $3^{1.5}$. Explain the method you used.

6. **e.** After about 114 years, about 10 grams will remain.

f. The half-life is approximately 34.3 years. At 34.3 years there will be 50.01 gm left, which is approximately half of the original amount.

Organizing

1.

Graph	Table	Equation
I	C	a
II	A	b
III	B	d
IV	D	c

One of the most important clues to notice is whether the function is increasing or decreasing. (Does the curve rise or fall? Do the values in the table increase or decrease?) Comparing the bases in the equations will give you good information—equations a and b are both decreasing and equation b is decreasing faster; equations c and d are increasing and equation d is increasing faster. Finding these similar patterns in the tables and graphs allows students to complete this task.

2. **a.**

X	Y₁
0	1
.1	1.1487
.2	1.3195
.3	1.5157
.4	1.7411
.5	2
.6	2.2974

X=0

X	Y₁
.7	2.639
.8	3.0314
.9	3.4822
1	4
1.1	4.5948
1.2	5.278
1.3	6.0629

X=1.3

X	Y₁
1.4	6.9644
1.5	8
1.6	9.1896
1.7	10.556
1.8	12.126
1.9	13.929
2	16

X=2

X	Y₁
2.1	18.379
2.2	21.112
2.3	24.251
2.4	27.858
2.5	32
2.6	36.758
2.7	42.224

X=2.7

X	Y₁
2.8	48.503
2.9	55.715
3	64
3.1	73.517
3.2	84.449
3.3	97.006
3.4	111.43

X=3.4

b.

X	Y₂
0	1
.25	.7746
.5	.6
.75	.46476
1	.36
1.25	.27885
1.5	.216

X=0

X	Y₂
1.75	.16731
2	.1296
2.25	.10039
2.5	.07776
2.75	.06023
3	.04666
3.25	.03614

X=3.25

X	Y₂
3.5	.02799
3.75	.02168
4	.0168
4.25	.01301
4.5	.01008
4.75	.00781
5	.00605

X=5

c. Student conjectures may vary. Sample conjectures are:

- If x is between s and t, then b^x is between b^s and b^t.
- If $0 < b < 1$, then b^x decreases as x increases.
- If $b > 1$, then b^x increases as x increases.

d. Student estimates will vary, but $3^{1.5}$ must be between 3 and 9. Some students may estimate 6 because it is halfway between 3 and 9. This is a reasonable estimate in this case. However, you may want to point out that this estimate will be high; it assumes a constant rate of change, but this function does not have a constant rate of change. It will increase less between 1 and 1.5 than it will between 1.5 and 2.

3. **a.** When $0 < b < 1$, the tables and graphs will be like the exponential decay models of Lesson 2. In these models, the value of the function approaches 0 as x becomes very large.

   b. When $b > 1$, the tables and graphs will be like the exponential growth models from Lesson 1. The value of the function will approach infinity as x becomes very large.

4. The smaller the value of the base is, the shorter the half-life will be. The graph that indicates a shorter half-life will decrease more quickly from the initial value.

Reflecting

1. Responses will vary. Be sure students justify their answers with good reasons.

2. No, this is not a true statement, because the rate of decrease is always changing. This would be true only if there were a constant rate of change. One good way for students to convince themselves of this is by looking at a specific example. One equation such as $y = 100(0.70)^x$ is particularly easy to examine because the percentage of the original dose that is still in the blood stream is easy to determine.

3. **a.** Student responses may vary. Any case where only integer domains make sense, such as the number of cutouts in the Sierpinski carpets, is acceptable.

   b. Fractional exponents make sense for continuous situations; for example, the amount of drug remaining in the body. The use of fractional exponents is sensible in most exponential growth and decay situations because the growth or decay is, in practical terms, continuous. The growth or decay does not occur only at the end of one hour or one day but rather it is always happening.

4. This is an exponential decay situation. The initial value is 500. The values of the function are decreasing, but not at a constant rate. Half of the substance is gone after approximately 1.35 time periods.

5. **a.** A linear model. The family and friends are assuming a constant rate of change.

   b. An exponential model. Usually drugs disappear at a decreasing rate.

3. For an equation of the form $y = a(b^x)$, what conclusions can you draw about the tables and the graphs of (x, y) values when b is

   a. between 0 and 1?

   b. greater than 1?

4. Suppose two equations $y = 100(b^x)$ and $y = 100(c^x)$ model the decay of 100 grams of two different radioactive substances. How can you tell which substance will have the shorter half-life by comparing the values of b and c? How will this difference appear in the graphs of the two equations?

Reflecting

1. Which example of an exponential decay pattern seems to you to be the most interesting or important example of exponential decay—the Sierpinski carpets, metabolizing of drugs in the body, bouncing of a golf ball, or decay of radioactive chemicals? Give reasons for your choice.

2. Suppose the makeup of a drug is such that one hour after a dose is administered to an individual's bloodstream, 70% remains active. Does it follow that one-half hour after administration of the same dose to the same person, 85% will remain active? Explain your reasoning.

3. When an exponential equation models a situation such as in the metabolizing of drugs in the body, fractional or decimal exponents are useful. In other situations, they may not be particularly meaningful.

   a. Give an example of an exponential growth or decay situation where use of fractional exponents would not make sense.

   b. What are some characteristics of exponential growth or decay situations that would suggest that use of fractional exponents is sensible?

4. Suppose a problem situation is modeled by the equation $y = 500(0.6^x)$. Tell as much as you can about the nature of the situation.

5. Suppose a person taking steroid drugs is hospitalized due to a side effect from the drug. Tests taken upon admittance show a steroid concentration of 1.0. The next test one day later shows a concentration of 0.75. Based on these results the person's family and friends assume that in three days the drug will be out of the person's system.

   a. What pattern of change are the family and friends assuming?

   b. What might be a more accurate pattern prediction? Why is this pattern more reasonable?

Extending

1. Fleas are one of the most common pests for dogs. If your dog has fleas, you can buy many different kinds of treatments, but those wear off over time. Suppose the half-life of one such treatment is 10 days.

   a. Make a table showing the fraction of an initial treatment that will be active after 0, 10, 20, 30, and 40 days.

   b. Experiment with your calculator or computer to find an equation of the form $y = b^x$ (where x is time in days) that matches the pattern in your table of Part a.

2. In Unit 3, "Linear Models," you solved linear equations of the form $ax + b = c$ and $ax + b = cx + d$ using several different methods. Solve each of the following *exponential equations* in at least two different ways.

   a. $2^x = 6$

   b. $2x = 2^x$

3. The following program creates a drawing of the Sierpinski Triangle (Modeling Task 2) in an interesting way. This program is from the *TI-83 Graphing Calculator Guidebook*.

Program: SIERPINS

```
:FnOff              :For(K,1,3000)        :.5(1+Y)→Y
:ClrDraw            :rand→N                :End
:PlotsOff           :If N≤1/3              :If 2/3<N
:AxesOff            :Then                  :Then
:0→Xmin             :.5X→X                 :.5(1+X)→X
:1→Xmax             :.5Y→Y                 :.5Y→Y
:0→Ymin             :End                   :End
:1→Ymax             :If 1/3<N and N≤2/3    :Pt - On(X,Y)
:rand→X             :Then                  :End
:rand→Y             :.5(.5+X)→ X           :StorePic 6
```

Reprinted by Permisssion of Texas Instruments.

---

   a. Enter the program in your calculator.

   b. After you execute the program, recall and display the picture by pressing RecallPic 6.

   c. How is the idea of *NOW* and *NEXT* used in the design of this program?

Extending

1. **a.**

Number of Days Since Treatment	0	10	20	30	40
Fraction of Initial Treatment Still Active	1	0.5	0.25	0.125	0.0625

 b. $y = (0.933)^x$ is very close but not exact.

2. Students may choose guess-and-adjust, a graphical method, or tables to obtain their answers.

 a. $x \approx 2.58$

 b. $x = 1$

3. **a.** Students should enter and run the program.

 b.

 c. The last point plotted is used in determining the next point that will be plotted.

See Assessment Resources, pages 213–218.

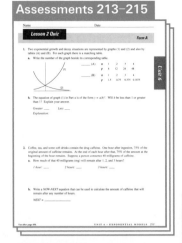

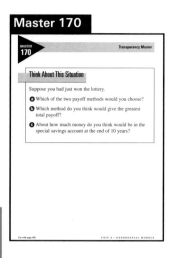
Lesson 3 *Compound Growth*

LESSON OVERVIEW This short lesson illustrates two very important families of exponential model applications, the growth of populations and money earning interest in a bank. In these applications, the constant multiplicative factor of change is usually given as a percent.

The key pattern to be observed is that if some quantity Q increases by r percent every day, month, or year, then the change can be predicted and calculated by use of exponential thinking:

$$Q_{n+1} = Q_n + \frac{r}{100} Q_n$$
$$= \left(1 + \frac{r}{100}\right)Q_n$$

If one tracks the pattern of this growth from its starting point, you get this exponential relation:

$$Q_n = \left(1 + \frac{r}{100}\right)^n Q_o$$

While that general form may look rather forbidding, in a special case it becomes quite simple. For instance, suppose that $500 is deposited in a bank account that pays 4% interest annually. It will grow to 500 + 0.04(500) or $520 the next year, then 1.04(520) or $540.80 the next year, and so on. With a calculator or using computer software, these values are very easy to find.

The study of population growth uses the same kind of compound growth rates. This results in a simple model of population growth; precise demographic models have to be more subtle, since the numbers of births and deaths in a population depend on the age distribution of that population as well as the total size of the population. By the end of this lesson, students will have begun to develop skill in analyzing the growth of populations and compound interest.

Lesson Objective

■ To recognize that if an initial quantity Q is growing at r% per year, then it can be modeled by the exponential form $y = Q\left(1 + \frac{r}{100}\right)^n$, and to apply this model when solving real-world applications

LAUNCH full-class discussion

Think About This Situation

See Teaching Master 170.

ⓐ You may wish to poll the class and quickly count the number of students who prefer each plan, keeping the result for later use.

See additional Teaching Notes on page T481G.

Lesson 3

Compound Growth

Every now and then we hear about somebody winning a big payoff in a state lottery somewhere. The winnings can be 1, 2, 5, or even as large as 50 million dollars. Those big money wins are usually paid off in annual installments for about 20 years. But some smaller prizes like $10,000 are paid at once. How would you react if this news report were actually about you?

Kalamazoo Teen Wins Big Lottery Prize—$20,000

A Kalamazoo teenager has just won $20,000 from a Michigan lottery ticket that she got as a birthday gift from her uncle. In a new lottery payoff scheme, the teen (whose name has been withheld) has two payoff choices: One option is to receive $1,000 payments each year for the next 20 years. In the other plan, the lottery will invest $10,000 in a special savings account that will earn 8% interest compounded annually for 10 years. At the end of that time she can withdraw the balance of the account.

Think About This Situation

Suppose you had just won the lottery.

a Which of the two payoff methods would you choose?

b Which method do you think would give the greatest total payoff?

c About how much money do you think would be in the special savings account at the end of 10 years?

INVESTIGATION 1 Just Like Money in the Bank

Of the two lottery payoff methods, one has quite a simple rule: $1,000 per year for 20 years, giving a total payoff of $20,000. The plan to put $10,000 in a savings account paying 8% **compound interest** might not be as familiar.

- After one year your balance will be:
  $10,000 + (0.08 \times 10,000) = 1.08 \times 10,000 = 10,800.$

- After the second year your balance will be:
  $10,800 + (0.08 \times 10,800) = 1.08 \times 10,800 = 11,664.$

During the next year the savings account balance will increase in the same way, starting from $11,664, and so on.

1. Write equations that will allow you to calculate the balance of this deposit
   a. for any year, using the balance from the year before.
   b. after any number of years *x*.

2. Use the equations to make a table and a plot showing the growth of this special savings account for a period of 10 years.

Time (in years)	0	1	2	3	4	...	9	10
Balance ($)	10,000	10,800	11,664					

3. Describe the pattern of growth in this savings account as time passes.
   a. Why is the balance not increasing at a constant rate?
   b. How could the pattern of increase be predicted from the shape of the graph of the modeling rules?

4. How long would it take to double the $10,000 savings account?

5. Compare the pattern of change and the final account balance in Activity 2 to that for each of the following possible savings plans over 10 years. Write a summary of your findings.
   a. Initial investment of $15,000 earning only 4% annual interest.
   b. Initial investment of $5,000 earning 12% annual interest.

Checkpoint

Most savings plans operate in a manner similar to the special lottery savings account. They may have different starting balances, different interest rates, or different periods of investment.

a Describe two ways to find the value of such a savings account at the end of each year from the start to year 10. Use methods based on

   ■ an equation relating *NOW* and *NEXT*.
   ■ an exponential equation $y = a(b^x)$.

b What is the shape of the graphs that you would expect?

c How will the rules change as the interest rate changes? As the amount of initial investment changes?

d Why does the dollar increase in the account get larger from one year to the next?

Be prepared to explain your methods and ideas to the entire class.

1. **a.** *NEXT* = (1.08)*NOW*, starting at $10,000.

   b. $y = 10,000(1.08)^x$

2.

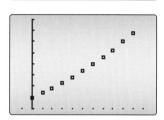

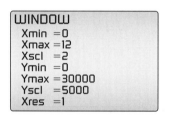

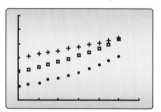

WINDOW	
Xmin	=–1
Xmax	=11
Xscl	=1
Ymin	=8000
Ymax	=23000
Yscl	=2000
Xres	=1

3. **a.** This happens because the interest paid also earns interest.

   b. Because the graph is curved upward, rather than being a straight line, we know the rate of increase is not constant. In fact, because the curve gets steeper as *x* increases, the rate of increase is increasing.

4. It will take about 9 years.

5.

WINDOW	
Xmin	=0
Xmax	=12
Xscl	=2
Ymin	=0
Ymax	=30000
Yscl	=5000
Xres	=1

+: Initial investment of $15,000 earning 4% annual interest

□: Initial investment of $10,000 earning 8% annual interest

•: Initial investment of $5,000 earning 12% annual interest

The scatterplot shows the pattern for the first 10 years. At the end of 10 years, the initial investment of $15,000 at 4% interest and the $10,000 investment at 8% interest are almost equal. It is also obvious from the scatterplot that the investment of $15,000 at 4% is going to fall behind, although for the first nine years it was greater than each of the others.

SHARE AND SUMMARIZE   full-class discussion

Checkpoint

See Teaching Master 171.

Consider, for example, a starting balance of $5,000 and an interest rate of 8%.

ⓐ ■ *NEXT* = *NOW* × (1.08), starting at 5,000.

On the calculator enter 5,000, then press ANS*1.08 and press the enter key 10 times.

■ Enter the equation $y = 5,000(1.08)^x$ in the functions list on the calculator. Set the table function to start at 0 and increment in steps of 1. By viewing the table, you can see the value of the investment at the end of each year.

> **See additional Teaching Notes on page T481G.**

Master 171

CONSTRUCTING A MATH TOOLKIT: Students should describe how the balance in a bank account can be modeled by an exponential equation of the form $y = a(b^x)$ and how *a*, *b*, *y*, and *x* relate to the situation (Teaching Master 200).

Unit 6

▶On Your Own

a. The population figures (in millions) for Brazil are in Y_1 and Nigeria's figures are in Y_2.

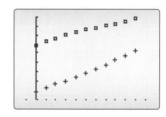

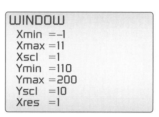

X	Y1	Y2
0	170	123
1	172.55	126.44
2	175.14	129.98
3	177.77	133.62
4	180.43	137.37
5	183.14	141.21
6	185.89	145.17

Y1 ▇ 170*(1.015^X)

X	Y1	Y2
5	183.14	141.21
6	185.89	145.17
7	188.67	149.23
8	191.5	153.41
9	194.38	157.7
10	197.29	162.12
11	200.25	166.66

Y2 ▇ 123*(1.028^X)

WINDOW
Xmin = −1
Xmax = 11
Xscl = 1
Ymin = 110
Ymax = 200
Yscl = 10
Xres = 1

- ■ The population of each country is increasing.
- ■ Nigeria's larger growth rate makes the scatterplot steeper over the 10-year period. The difference between the two populations gets smaller as the number of years increases.

b. $y = 170(1.015)^x$, for Brazil

$y = 123(1.028)^x$, for Nigeria

- ■ Based on these equations, Brazil's population will reach 300 million in approximately 39 years beyond year 2000.
- ■ Nigeria's population will reach 200 million in approximately 18 years beyond year 2000.

MORE

ASSIGNMENT *pp. 457–460*

Modeling: 1, and 2 or 3*
Organizing: 1, 2, and 4
Reflecting: 1
Extending: Choose one*

When choice is indicated, it is important to leave the choice to the student.
NOTE: *It is best if Organizing tasks are discussed as a whole class after they have been assigned as homework.*

Modeling

1. a.

X	Y1
0	5000
1	5250
2	5512.5
3	5788.1
4	6077.5
5	6381.4
6	6700.5

Y1 ▇ 5000(1.05)^X

X	Y1
7	7035.5
8	7387.3
9	7756.6
10	8144.5
11	8551.7
12	8979.3
13	9428.2

Y1 ▇ 5000(1.05)^X

X	Y1
14	9899.7
15	10395
16	10914
17	11460
18	12033
19	12635
20	13266

Y1 ▇ 5000(1.05)^X

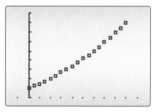

WINDOW
Xmin = −2
Xmax = 20
Xscl = 2
Ymin = 4000
Ymax = 13000
Yscl = 1000
Xres = 1

b. The patterns of growth of the two accounts are similar. But with an initial savings of $10,000, each value would be twice as large as with the $5,000 initial savings.

On Your Own

The world population and populations of individual countries grow in much the same pattern as money earning interest in a bank.

i. Brazil is the most populous country in South America. In 2000, its population was about 170 million. It is growing at a rate of about 1.5% per year.

ii. Nigeria is the most populous country in Africa. Its 2000 population was about 123 million. It is growing at a rate of about 2.8% per year.

a. Assuming these growth rates continue, make a table showing the predicted populations of these two countries in each of the 10 years after 2000. Then make a scatterplot of the data for each country.

- Describe the patterns of growth expected in each country.

- Explain how the different patterns of growth are shown in the scatterplots.

b. Write equations to predict the populations of these countries for any number of years x in the future. Use the equations

- to estimate when Brazil's population might reach 300 million.

- to estimate when Nigeria's population might reach 200 million.

MORE
Modeling • Organizing • Reflecting • Extending

Modeling

1. Suppose that a local benefactor wants to offer college scholarships to every child born into a community. When a child is born, the benefactor puts $5,000 in a special savings fund earning 5% interest per year.

   a. Make a table and graph of an account showing values each year for 18 years.

   b. Compare the pattern of growth of the account in Part a to one in which the initial deposit was $10,000. Compare values of each account after 18 years.

c. Compare the pattern of growth of the account in Part a to one in which the interest rate was 10% and the initial deposit was $5,000. Compare values of each account after 18 years.

d. Compare values of the accounts in Parts b and c after 18 years. Explain why your finding makes sense.

2. In 2000, the population of Iraq was 23.1 million and was growing at a rate of about 2.8% per year, one of the fastest growth rates in the world.

a. Make a table showing the projected population of Iraq in each of the eight years after 2000.

b. Write two different kinds of equations that could be used to calculate population estimates for Iraq at any time in the future.

c. Estimate the population of Iraq in 2020.

d. What factors might make the estimate of Part c an inaccurate forecast?

3. In Unit 2, "Patterns of Change," you studied growth in the population of Arctic bowhead whales. The natural growth rate was about 3.1% and estimates place the 1993 population between 6,900 and 9,200. The harvest by Inuit people is very small in relation to the total population. Disregard the harvest for this task.

a. If growth continued at 3.1%, what populations would be predicted for each year to 2010? Make tables based on both 1993 population estimates.

b. How would the pattern of results in Part a change if the growth rate were and continued to be 7%, as some scientists believe it is?

c. Write two different types of equations that can be used to calculate population estimates for the different possible combinations of initial population and growth rate estimates.

d. Find the likely time for the whale population to double in size under each set of assumptions.

Organizing

1. Consider the four exponential equations:

   i. $y = 5(1.2^x)$ **ii.** $y = 5(1.75^x)$

   iii. $y = 5(2.5^x)$ **iv.** $y = 5(3.25^x)$

a. Sketch the patterns of graphs you expect from these four equations; then check your estimates with your calculator or computer.

1. c. The two plans start at the same value but the 10% interest fund increases faster. Doubling the interest rate more than doubles the earnings. After 18 years, the value of the account at 5% interest is $12,033 and at 10% interest is $27,800.

d. The value of the account in Part b is $24,066. This is less than the value of the account in Part c because of the greater rate in Part c.

2. a. Population Estimates for Iraq (in millions)

Year	Population	Year	Population
2001	23.7	2005	26.5
2002	24.4	2006	27.3
2003	25.1	2007	28.0
2004	25.8	2008	28.8

b. Representing the number of years beyond 2000 by x, we have $y = 23.1(1.028)^x$ and $NEXT = NOW(1.028)$, starting at 23.1 (for 2000).

c. The population of Iraq in 2020 will be approximately 40.1 million.

d. Mortality and birth rates might change by the year 2020.

> NOTE: Student methods for creating this table may vary. Students may create the table by hand, possibly using the ANS key to repeat multiplication. They may instead formulate the equation first and use a calculator table or list. However, if students use the exact nmber for the date, an overflow error may occur when doing an exponential regression. If this occurs, it would be valuable for students to determine why it occurred.

Unit 6

3. a. Let $x = 0$ for year 1993.

X	Y₁	Y₂
	6900	9200
1	7113.9	9485.2
2	7334.4	9779.2
3	7561.8	10082
4	7796.2	10395
5	8037.9	10717
6	8287.1	11049

X=0

X	Y₁	Y₂
	8544	11392
8	8808.8	11745
9	9081.9	12109
10	9363.4	12485
11	9653.7	12872
12	9953	13271
13	10262	13682

X=7

X	Y₁	Y₂
	9653.7	12872
12	9953	13271
13	10262	13682
14	10580	14106
15	10908	14543
16	11246	14994
17	11594	15459

X=11

b. The pattern would be very similar, but the population increases would be greater each year. The low estimate for the year 2010 at the 7% growth rate is 21,796 and the high estimate is 29,061.

c. *NOW-NEXT* **Equations**
Low estimates and 3.1% growth rate: $NEXT = NOW(1.031)$, starting at 6,900
Low estimates and 7% growth rate: $NEXT = NOW(1.07)$, starting at 6,900
High estimates and 3.1% growth rate: $NEXT = NOW(1.031)$, starting at 9,200
High estimates and 7% growth rate: $NEXT = NOW(1.07)$, starting at 9,200

Exponential Equations
Low estimates and 3.1% growth rate: $y = 6,900(1.031)^x$
Low estimates and 7% growth rate: $y = 6,900(1.07)^x$
High estimates and 3.1% growth rate: $y = 9,200(1.031)^x$
High estimates and 7% growth rate: $y = 9,200(1.07)^x$

d. Estimates for the number of years until the population doubles follow:
Low estimates and 3.1% growth rate: y is approximately 22.7 years.
Low estimates and 7% growth rate: y is approximately 10.3 years.
High estimates and 3.1% growth rate: y is approximately 22.7 years.
High estimates and 7% growth rate: y is approximately 10.3 years.

Organizing

1. a. See margin.

1a.

$y = 5(1.2^x)$

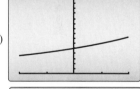

$y = 5(1.75^x)$

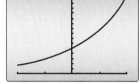

$y = 5(2.5^x)$

$y = 5(3.25^x)$

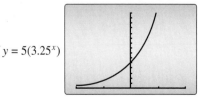

1. b.

X	Y1
1	6
2	7.2
3	8.64
4	10.368
5	12.442
6	14.93
7	17.916

$Y_1 = 5(1.2^{\wedge}X)$

X	Y1
1	8.75
2	15.313
3	26.797
4	46.895
5	82.065
6	143.61
7	251.33

$Y_1 = 5(1.75^{\wedge}X)$

X	Y1
1	12.5
2	31.25
3	78.125
4	195.31
5	488.28
6	1220.7
7	3051.8

$Y_1 = 5(2.5^{\wedge}X)$

X	Y1
1	16.25
2	52.813
3	171.64
4	557.83
5	1813
6	5892.1
7	19149

$Y_1 = 5(3.25^{\wedge}X)$

In all of these tables, you can see that the *y* value is increasing at an increasing rate. As you look at the examples from left to right, you can see that the values in the tables increase faster and the graphs are steeper when the base is larger. The coefficient 5 is the *y*-intercept.

2. a.

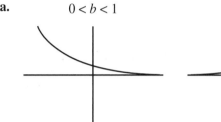

$$0 < b < 1 \qquad\qquad 1 < b$$

b. The value of *a* is the *y*-intercept.

3. a. The U.S. population will be approximately 552 million at 77.4 years after 2000.

b. It would take 110.4 years to double the population if the rate of growth was 2.5 million per year.

c.

Interest Rate	Approximate Doubling Time (in years)
2%	35
4%	18
6%	12
8%	9
12%	6

d. At a 3% rate, it will take about 24 years to double. The larger the rate, the less time it takes to double because the change increases more rapidly. This relationship is an *inverse variation* relationship. So if the interest rate is doubled, the amount of time is divided by two.

4. The distributive property of multiplication over addition justifies each of the calculations.

See additional Teaching Notes on page T481H.

b. Make tables of (x, y) values for the four equations and explain how the patterns in those tables fit the shape of the graphs in Part a.

2. Think about the shapes of graphs of exponential equations.

a. Sketch the graph shape you would expect from an exponential equation $y = a(b^x)$ when $0 < b < 1$. Sketch the shape you would expect when $b > 1$.

b. How does the value of a affect the graph?

3. One way to think about rates of growth is to calculate the time it will take for a quantity to double in value. For example, it is common to ask how long it will take a bank investment or a country's population to double.

a. If the U.S. population in 2000 was about 276 million and growing exponentially at a rate of 0.9% per year, how long will it take for the U.S. population to double?

b. One year's growth is 0.9% of 276 million, or about 2.5 million. How long would it take the U.S. population to double if it increased *linearly* at the rate of 2.5 million per year?

c. How long does it take a bank deposit of $5,000 to double if it earns interest compounded annually at the rate of 2%? At a 4% rate? At a 6% rate? At an 8% rate? At a 12% rate?

d. Examine your (*rate*, *time to double*) data in Part c. Do you see a pattern that would allow you to predict the doubling time for an investment of $5,000 at an interest rate of 3% compounded annually? Check your prediction. If your prediction was not close, search for another pattern for predicting doubling time and check it.

4. What property of addition and multiplication justifies each of the following calculations in figuring compound interest?

- $10,000 + 0.06(10,000) = 1.06(10,000)$

- $10,600 + 0.06(10,600) = 1.06(10,600)$

- $P + rP = (1 + r)P$

Reflecting

1. What characteristic of money earning interest in the bank and growth of human or animal populations makes them grow in similar exponential patterns?

2. Which of these two offers would you take to invest a $500 savings? Justify your choice.

   i. 4% interest paid each year on the balance in that year

   ii. $20 interest paid each year (Notice: $20 = 4% of $500.)

LESSON 3 • COMPOUND GROWTH   459

3. Refer to the savings fund description in Modeling Task 1 and complete Part a if you have not already done so. Calculate *differences* between the value of the account at the beginning and end of years 1, 5, 11, and 18. What do these four differences say about the rate at which the savings account grows?

Extending

1. Banks frequently pay interest more often than once each year. Suppose your bank pays interest compounded *quarterly*. If the annual percentage rate is 4%, then the bank pays 1% interest at the end of each 3-month period.

   a. Explore the growth of a $1,000 deposit in such a bank over 5 years.

   b. Compare the quarterly compounding with annual compounding at 4%.

   c. Repeat the calculations and comparisons if the annual rate is 8%.

2. Many people borrow money from a bank to buy a car, a home, or to pay for a college education. However, they have to pay back the amount borrowed plus interest. To consider a simple case, suppose that for a car loan of $9,000 a bank charges 6% annual rate of interest compounded quarterly and the repayment is done in quarterly installments. One way to figure the balance on this loan at any time is to use the equation:

   new balance = 1.015 × *old balance* − *payment*

   a. Use this equation to find the balance due on this loan for each quarterly period from 0 to 20, assuming that the quarterly payments are all $250.

   b. Experiment with different payment amounts to see what quarterly payment will repay the entire loan in 20 payments (5 years).

   c. Experiment with different loan amounts, interest rates, and quarterly payments to see how those factors are related to each other. Write a brief report of your findings.

3. The value of purchased products such as automobiles *depreciates* from year to year.

   a. Would you suspect the pattern of change in value of an automobile from year to year is linear? Exponential?

   b. Select a 1995 automobile of your choice. Research the initial cost of the car and its value over the years since 1995.

   c. Does the plot of (*time since purchase*, *value*) data show an exponential pattern? If so, find an exponential model that fits the data well. Use your model to predict the value of the car when it is 10 years old.

   d. Compare your findings with those of other classmates who completed this task. Which 1995 automobile researched held its value best? Explain your reasoning.

3. The difference in the value of the account at the end and at the beginning of year 1 is $250; at the end and beginning of year 5 is $303.90; at the end and beginning of year 11 is $407.20; at the end and beginning of year 18 is $573. These figures show that the *rate* at which the savings account grows is increasing.

Extending

1. a. The tables below show the value of the account over 5 years. The first column (X) shows the number of 3-month compounding periods, and the second column (Y_1) shows the account balances.

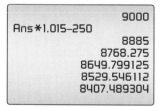

X	Y_1
0	1000
1	1010
2	1020.1
3	1030.3
4	1040.6
5	1051
6	1061.5

$Y_1 = 1000(1.01)^X$

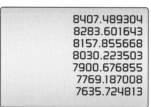

X	Y_1
7	1072.1
8	1082.9
9	1093.7
10	1104.6
11	1115.7
12	1126.8
13	1138.1

$Y_1 = 1000(1.01)^X$

X	Y_1
14	1149.5
15	1161
16	1172.6
17	1184.3
18	1196.1
19	1208.1
20	1220.2

$Y_1 = 1000(1.01)^X$

b. The value of the account compounded quarterly is $1{,}000(1.01)^{20} = \$1{,}220.19$. The value of the account compounded annually is $1{,}000(1.04)^5 = \$1{,}216.65$.

Compounding the interest quarterly gives you $3.54 more than compounding the interest annually.

c. Compounding the interest quarterly yields $1{,}000(1.02)^{20} = \$1{,}485.95$, while compounding the interest annually yields $1{,}000(1.08)^5 = \$1{,}469.33$. There is a difference of $16.62.

2. a.

Periods 0 to 5

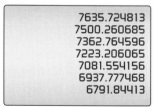

```
                 9000
Ans*1.015-250
                 8885
            8768.275
         8649.799125
         8529.546112
         8407.489304
```

Periods 5 to 11

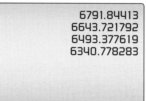

```
         8407.489304
         8283.601643
         8157.855668
         8030.223503
         7900.676855
         7769.187008
         7635.724813
```

Periods 11 to 17

```
         7635.724813
         7500.260685
         7362.764596
         7223.206065
         7081.554156
         6937.777468
          6791.84413
```

Periods 17 to 20

```
          6791.84413
         6643.721792
         6493.377619
         6340.778283
```

b. A payment of about $524.25 will repay the loan in 20 quarterly payments.

c. Responses will vary, but students should include such ideas as the following: the lower the amount of the loan, the sooner it will be paid off; the lower the interest rate, the lower the monthly payment; and the more the monthly payment, the sooner the loan will be paid off.

See additional Teaching Notes on page T481H.

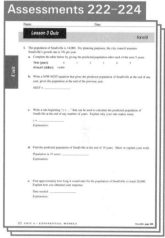

Unit 6

Lesson 4 — *Modeling Exponential Patterns in Data*

LESSON OVERVIEW This lesson engages students in looking at a variety of situations in which data can be modeled with exponential models. By doing the experiments, students get a tactile and visual sense of how exponential change occurs (and why it is different from linear change). Several interesting data sets in this lesson will help students get a strong numerical sense about situations that "increase at an increasing rate" or "decrease at a decreasing rate."

The best modeling growth rates in the various situations are not going to be predicted easily by simply analyzing the conditions of the experiment or the data sources. Because of this, the graphing calculator or computer software curve-fitting routines should be used. However, it is important to have students compare those fits with the actual data and to ask themselves whether the fit seems reasonable. (Some of the given data sets are not very close to exponential patterns.)

Lesson Objectives

- ■ To experience exponential change in a visual and tactile manner by completing investigations that result in exponential models
- ■ To use the graphing calculator or computer software to determine exponential models for real-world data, modeling both increasing and decreasing exponential situations
- ■ To collect a data set, create a scatterplot, and determine an exponential model using the characteristics of the scatterplot and data, or using the graphing calculator or computer software
- ■ To appreciate the importance of exponential models in a world where change often occurs at an ever increasing rate

LAUNCH full-class discussion

Think About This Situation

See Teaching Master 172.

At this point, the student should have a good understanding of exponential growth. This should be reflected in their confidence about Part a. In Part b, they are asked only to describe how to find the equation, not what the equation would be.

ⓐ The graph looks like an exponential model.

ⓑ The students might suggest experiments with different values of a and b in the model $y = a(b^x)$.

ⓒ They might use it to predict the wolf population in the future. They might use it to help support changes in policy.

Lesson 4

Modeling Exponential Patterns in Data

Our planet Earth is home for millions of different species of animal and plant life. Many species of life become *extinct* every day. Much loss is due to human actions that change the environment for animal and plant life. The endangerment of life forms often can be reversed by protection of species and their habitats.

For example, the Kenai Peninsula of Alaska is a natural home for wolves, moose, bear, and caribou. When a gold rush in 1895–96 brought thousands of prospectors to the area, hunting and changes to the environment reduced all those populations. Wolves disappeared from the Kenai Peninsula by about 1915.

In the late 1950s a few wolves reappeared on the Kenai Peninsula. They were protected from hunting in 1961. The graph at the right shows the growth of the Kenai wolf population during the decade after it became a protected species.

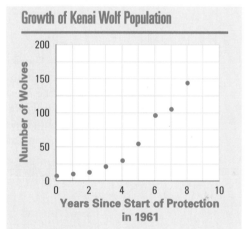

Growth of Kenai Wolf Population

Think About This Situation

Study the pattern of change in the Kenai wolf population.

a What sort of graph model do you think would best fit the trend in wolf population data?

b How would you find equations modeling the growth of the wolf population on the Kenai Peninsula over time?

c How might a Natural Resources Department use your equations?

INVESTIGATION 1 ► Popcorn and Thumbtacks

This investigation includes four experiments that give you practice in modeling exponential patterns in data. In each case, you will collect some data showing how a variable changes over time. Then you will make a table and a scatterplot of that data. Next you will experiment to find an equation relating *x* and *y* to fit the pattern in your data. Finally, you will use the equation to make predictions. The main steps are outlined in Experiment 1. Apply the same steps in the other three experiments.

Share the work so that each group does Experiment 1 and one of the remaining three experiments. Compare results to see similarities and differences in outcomes of the same and different experiments.

Experiment 1

Begin this experiment with a paper plate divided into four equal sections. Shade one of the sections, as shown here. You also need a paper cup containing 200 kernels of unpopped popcorn.

Pour the kernels of corn from the cup onto the plate at its center. Shake the plate gently to spread the kernels around. Then *remove* and count all kernels that end up on the shaded sector. (This ends Stage 1 of the experiment.) For the next stage, repeat the shake-remove process with the kernels that remain.

1. **Collect Data** Collect the data from your experiment in a table like this:

Stage Number	0	1	2	3	4	5	6	7
Kernels Left	200							

2. **Display Data** Make a scatterplot of the (*stage*, *kernels left*) data.

3. **Analyze Data** Write a short description of the pattern in the data table and scatterplot.

   a. Experiment with entering different equations in the "Y=" function list. See if you can find one that fits the pattern well.

   b. Use the **exponential regression** feature of your calculator or computer software to find the equation of the best-fitting exponential model.

INVESTIGATION 1 Popcorn and Thumbtacks

In this investigation, it is not necessary to have each group do all four experiments. However, it is important for each experiment to be done by at least two groups. Each group should display the graph and the model so that the class can see all of the results at one time.

Experiment 1

Before you start the experiment, discuss with students whether kernels which fall *on* the line should be removed or not. Ask them, do we all need to make the same decision about this issue? If we consistently remove the kernels on the line along with those kernels in the shaded region, how would we expect our data to compare to those of another group who remove only those kernels that fall strictly within the shaded area? (If students are consistent in their process, then the data amount remaining will decrease faster if they remove kernels on the line also. In one case slightly more than 25% should be removed, and in the other slightly less. You should be able to see this reflected in the table and in the symbolic model, and if both methods are used, you can draw attention to this when students share their work.)

As you circulate around the room, you may want to ask students what a particular pair of variables means. *For example:*

....	....	4	....	....
....	....	61	....	....

(The pair (4, 61) means that on the fourth stage there are 61 kernels left.) Some students will forget that the graph represents the relationship between the number of kernels *left* and number of stages, not between kernels *removed* and number of stages. Also, when they try to find the decay factor they may not have a very efficient strategy. Some will guess at some decimal and multiply each entry by this to see if it produces the next entry. If you see students in a fruitless guess-and-check, you might want to refer to an easier set of data, such as the following:

0	1	2	3	....
200	100	50	25	....

The decay factor is obviously 0.5, and it is very easy to see that succeeding ratios, $\frac{100}{200}$, $\frac{50}{100}$, or $\frac{25}{50}$, will give this ratio. Of course, in the case of the popcorn experiment we can not expect to get exactly the same ratio each time.

When students have been experimenting for some time, trying to write a symbolic model that fits the data, you might ask them what fraction of the kernels was removed. This should elicit the answer that $\frac{1}{4}$ was removed, or 25%. So what fraction should be left? (This is the same conversation you probably had when students were removing $\frac{1}{9}$ of Sierpenski's carpet at each stage.) With broad hints like this, everyone should be able to come up with a decay factor that represents the 75% retention.

See additional Teaching Notes on page T481H.

Unit 6

4. **Apply Model** Students should use their exponential equations to make these predictions.

    a. Look for good reasoning that might explain the differences between their experimental outcomes and the model.

    b. Student responses will vary. Be sure that both the question and the answer are reasonable. Some possible questions might be:

    After how many stages will fewer than half the kernels be left on the plate?

    What percentage of the original kernels will be left after 5 stages?

Experiment 2

As you circulate, again you may want to ask for an interpretation of a data pair. This time you might want to remark on the growth of the data. "I see you have more than 100% of your last result each time," or some such remark helps students focus on a sensible growth factor, without robbing them of the opportunity to experiment. Some will simply guess and check different percentages. Ideally, you would like students to see that to create an increase from 47 to 59 kernels, you have to multiply 47 by $\frac{59}{47}$. If students do not refer at all to the data in making their guesses, you might want to set up a simpler table as an example, such as:

....	3	4	5	6	....	....
....	90	270	810	2,430	....	....

The data in this example grow by multiplying by 3 each time $\left(\frac{270}{90} = \frac{810}{270} = \cdots = 3\right)$. This may help students see what to do with the messier experimental data.

1. **Collect Data** Answers will vary; the following is given as a sample.

Stage Number	0	1	2	3	4	5	6	7
Kernels Left	20	26	30	37	47	59	75	93

2. **Display Data** Our sample (*stage number*, *number of kernels*) data are displayed below.

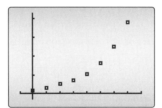

```
WINDOW
Xmin =-1
Xmax =8
Xscl =1
Ymin =10
Ymax =100
Yscl =10
Xres =1
```

3. **Analyze Data** The data table shows that the number of kernels of corn is increasing, but not at a constant rate. The increases are smaller initially and then they gradually become larger with each stage. The graph shows a curve where as x increases, the values for y increase at an ever increasing rate.

    The exponential model $y = 20(1.25)^x$ ideally describes this experiment. Each time, 25% of the current number of kernels are added. This is represented by the rate of 1.25. Since you start with 20, your initial value when $x = 0$ is 20, which means $a = 20$.

4. **Apply Model** Student questions will vary. Some possible questions are:

    How many stages will it take for the number of kernels to double?

    How many kernels would you add between the 9th and 10th stages?

See additional Teaching Notes on page T481I.

c. Write the exponential equation $y = a(b^x)$ that you believe fits your data best.

d. Explain how the values of a and b relate to the experiment you have done. What do they tell about stages and kernels of corn?

4. Apply Model Use your exponential equation to do the following:

a. Predict the number of kernels of corn left after Stage 3 and Stage 7. Compare your predictions with the data table. Explain any differences you observe.

b. Write a question about the experiment that can be answered by using your modeling equation. Then show how you would use the equation to find the answer.

Experiment 2

Begin this experiment by pouring 20 kernels of corn onto the plate that has been divided into quarters. After shaking the plate to spread the kernels, count the number of kernels that land on the shaded sector of the plate. *Add that number of kernels to the test supply.* (This ends Stage 1.) Repeat the shake-count-add process several times.

Record the data in a table of (*stage, supply of kernels after adding*) data. Plot that data. Find an equation that models the relation between stage number and number of kernels. Explain the relation between the equation and the experiment. Compare values predicted by your model with data table entries. Write a question about the experiment. Use your equation to answer the question.

Experiment 3

Begin this experiment with a collection of 200 identical thumbtacks. Toss those tacks onto a flat surface and *remove* all tacks that land with the point up. Count and record the number of tacks remaining. (This ends Stage 1.)

Point Up   **Point Down**

Toss the remaining tacks again and *remove* all tacks that land with their point up. Record the number of tacks left. Repeat the toss-remove-count process several times.

Record the data in a table of (*stage, tacks left*) data. Plot that data. Find an equation that models the relation between stage number and number of tacks. Explain the relation between the equation and the experiment. Compare values predicted by your model with data table entries. Write a question about the experiment. Use your equation to answer the question.

Experiment 4

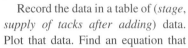

Begin this experiment by tossing 10 tacks onto a flat surface. Count the number of tacks that land with their point down and *add* that number of tacks to the test supply. (This ends Stage 1.) Repeat the toss-count-add process several times.

Record the data in a table of (*stage, supply of tacks after adding*) data. Plot that data. Find an equation that models the relation between the stage and the number of tacks. Explain the relation between the equation and the experiment. Compare values predicted by your equation with data table entries. Write a question about the experiment. Use your equation to answer the question.

Checkpoint

After each experiment has been reported to your class, consider the following questions about exponential patterns in data, their graphs, and their equations $y = a(b^x)$.

a What does the value of *a* indicate about each of the experiments? What does it indicate about the table of values for any exponential relation?

b What does the value of *b* indicate about each of the experiments? What does it indicate about the table of values for any exponential relation?

c In what sorts of problem situations can you expect an exponential model for which the value of *b* is between 0 and 1?

d In what sorts of problem situations can you expect an exponential model for which the value of *b* is greater than 1?

e What changes in data, graphs, and equation models would you expect if the experiments were changed

- by dividing the paper plate differently in the corn kernel experiment?

- by using different tacks, with shorter or longer points, in the tack experiment?

Be prepared to explain your ideas to the entire class.

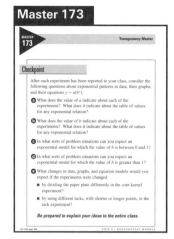

Master 173

Experiment 4

1. **Collect Data** Answers will vary; the following is given as a sample.

Stage Number	0	1	2	3	4	5	6	7
Number of Tacks	10	15	24	35	54	83	125	190

2. **Display Data** Our sample (*stage number, number of tacks*) data are displayed below.

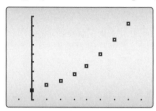

```
WINDOW
Xmin =–1
Xmax =8
Xscl =1
Ymin =–10
Ymax =210
Yscl =50
Xres =1
```

3. **Analyze Data** The data table shows that the number of tacks is increasing, but not at a constant rate. The increases are smaller initially and then gradually become larger with each stage. The graph shows a curve where as x increases, the values for y increase at an increasing rate. The exponential model that represents the data pattern is $y = 10(1.52)^x$.

4. **Apply Model** One possible question is:
   How many stages will it take to get 150 tacks?

SHARE AND SUMMARIZE   full-class discussion

Checkpoint

See Teaching Master 173.

This Checkpoint allows students to formalize what they have determined collectively from the four experiments. Before starting on the Checkpoint, be sure each group has presented its experiment to the others, and that each has at least addressed the problem of how to choose the growth or decay factor from the data. Each group should explain how the important facts in the experiment (the starting number and the decay factor) are represented in the symbolic model. They should refer to the real situation and how this is modeled by the equation. (This would be the time to discuss differences in the decay factor, caused by the choice made: removing all the kernels strictly in the shaded area, or in the shaded area and on the line. The decay factor will be a little more than 75% remaining or a little less.) It may be helpful to have the graphs and equations displayed while students work on this Checkpoint.

ⓐ The initial number of objects for the experiments is a. In the table of values, when $x = 0$ then $y = a$.

ⓑ In the experiments, the values change by a factor of b. You can find the value of b in the table of values by taking any function value and dividing it by the previous value. Your result should be very close to b.

ⓒ If $0 < b < 1$, then the problem situations are ones representing exponential decay, such as radioactive decay or metabolic decay.

See additional Teaching Notes on page T481I.

Unit 6

Students can now begin
Modeling Task 1, 2, 3, or 4 or
Organizing Task 1 or 4 from the
MORE assignment following
Investigation 2. (Modeling
Task 3 requires 200 plastic
spoons, which probably aren't
readily available in most
homes. You may want to have
a supply at school, and let
students conduct the experiment in class, or borrow the
spoons.)

APPLY   **individual task**

▶On Your Own

a. The pattern of (*stage number*, *dice remaining*) data would show exponential decrease. The number of dice remaining after each stage is multiplied by approximately $\frac{2}{3}$ to get the next entry.

b. The scatterplot would have the left-most value of (0, 300) and then have other values representing a decay rate of approximately $\frac{2}{6}$ or $\frac{1}{3}$.

c. $y = 300(0.67)^x$

d. ■ The two students probably worked together.
  ■ The student probably did not actually do the experiment, but simply reported theoretical data.

Unit 6

> ## On Your Own

Suppose you have a collection of 300 dice. You toss them and remove all that show ones or sixes. Then you count and record the number of dice remaining. You repeat this procedure until you have only a few dice left.

a. What pattern of (*toss number, dice remaining*) data would you expect?

b. What would a scatterplot of the (*toss number, dice remaining*) data look like?

c. What equation would you expect as a good model of the data?

d. Suppose your teacher gives a homework assignment to conduct the dice-tossing experiment for ten tosses. If you were the teacher, what would you think:

- If two students reported exactly the same data?
- If one student's data fit exactly the equation $y = a(b^x)$ that was reported as the most likely model for that data pattern?

INVESTIGATION 2 Another Day Older ... and Deeper in Debt

By the end of 1995, the national debt of the United States government was about $5,000,000,000,000. The debt was growing by nearly $900,000,000 every day. The numbers may seem too large to comprehend and the national debt may seem unrelated to your life. But on February 17, 1993, the *Chicago Tribune* reported that a large group of young people had gathered to make their position on the national debt known. These young people were concerned about government spending in this country and its long range implications. How will the national debt affect your financial future? Is the damage to the financial health of future generations beyond repair?

Danziger © 1993 *The Christian Science Monitor*

1. Consider the data table below which gives the federal debt in trillions of dollars from 1988 to 1993.

Year	1988	1989	1990	1991	1992	1993
Debt in $ Trillion	2.6	2.9	3.2	3.6	4.0	4.4

Source: U.S. Bureau of the Census, *Statistical Abstract of the United States: 1995* (115th edition). Washington, DC, 1995.

a. Enter these data in your calculator or computer using 0 for 1988, 1 for 1989, and so on. Make a scatterplot.

b. What patterns in the data and the plot suggest that a linear model might fit the trend in national debt? What patterns in the data are unlike linear models?

c. Use your calculator or computer software to find a linear rule for the (*year, debt*) data that you believe fits well. Find an exponential rule that seems to fit well, also.

■ Use the two rules to make tables and graphs. Describe the similarities and differences.

■ Use each model equation to estimate the national debt in the years 2005, 2010, 2020, and 2030.

d. Which of the two models do you think is better for describing and predicting the American national debt? Compare your choice with those of other groups. Resolve any differences between groups.

2. Early estimates of the national debt data for 1994 indicated that the rate of increase might be slowing. The debt figure for 1994 actually turned out to be around 4.6 trillion. Subsequent data, shown in the table below, confirm that the rate of increase is slowing.

Year	1995	1996	1997	1998	1999	2000
Debt in $ Trillion	4.97	5.22	5.41	5.5	5.66	5.67

Source: U.S. Bureau of the Census, *Statistical Abstract of the United States: 2000.* Washington, DC, 2000.

a. How do these additional values affect the pattern of the data plot?

b. How might they affect equations of good linear and exponential models?

c. How might they affect the long-range projection of the national debt?

d. Do you think today's young people have as much need to be concerned about the national debt as those who gathered in 1993?

INVESTIGATION 2 Another Day Older . . . and Deeper in Debt

In this investigation, students explore exponential growth in the context of debt.

1. **a.**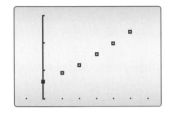

```
WINDOW
Xmin =-1
Xmax =6
Xscl =1
Ymin =2
Ymax =5
Yscl =1
Xres =1
```

b. The scatterplot looks fairly linear, but looking at the table of values shows that the amount of increase is not constant from one y value to the next.

c.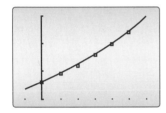

```
Plot1   Plot2   Plot3
\Y1 =2.6034045946
735*1.1119171601
51^X
\Y2 =.36285714285
714X+2.542857142
8572
\Y3 =
```

X	Y1	Y2
6	4.9201	4.72
7	5.4708	5.0829
8	6.083	5.4457
9	6.7638	5.8086
10	7.5208	6.1714
11	8.3625	6.5343
12	9.2985	6.8971

Y1 =2.6034045946...

Y_1 is an exponential model for the data given and Y_2 is a linear model. These models were found using the exponential and linear regression features of the TI-83.

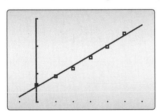

Year	2005	2010	2020	2030
Debt in $ Trillions using Exponential Model	15.80	26.86	77.60	224.17
Debt in $ Trillions using Linear Model	8.71	10.53	14.15	17.78

The graphs above show the models graphed on the scatterplot of the original data. You can see that the models are relatively close up to the year 2000 (when $x = 12$), but they become very widespread after that point. The linear model shows a gradual and constant increase, and the exponential model shows relatively sharp increases.

d. Since we must pay interest on the debt, the debt continues to grow at an increasing rate. Thus, the exponential model is probably a better representation.

2. **a.** The new plot is neither linear nor exponential in appearance.

b. The new data points suggest that neither a linear nor an exponenetial model represents the new pattern.

c. This would indicate that the national debt would be increasing at a slower rate. Neither the long-range projection provided by the linear model nor the one provided by the exponential model would be reasonable.

d. If the current trend continues, today's youth do not have as much to be concerned about becuase the growth of the debt has slowed dramatically; however the debt is still substantial.

Unit 6

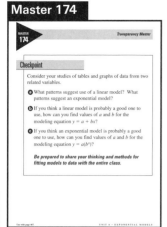
SHARE AND SUMMARIZE   full-class discussion

Checkpoint

This Checkpoint is very important to the general understanding of both linear and exponential models. If students do not seem to grasp these ideas, it is important to work on some of the MORE tasks and revisit this Checkpoint.

See Teaching Master 174.

ⓐ Data that suggest a constant rate of change usually are going to be linear, unless you are not looking at the whole picture. If it looks as if the rate is changing at an increasing or decreasing rate, and if the curve approaches the x-axis on either the left or the right, this would suggest an exponential model.

ⓑ You can find the value for a by examining where the line crosses the y-axis. The value for b is the slope of the line. Take any two points and calculate the difference in the y-coordinates divided by the difference in the x-coordinates.

ⓒ You can determine the value for a by examining where the curve crosses the y-axis. To determine the base b, determine the ratio of the y values between successive points where the change in the x values is 1. For example, using the following data set, a is 20 because the plot contains the point $(0, 20)$, and b is 2.5 because $\frac{50}{20} = \frac{125}{50} = \frac{312.5}{125} = \frac{781.25}{312.5} = 2.5$.

$$\{(0, 20), (1, 50), (2, 125), (3, 312.5), (4, 781.25)\}$$

APPLY   individual task

▶On Your Own

a.

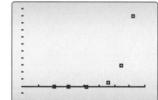

```
WINDOW
 Xmin =5
 Xmax =9
 Xscl =.5
 Ymin =-500
 Ymax =5500
 Yscl =500
 Xres =1
```

b. The curve approaches the x-axis (on the left), and as x becomes very large, the curve increases at an increasing rate.

c.
```
ExpReg
 y=a*b^x
 a=6.120973E-10
 b=31.74619231
```

An approximate exponential model for these data is $y = 6.12(31.746)^x \times 10^{-10}$ or $6.12 \times 10^{-10}(31.746)^x$.

Checkpoint

Consider your studies of tables and graphs of data from two related variables.

ⓐ What patterns suggest use of a linear model? What patterns suggest an exponential model?

ⓑ If you think a linear model is probably a good one to use, how can you find values of a and b for the modeling equation $y = a + bx$?

ⓒ If you think an exponential model is probably a good one to use, how can you find values of a and b for the modeling equation $y = a(b^x)$?

Be prepared to share your thinking and methods for fitting models to data with the entire class.

▶ On Your Own

Earthquakes are among the most damaging kinds of natural disasters. The size of an earthquake is generally reported as a rating on the *Richter scale*—usually a number between 1 and 9. That Richter scale rating indicates the energy released by the shaking of the ground and the height of the shock waves recorded on seismographs.

The data in the following table show Richter scale ratings and amounts of energy released for six earthquakes.

Earthquake Location	Richter Scale Rating	Energy (in sextillion ergs)
San Francisco, CA, 1906	8.25	1,500
Yugoslavia, 1963	6.0	0.63
Alaska, 1964	8.6	5,000
Peru, 1970	7.8	320
Italy, 1976	6.5	3.5
Loma Prieta, CA, 1989	7.1	28

a. Use your calculator or computer software to make a scatterplot for these data.

b. What pattern makes it reasonable to think that this is an exponential relation?

c. Use your calculator or computer software to find an algebraic model that fits the data pattern well.

d. Use the model to estimate energy released by earthquakes listed in the following chart.

Earthquake Location	Richter Scale Rating	Energy (in sextillion ergs)
Quetta, India, 1906	7.5	
Kwanto, Japan, 1923	8.2	
Chillan, Chile, 1939	7.75	
Agadir, Morocco, 1960	5.9	
Iran, 1968	7.4	
Tangshan, China, 1976	7.6	
Northridge, CA, 1994	6.7	
Kobe, Japan, 1995	7.2	

MORE
Modeling • Organizing • Reflecting • Extending

Modeling

1. Suppose you are given a collection of 200 new pennies and directed to perform this experiment: Shake the pennies and drop them on a flat surface. *Remove* all pennies that land heads up. Count and record the number of pennies remaining. Repeat the shake-drop-remove-count process several times.

   a. What pattern of (*drop number, pennies left*) data would you expect from this experiment?

   b. What pattern would you expect in a scatterplot of the data?

   c. What equations would you expect to be good models of the data?

   d. Conduct the experiment to test your predictions.

2. Suppose you are given a collection of new pennies and directed to perform this experiment: Start with a cup holding 10 pennies. Shake the pennies and drop them on a flat surface. Count the pennies that turn up tails. *Add* that number of pennies to your cup and record the number of pennies now in the cup. Repeat the shake-drop-count-add process several times.

   a. What pattern of (*drop number, number of pennies*) data would you expect from this experiment?

d. Answers may vary depending on the window used, if the trace function was used, and the number of places to which the algebraic model was rounded.

Earthquake Location	Richter Scale Rating	Energy (in sextillion ergs)
India, Quetta, 1906	7.5	112.07
Japan, Kwanto, 1923	8.2	1,260.93
Chile, Chillan, 1939	7.75	266.03
Morocco, Agadir, 1960	5.9	0.44
Iran, 1968	7.4	79.31
China, Tangshan, 1976	7.6	158.37
Northridge, CA, 1994	6.7	7.05
Japan, Kobe, 1995	7.2	39.72

MORE   independent assignment

Modeling

1. a. Since the probability of one coin landing heads up is 50%, you would expect to reduce the number of pennies by 50% with each successive drop.

b. The scatterplot should show the initial number of pennies, 200, as the *y*-intercept. Each successive point should have a *y* value of about half of the previous *y* value. In other words, the curve would show a decreasing curve that approaches the *x*-axis as *x* increases.

c. The exponential model $y = 200(0.5)^x$ should be close.

d. Students should collect data and then look back at their predictions.

2. a. For each successive drop, the number of pennies would be 1.5 times the previous number.

MORE
ASSIGNMENT   *pp. 468–476*

Modeling: Choose one of 1–4, and 5 or 6*

Organizing: 1, 3, and 4

Reflecting: Choose one*

Extending: 2, and 3 or 4*

*When choice is indicated, it is important to leave the choice to the student.
NOTE: *It is best if Organizing tasks are discussed as a whole class after they have been assigned as homework.*

Unit 6

2. **b.** The *y*-intercept would be 10 because you start with 10 coins. Each successive *y* value would be 1.5 times greater than the previous *y* value, making the curve rise to the right at an increasing rate.

    c. $y = 10(1.5)^x$

    d. Students should collect data and then look back at their predictions.

3. Responses will vary for this item, but the basic patterns should be similar to the investigations that the students have done already with popcorn and thumbtacks. This task will be an exponential decay model $y = 200b^x$, where the value of *b* is 1 minus the probability that the spoon will land rightside up.

4. Responses will vary for this item, but the basic patterns should be similar to the investigations that the students have completed with popcorn and thumbtacks. This task will be modeled by the exponential growth equation $y = 200b^x$, where the value of *b* is 1 plus the probability that the spoon will land rightside up.

b. What pattern would you expect in a scatterplot of the data?

c. What equations would you expect to be good models of the data?

d. Conduct the experiment to test your predictions.

3. Try this experiment with a supply of about 200 plastic spoons. Toss the spoons onto a flat surface and *remove* all spoons that land right side up. Count and record the number of spoons remaining. Repeat this toss-remove-count process several times.

   a. Record the (*toss number, number of spoons*) data in a table.

   b. Make a scatterplot of the data.

   c. Find an equation that models the relation between toss number and number of spoons. Explain the relation between the equation and the experiment.

   d. Write a question about this experiment. Use your model to answer the question.

4. Try this spoons experiment. Start with a supply of about 15 plastic spoons. Toss the spoons onto a flat surface and count the spoons that land right side up. *Add* that number of new spoons to your test collection. Then repeat the toss-count-add process several times.

   a. Record the (*toss number*, *number of spoons*) data in a table.

   b. Plot the data.

   c. Find an equation that models the relation between toss number and number of spoons.

   d. Explain the relation between the equation and the experiment. How is the equation related to the experiment in Modeling Task 3?

5. With improved health care and advances in medicine, people continue to live longer. The American Hospital Association has predicted that the nursing home population will increase rapidly. It has made the following projections.

Projected Nursing Home Population

Year	1985	1990	2000	2010	2020	2030	2040	2050
Population (millions)	1.30	1.45	1.80	2.30	2.55	3.35	4.30	4.80

Source: Person, J.E. Jr., ed., *Statistical Forecasts of the United States*. Detroit: Gale Research, Inc. 1993.

LESSON 4 • MODELING EXPONENTIAL PATTERNS IN DATA **469**

a. Find linear and exponential models that fit these data well. Use 0 for 1985, 5 for 1990, 10 for 2000, and so on.

b. In the equation $y = a + bx$ for the linear model, what do the values of a and b indicate about the projected pattern of change in nursing home populations?

c. In the equation $y = a(b^x)$ for the exponential model, what do the values of a and b indicate about the projected pattern of change in nursing home populations?

d. Which model do you believe was used to make the projections in the table?

e. What is the projected number of elderly who will be receiving nursing home care when you are eighty years old?

6. Life began on earth millions of years ago. Our species, *Homo Sapiens*, dates back only 300,000 years. The black rhinoceros, the second largest of all land mammals, has walked the earth for 40,000,000 years. In less than a century, the very existence of this species has been threatened. Prior to the 19th century, over 1,000,000 black rhinos roamed the plains of Africa. That number has been drastically reduced by hunting over the years. Recent data on the black rhino population is shown in the table below.

African Black Rhino Population

Year	1970	1980	1984	1986	1993
Population (in 1000s)	65	15	9	3.8	2.3

Source: Nowak, R.M., *Mammals of the World*, fifth ed., vol. 2. Johns Hopkins University Press: Baltimore, 1991; www.rhinos-irf.org/rhinos/black.html

a. Make a scatterplot of these data and find an exponential equation that models the pattern in the data well. Use 0 for 1970, 10 for 1980, and so on.

b. Use the model from Part a to predict the black rhino population in the year 2010.

c. Use your model to predict the time when the black rhino population will be less than 1,000.

d. Find a linear model for the black rhino data that you believe fits the data well. Answer Parts b and c again using that model.

5. a. Using 0 for 1985, 5 for 1990, 15 for 2000, *etc.*, we have the following:

$y = 1.06158 + 0.05452x$ $y = 1.31569(1.02075)^x$

 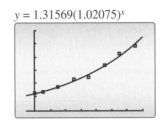

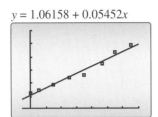

```
WINDOW
Xmin =-5
Xmax =70
Xscl =10
Ymin =0
Ymax =6
Yscl =1
Xres =1
```

b. The value of *a* gives the initial nursing home population in 1985. The value of *b* is the increase per year. For the model in Part a, the 1985 population is about 1.06 million, and the population increases by about 0.0545 million each year.

c. The value of *a* gives the initial nursing home population in 1985, and *b* gives the ratio between populations from year to year. According to the model used in Part a, the initial population is 1.32 million, and this increases by a factor of 1.02 or by 2%, each year.

d. The exponential model probably was used because the curve seems to be a better fit for the scatterplot.

e. Answers will vary depending on the age of the students and the model that they use. In the table at the right, 80 represents the year 2065, Y_1 gives linear model projections, and Y_2 gives exponential model projections (in millions).

X	Y₁	Y₂
79	5.3686	6.6654
80	5.4232	6.8037
81	5.4777	6.9449
82	5.5322	7.089
83	5.5867	7.2361
84	5.6412	7.3863
85	5.6958	7.5395

$Y_1 \blacksquare 1.0615819209...$

6. a. Using $x = 0$ for 1970, $x = 10$ for 1980, and so on, we have the following:

$y = 63.55053(0.85987)^x$

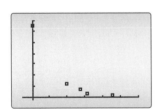 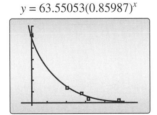

```
WINDOW
Xmin =-2
Xmax =30
Xscl =5
Ymin =-10
Ymax =75
Yscl =10
Xres =1
```

b. For the year 2010, the model predicts approximately 151 rhinos.

c. The prediction is that the rhino population will be less than 1,000 by the 28th year, which is 1998.

X	Y₁
24	1.6962
25	1.4585
26	1.2541
27	1.0784
28	.92724
29	.7973
30	.68557

$X = 28$

d. The population in 2010 is shown as the *y* value corresponding to $x = 40$. Since this number is negative, the model predicts that rhinos will be extinct by the year 2010. The rhino population will be less than 1,000 after the year 19, or 1989. (Clearly, this is not the case, since our data show 2,300 in 1993.)

$y = 54.49 - 2.82x$

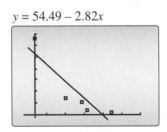

Unit 6

6. e.

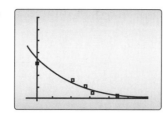

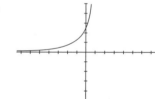

```
ExpReg
 y=a*b^x
 a=35.50910533
 b=.8895348778
 r²=.9231461086
 r=-.9608049274
```

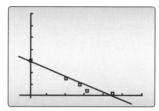

```
LinReg
 y=a+bx
 a=28.14554318
 b=-1.279805014
 r²=.9345896332
 r=-.9667417614
```

Students might choose the exponential model because they believe that the overall patterns are more like the patterns found in population problems. On the other hand, the linear model seems to fit these points about as well. A linear model might be reasonable if you consider the intervention of humans in nature.

f. In 1996, strict anti-poaching efforts were made and have resulted in significant positive change for the black rhino population.

Organizing

1. a.

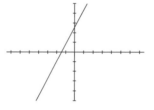

The *y*-intercept is 5 and the constant rate of change is 3.

b.

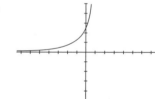

The *y*-intercept is 5 and the common ratio is 3. (This is an example of exponential growth.)

c.

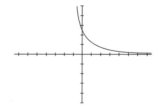

The *y*-intercept is 5 and the common ratio is $\frac{1}{3}$. (This is an example of exponential decay.)

See additional Teaching Notes on page T481J.

e. A model based on very few data points is sometimes inaccurate, especially if one data point has an incorrect value. Suppose the 1970 black rhino population was actually only 30,000. Find what you believe is a good-fitting model in that case.

f. The actual black rhino population in 2000 was approximately 2,700. What might account for the break in the pattern suggested by earlier data?

Organizing

1. Without using your calculator or computer, sketch graphs for each of the following equations. Explain the reasoning you used in making each sketch.

a. $y = 3x + 5$

b. $y = 5(3^x)$

c. $y = 5\left(\frac{1}{3}\right)^x$

2. Make tables of sample (x, y) data that fit the conditions below. Use values for x from 0 to 8. Explain your reasoning in making each table.

a. The y values increase exponentially from an initial value of 5.

b. The y values increase exponentially from an initial value of 5 at a greater rate than the example in Part a.

c. The y values increase linearly from an initial value of 5.

d. The y values decrease exponentially from an initial value of 25.

e. The y values decrease linearly from an initial value of 25.

3. Complete a table like the one below so that it shows:

a. a pattern of linear growth. Write a linear equation that describes the pattern.

b. a pattern of exponential growth. Write an exponential equation that describes the pattern.

x	0	1	2	3	4	5
y	10	20				

4. When a fair coin is flipped, the outcome of "heads" or "tails" is equally likely. So the probability of a flipped coin landing heads up is $\frac{1}{2}$ or 0.5. Refer back to Experiment 3 of this lesson.

   a. If one of the thumbtacks is tossed in the air, what do you think is the probability that it will land with the point up?

   b. Toss a thumbtack in the air 100 times and count the number of times the tack lands with the point up. Use the results of your experiment to get a better estimate of the probability in Part a.

   c. What do the results of your experiment in Part b tell you about the probability that a tack tossed in the air will land point down?

   d. How, if at all, is the probability of a tack landing point up reflected in the equation model for Experiment 3?

Reflecting

1. A thousand-dollar bill is about 0.0043 inches thick. Imagine a stack of thousand-dollar bills whose total value is a trillion dollars. How high would the stack of bills be? If you created a stack of thousand-dollar bills whose value is that of the current national debt, about how many miles high would the stack be? Does this help show the seriousness of the debt you and your classmates will be inheriting?

2. Jail overcrowding is an issue in many states. Drug use and drug-related crime have contributed to the problem. Average operating costs of $25,000 per inmate and construction costs of $50,000 per cell will be an incredible burden on these jail systems. Examine the data in the following table, which gives the total number of jail inmates for the years 1993 through 1999.

U. S. Jail Inmates (excluding federal and state prisons)

Year	1993	1994	1995	1996	1997	1998	1999
Jail Population	459,804	486,474	507,044	518,492	567,079	592,462	605,943

Source: *Statistical Abstract of the United States: 2000.* Washington, DC: U.S. Bureau of the Census, 2000.

   a. What sort of model seems best for projecting this growth pattern into the future—linear, exponential, or some other type?

4. **a.** Responses will depend on the type of tacks used in Experiment 3.

b. Student responses will vary.

c. The probability that a tack tossed in the air will land point down is 1 minus the probability that it will land point up.

d. Student responses will vary, but the base should be approximately equal to the probability that the tack will land point down. Thus, 1 minus the base should be the probability that the tack will land point up.

Reflecting

1. 1,000,000,000 bills $\times$ 0.0043 inches per bill = 4,300,000 inches

   The height of a stack of $1,000 bills whose value is that of the current national debt will depend on the debt. The necessary calculation is:

   $$Debt \div 1,000 \times 0.0043 \div 5,280 \div 12$$

   For the year 2000, the national debt was approximately $5.67 trillion. This amount could be represented by a stack of $1,000 bills about 385 miles high.

2. **a.** Based on the graphs below, the linear model does not seem to be better than the exponential model. It is difficult to claim either model as best without further data since these data vary around both models in a similar pattern.

   Note: x represents years after 1993.

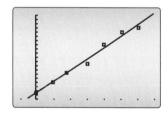
```
LinReg
 y=a+bx
 a=457782.4286
 b=25372.42857
```

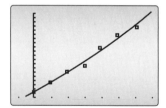
```
ExpReg
 y=a*b^x
 a=460653.9165
 b=1.048798424
```

Unit 6

2. b. Using the linear model above, $Y_1(12) \approx 762,252$ and $Y_1(6) = 610,017$. By 2005, 762,252 – 610,017 or 152,235 new inmates will need to be housed in new cells. Assuming 2 new prisoners in each new cell, the cost for this would be $152,235 \times (50,000/2 + 25,000)$ or 7.6118×10^9 (over $7 billion).

c. Responses will vary. The money could come from increased taxes, sale of property seized from criminals, lotteries, and so on.

3. a. x represents years since 1975.

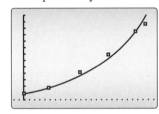 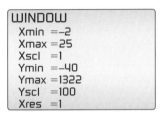

The exponential model $y = 149.74(1.10)^x$ gives the following predictions: in 2005 the health care spending will be $2,612.9 billion, and in 2010 it will be $4,208.1 billion.

b. The number of elderly people, the AIDS epidemic, and the basic population increase might be mentioned as factors that would cause health care costs to increase.

c.

Year	1975	1980	1985	1990	1995	1998
Spending per capita in $	611	1,083	1,803	2,796	3,776	4,240

d.

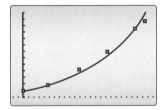

An equation for the graph above is $y = 692.18(1.088)^x$. The cost per capita for health care may be growing exponentially at a rate of about 8.8% per year. The linear model $y = 382.2 + 164.6x$ is also a good fit for the data, indicating an increase of about $165 each year. In either case, this means that if personal income is not rising at the same rate (or higher), then a greater percentage of personal income will be spent on health care, and less money will be available for purchasing the goods and services which fuel the economy.

Unit 6

b. Assume that the jails in these states were all full in 1999. Make a reasonable estimate of the number of additional cells that will be needed by 2005. Estimate the construction and operating costs for the additional cells.

c. Where might the money for the increased costs come from?

3. Health care spending has been another factor in American life which has shown exponential growth. Using the data below, create a scatterplot and find an algebraic model to closely fit this data.

Total U.S. Spending on Health Care

Year	1975	1980	1985	1990	1995	1998
Spending in $ Billion	132	247	429	699	993	1,149

Source: *Statistical Abstract of the United States: 2000.* Washington, DC: U.S. Bureau of the Census, 2000.

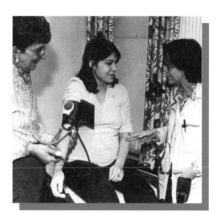

a. Predict the health care spending total for 2005 and 2010.

b. Besides inflation, what factors do you think would cause this dramatic rise in the cost for health care?

c. "Cost per capita" indicates the expense per person and therefore adjusts to reflect changes in population. The population of the U.S. for the given years is indicated in the following table. Calculate the health care cost per capita.

U.S. Population

Year	1975	1980	1985	1990	1995	1998
Population in Millions	216	228	238	250	263	271

Source: *Statistical Abstract of the United States: 2000.* Washington, DC: U.S. Bureau of the Census, 2000.

d. Is the cost per capita for health care also growing exponentially? What implications would this have for the future of health care in this country?

Extending

1. The following data were collected using a Geiger counter and a sample of radioactive barium-137. A Geiger counter measures the level of radioactivity in a sample.

Geiger Counter Readings for Barium-137

Time in Minutes	0	1	2	3	4	5	6
Counts per Minute	10,094	8,105	5,832	4,553	3,339	2,648	2,035

a. Make a scatterplot of the data.

b. Use your calculator or computer software and what you know about exponential models to determine the half-life of this radioactive substance.

2. The following data is from the *HIV/AIDS Surveillance Report*.

AIDS Cases and Fatalities

Year	1995	1996	1997	1998	1999
Estimated Population Livng with AIDS	216,796	240,184	268,242	293,702	320,282
Fatalities Adults/Adolescents	49,284	50,070	37,356	21,704	17,806
Fatalities Children < 13 years	542	431	219	124	113

Source: U.S. Department of Health and Human Services. *HIV/AIDS Surveillance Report 12, No. 2* (July 2000).

a. Make a scatterplot for each of the three sets of data included in the table, showing how those variables have changed over time. Describe the patterns in the scatterplots.

b. Find a model you believe will help you make the best predictions about the number of persons living with AIDS in the future. Use your model to predict the number of persons who will be living with AIDS in 2010.

c. Find a model for the child AIDS fatalities data. Assuming the pattern will continue, use your model to predict the number of AIDS fatalities for children in the year 2010.

Extending

1. a.

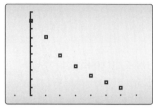

```
WINDOW
 Xmin =-1
 Xmax =7
 Xscl =1
 Ymin =1000
 Ymax =11000
 Yscl =1000
 Xres =1
```

b.

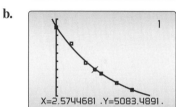

X=2.5744681 .Y=5083.4891 .

```
ExpReg
 y=a*b^x
  a=10223.86645
  b=.7623066708
```

Since you start with 10,094 and after almost 2.6 minutes you are down to 5,083, the half-life of Barium-137 is about 2.6 minutes.

2. a.

Estimated Number of Persons Living with AIDS

```
WINDOW
 Xmin =-1
 Xmax =5
 Xscl =1
 Ymin =200000
 Ymax =340000
 Yscl =10000
 Xres =1
```

The number of people living with AIDS seems to fit a linear pattern, increasing at a constant rate each year. In the United States, AIDS victims have access to new drugs and treatments. While there is no cure for AIDS, many more people are living with the disease and fewer are dying from AIDS.

Fatalities Adult/Adolescent

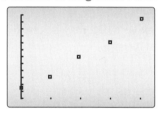

```
WINDOW
 Xmin =-1
 Xmax =5
 Xscl =1
 Ymin =13000
 Ymax =56000
 Yscl =10000
 Xres =1
```

The adult/adolescent fatalities do not appear to fit any of the patterns studied so far, although it may be decreasing exponentially after 1996.

Fatalities Children <13

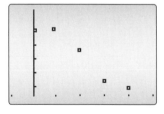

```
WINDOW
 Xmin =-1
 Xmax =5
 Xscl =1
 Ymin =40
 Ymax =620
 Yscl =100
 Xres =1
```

The child fatalities are decreasing at a decreasing rate and so might be exhibiting exponential decay.

b. Using the linear model $y = 26{,}049x + 215{,}743.2$ (where x is the number of years after 1995), there will be 606,478 people living with AIDS in 2010.

Unit 6

2. c.

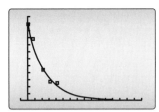

Using the exponential model $y = 564.5(0.645)^x$, $564.5(0.645)^{15} \approx 0.785 < 1$. So we might not expect any child fatalities due to AIDS in 2010.

d.

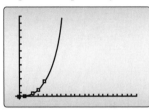

- In 1986, you probably would have still used an exponential model, but the model would reflect exponential growth instead of decay. A possible model would be $y = 7.915(1.897)^x$, where x represents the number of years since 1981.
- Using this model gives a prediction of 9.17×10^8 or 917 million child fatalities due to AIDS in 2010, a drastically grimmer forecast than that given by our model in Part c.
- The change in the pattern of child fatalities due to AIDS may be due to increased awareness of the disease, greater education about how to avoid infection, and to medical advances.

3. a.

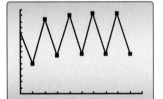

Time in Minutes	Cigarette #1 Nicotine	Cigarette #2 Nicotine	Cigarette #3 Nicotine	Cigarette #4 Nicotine	Cigarette #5 Nicotine	Total Nicotine
0	100					100
20	50					50
40	25	100				125
60	12.5	50				62.5
80	6.25	25	100			131.25
100	3.125	12.5	50			65.625
120	1.5625	6.25	25	100		132.8125
140	0.78125	3.125	12.5	50		66.40625
160	0.390625	1.5625	6.25	25	100	133.203125
180	0.195313	0.78125	3.125	12.5	50	66.601563

The connected scatterplot shows the nicotine levels over the three-hour time period. The level of nicotine is continually going up and down, but the overall pattern is that the amount of nicotine is slowly increasing.

b. The pattern of increases and decreases would continue, but the overall levels would be higher, and the spikes would occur twice as often.

c. Regardless of the total nicotine in the body, half of that amount will disappear every 20 minutes, so the nicotine levels will drop fairly quickly. As you can see from the plot above, if a person smokes a cigarette every 40 minutes the minimum nicotine level will be 50, until they break the schedule.

d. Suppose you were making the same prediction in 1986 using the earlier data given in the table below:

Year	1981	1982	1983	1984	1985
AIDS Fatalities Children < 13 years	9	13	29	48	115

Source: U.S. Department of Heath and Human Services. *HIV/AIDS Surveillance Report 5, no. 2* (July 1993).

■ What model would you have used based on only the data available at that time?

■ Does that model give you the same prediction for AIDS fatalities for children in 2010 as your model from Part c?

■ What changes in conditions might explain the differences?

3. Cigarette smoke contains nicotine, a very addictive and harmful chemical that affects the brain, nervous system, and lungs. The productivity losses and health care costs associated with cigarette smoke are considerable.

Suppose an individual smokes one cigarette every 40 minutes over a period of three hours and that each cigarette introduces 100 units of nicotine into the bloodstream. The half-life of nicotine is 20 minutes.

a. Create a chart that keeps track of the amount of nicotine which remains in the body over the three-hour time period in 20-minute intervals. Plot these totals over time. Then describe the pattern of nicotine build-up in the body of a smoker.

b. How would the data change if the individual smokes a cigarette every 20 minutes?

c. Because nicotine is a very addictive drug, it is difficult for a smoker to break the habit. Suppose a long-time smoker decides to quit "cold turkey." That is, rather than reducing the number of cigarettes smoked each day, the smoker resolves never to pick up another cigarette. How will the level of nicotine in that smoker's bloodstream change over time?

4. Alcohol is another dangerous drug. Driving after excessive drinking is not only punishable by law but also potentially fatal. The National Highway Safety Administration reported 2,238 youth alcohol-related traffic fatalities in 1999— an average of 6 fatalities each day.

Unit 6

While legal limits of blood alcohol concentration (BAC) are different in each state, the American Medical Association recommends that a limit of 0.05 be used.

There are many factors that affect a person's BAC. Some factors include body weight, gender, and the amount of alcohol drunk. The following chart contains typical data relating body weights and number of drinks consumed to approximate blood alcohol concentration. (Because of individual differences, this chart should not be considered to apply to everyone.)

Approximate Blood Alcohol Concentration

Weight (in pounds)	1 Drink	2 Drinks	3 Drinks	4 Drinks	5 Drinks
100	0.05	0.09	0.14	0.18	0.23
120	0.04	0.08	0.11	0.15	0.19
140	0.03	0.07	0.10	0.13	0.16
160	0.03	0.06	0.09	0.11	0.14
180	0.03	0.05	0.08	0.10	0.13

Source: National Highway Traffic Safety Administration, *Driving under the influence: A report to Congress on alcohol limits*. Washington, DC., 1992.

a. As time passes since alcohol was consumed, a person's body metabolizes the drug. Again, the rate at which this happens is different for each person. For most people, their BAC would drop at a rate of at least 0.01 each hour. Suppose a 120 lb. person had consumed three drinks. Using the table above and a burnoff rate of 0.01 per hour, when would this person satisfy the AMA's suggested limit of 0.05? How would this change if the person weighed 180 pounds and had consumed four drinks?

b. Prepare a graphical display of the data in the chart. Describe any patterns you see in the display.

c. Create a table showing the change in blood alcohol level over time, for a 140 lb. person who has consumed five drinks. Make a scatterplot of this data.

d. What type of model would best fit the scatterplot in Part c?

e. Based on your work in Investigation 3 of Lesson 2 and in Extending Task 3 on the previous page, what type of model best describes the amount of substance in the body over time for steroids, nicotine, and penicillin?

4. a. The 120-pound person would have a blood alcohol concentration (BAC) of 0.11 after 3 drinks, and the 180-pound person would have a BAC of 0.10 after 4 drinks. The 120-pound person would have to wait 6 hours, and the 180-pound person 5 hours, before reaching the suggested 0.05 limit. (The value 0.05 refers to 0.05 gram per 100 milliliters of blood.)

b.

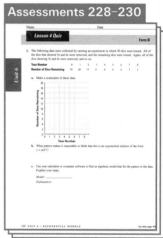

The pattern is a series of lines representing the blood alcohol concentrations for different weight individuals. The less a person weighs, the greater the slope of the line representing the BAC.

c.

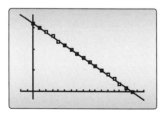

WINDOW
Xmin =-2
Xmax =18
Xscl =1
Ymin =-.02
Ymax =.18
Yscl =.05
Xres =1

d. A linear model would be best. The blood alcohol level decreases by a constant amount each hour.

LinReg
y=a+bx
a=.16
b=-.01

e. All of these substances metabolize exponentially.

See Assessment Resources, pages 225–230.

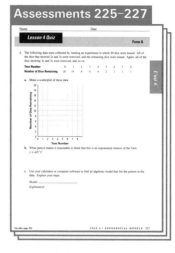

Assessments 225–227

Assessments 228–230

Unit 6

Lesson 5 *Looking Back*

This short lesson offers a set of problems in which students can review and consolidate their insights and skills. By this point in the unit, students should be comfortable with tasks that require identifying exponential growth and decay situations—whether they are given data, graphs, verbal descriptions, or algebraic rules. They should be comfortable translating back and forth between the table, graph, and symbolic model.

The first task presents a different context, in which is embedded the same exponential growth pattern students have been investigating. Tasks 2, 3, and 4 are written about familiar contexts. Task 4 compares exponential growth with linear growth, graphically and symbolically. Task 5 lends itself to extensions about other rules for how exponential expressions behave, if this is appropriate for your students.

One way to summarize the results would be to give each group of students a transparency and overhead marker, and ask them to be responsible for noting and explaining (to the whole class) their answers for one particular task.

1. **a.** 100
   b. 1,000
   c. 10,000
   d.

Digits	1	2	3	4	5	6	7	8	9
Codes	10	10^2	10^3	10^4	10^5	10^6	10^7	10^8	10^9

   e. $NEXT = NOW \times 10$, starting with 10
   f. $C = 10^D$

Lesson 5 — *Looking Back*

Many interesting and important patterns of change involve quantities changing as time passes. Populations of animals, bacteria, and plants grow over time. Drugs in the blood and radioactive chemicals in the environment decay over time. Most people hope that their bank savings account grows quickly over time. In many of the examples, the change is modeled well by exponential rules of the form $y = a(b^x)$.

When you find an exponential model for change in a variable, that model can be used to make useful predictions of events in the future. Test your understanding of exponential models on the following problems.

1. Code numbers are used in hundreds of ways every day—from student and social security numbers to product codes in stores and membership numbers in clubs.

   a. How many different 2-digit codes can be created using the digits 0, 1, 2, 3, 4, 5, 6, 7, 8, and 9 (for example, 33, 54, 72 or 02)?

   b. How many different 3-digit codes can be created using those digits?

   c. How many different 4-digit codes can be created using those digits?

   d. Using any patterns you may see, complete a table like the one below showing the relation between number of digits and number of different possible codes.

Number of Digits	1	2	3	4	5	6	7	8	9
Number of Codes									

   e. Write an equation using *NOW* and *NEXT* to describe the pattern in the table of Part d.

   f. Write an equation that shows how to calculate the number of codes C for any number of digits D used.

g. Kitchenware stores stock thousands of different items. How many digits would you need in order to have code numbers for up to 8,500 different items?

h. How will your answers to Parts a through f change if the codes were to begin with a single letter of the alphabet (A, B, C, ... , or Z) as in A23 or S75?

2. In one professional golf tournament, the money a player wins depends on her finishing place in the standings. The first place finisher wins $\frac{1}{2}$ of the $1,048,576 in total prize money. The second place finisher wins $\frac{1}{2}$ of what is left; then the third place finisher wins $\frac{1}{2}$ of what is left, and so on.

U.S. Women's Open Champion Annika Sorenstam

a. What fraction of the *total* prize money is won

- by the second place finisher?
- by the third place finisher?
- by the fourth place finisher?

b. Write a rule showing how to calculate the share of the prize money won by the player finishing in *n*th place, for any *n*.

c. Make a table showing the actual prize money in dollars (not fraction of the total prize money) won by each of the first ten place finishers.

Place	1	2	3	4	5	6	7	8	9	10
Prize (dollars)										

d. Write a rule showing how to calculate the actual prize money in dollars won by the player finishing in place *n*. How much money would be won by the 15th place finisher?

e. How would your answers to Parts a through d change if

- the total prize money were reduced to $500,000?
- the fraction used were $\frac{1}{4}$ instead of $\frac{1}{2}$?

f. When prize monies are awarded using either fraction, $\frac{1}{2}$ or $\frac{1}{4}$, could the tournament organizers end up giving away more than the stated total prize amount? Explain your response.

3. Growth of protected wild animal populations like the Alaskan wolves can be simulated as follows:

1. **g.** A four-digit code would allow for coding 10,000 items.

   h. All of the answers to Parts a–c would be multiplied by 26. The *NOW-NEXT* equation would be *NEXT = NOW* × 10, starting with 26. The exponential equation would be $C = 26(10^D)$.

2. **a.** ■ The second-place finisher wins $\frac{1}{4}$ of the total prize money.

   ■ The third-place finisher wins $\frac{1}{8}$ of the total prize money.

   ■ The fourth-place finisher wins $\frac{1}{16}$ of the total prize money.

   b. $P = \left(\frac{1}{2}\right)^n$

   c.

Place	1	2	3	4	5	6	7	8	9	10
Prize $	524,288	262,144	131,072	65,536	32,768	16,384	8,192	4,096	2,048	1,024

   d. $P = \$1,048,576\left(\frac{1}{2}\right)^n$
   The 15th-place finisher would win $32.

   e. ■ Reducing the prize money to $500,000:

   a–b. No change

   c.

Place	1	2	3	4	5	6	7	8	9	10
Prize $	250,000	125,000	62,500	31,250	15,625	7,812.50	3,906.25	1,953.12	976.56	488.28

   d. $P = \$500,000\left(\frac{1}{2}\right)^n$
   The 15th-place finisher would win $15.25.

   ■ Using a fraction of $\frac{1}{4}$:

   a. The second-, third-, and fourth-place finishers would win $\frac{1}{16}$, $\frac{1}{64}$, and $\frac{1}{256}$ of the total prize money, respectively.

   b. $P = \left(\frac{1}{4}\right)^n$

   c.

Place	1	2	3	4	5	6	7	8	9	10
Prize $	262,144	65,536	16,384	4,096	1,024	256	64	16	4	1

   d. $P = \$1,048,576\left(\frac{1}{4}\right)^n$
   The 15th-place finisher would win nothing.

   f. No. The first-place finisher wins half (or one-fourth) of the total prize money. The second-place finisher wins half (or one-fourth) of the prize money *that remains*. Each successive finisher wins half (or one-fourth) of what remains, so the tournament organizers cannot give away more than the total prize amount. (Observant students may realize that under the $\frac{1}{4}$ scheme, only a third of the money would be given away.)

3. **a.** It seems fair because there are some males and some females and some that do not survive. This seems to be realistic. However, it does not seem reasonable that this pattern would repeat itself exactly every time. Perhaps one time there would be all males, or all females, and other times a mixture. Maybe all the pups live in certain litters, but in others more of the offspring do not survive. This model also does not take into consideration lifespans or how many life-bearing years a female may have.

    b.

Stage	0	1	2	3	4	5	6	7	8
Wolf Count	4	12	36	108	324	972	2,916	8,748	26,244

    c. One linear model is $y = 2,296.5x - 4,812.4$.
    The exponential model is $y = 4(3)^x$.
    The exponential model is a perfect fit for the data. A scatterplot of the data shows a linear relationship would not be a good model.

    d. The typical patterns are very helpful in deciding which model is best. If the data are linear, the scatterplot will form a fairly straight line and the table will have a constant difference. If the data are exponential, the graph will curve, and the difference will increase or decrease.

    e. There are more and more wolves producing pups.

    f. The numbers would stay the same for stages 0 through 5. After that, the growth rate would slow down because a certain number would be subtracted each year.

■ Assume that the population starts with 4 adult wolves, 2 male and 2 female.

■ Assume that each year, each female produces 4 pups who survive (assume 2 male and 2 female survivors in each litter). Thus, at the end of the first year there will be 12 wolves (6 male and 6 female). At the end of the next year, there will be 36 wolves (18 male and 18 female), and so on.

a. In what ways does this seem a reasonable simulation of the population growth? What modeling assumptions seem unlikely to be accurate?

b. Make a table showing the number of wolves at each stage (assume no deaths).

Stage	0	1	2	3	4	5	6	7	8
Wolf Count	4	12	36						

c. Use your calculator or computer software to find both linear and exponential models for the data in your table. Compare the fit of the two models to the data pattern. Explain which you feel is the better model.

d. What patterns of change will occur in the graph and in the table of values of a linear model? Of an exponential model? How do those typical patterns help you to decide which model is best in Part c?

e. Why does the wolf population grow at a faster rate as time passes?

f. How would the numbers in your table change if you assumed that wolves lived only 5 years? How does that affect the growth rate of the population?

4. In a study of ways that young people handle money, four high school students were given $200 at the start of a school year. They were asked to keep records of what they did with that money for the next 10 months.

■ Cheryl put the money away for safe keeping and worked so she could add 10% to the total every month.

■ James put his money in a box at home and added $10 each month.

■ Jennifer put her money in a box at home and spent $10 each month.

■ Delano put his money in a box at home. At the start of each month, he took out 10% of his balance for spending in that month.

Unit 6

a. The following four graphs show possible patterns for the savings of the students over time. Match each student's saving or spending pattern to the graph that best fits it. Explain your reasoning.

i.

ii.

iii.

iv.

b. Match each graph from Part a to the type of rule you would expect to produce it, $y = a + bx$ or $y = a(b^x)$. Then explain what you can expect for values of a and b in each rule.

5. If x is a whole number, calculations like 2^x, 3^x or $\left(\frac{1}{2}\right)^x$ involve many multiplications. For example, $2^{10} = 2 \times 2 \times 2 \times 2 \times 2 \times 2 \times 2 \times 2 \times 2 \times 2$. On a calculator, you can reduce the number of operations by using an exponential key such as 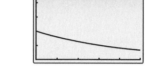 . What could you do on a basic four-function calculator that has no exponential key? Answer Parts a through d assuming you have only number keys, an = (ENTER) key, and the multiplication key (✕).

a. How could you calculate 2^{10} with fewer than nine ✕ keystrokes (no addition allowed)?

b. How could you use the fact that $2^{10} = 1,024$ to calculate 2^{20} with only one ✕ keystroke?

c. How could you use the fact that $2^{10} = 1,024$ and $2^5 = 32$ to calculate 2^{15} with only one ✕ keystroke?

d. How could you calculate 3^{12} in several different ways with only the ✕ key?

e. How could you calculate $3^{12} \times 3^8$ with only an exponential key?

f. Look back at the results of your work on Parts a–e for a pattern that will complete calculations of this type: $2^m \times 2^n = 2^?$ for any nonnegative, whole-number values of n and m. Explain the rule your group invents using the meaning of exponents.

g. Explain why the rule you came up with in Part f also applies when the base 2 is replaced by 3 or 6 or 1.5 or any other positive number.

4. a.   **i.** Jennifer, because this graph shows a constant decrease

      ii. James, because the graph shows a constant increase

      iii. Cheryl, because the graph shows exponential growth

      iv. Delano, because the graph shows the pattern of exponential decay

  b.   **i.** $y = a + bx$; a would be \$200 and b would be -10.

      ii. $y = a + bx$; a would be \$200 and b would be 10.

      iii. $y = a(b^x)$; a would be \$200 and b would be 1.10.

      iv. $y = a(b^x)$; a would be \$200 and b would be 0.90.

5. a. One possible response is $4 \times 4 \times 4 \times 4 \times 4$, then $\boxed{\text{ENTER}}$.

  b. $2^{10} = 1{,}024$, $2^{20} = 2^{10} \times 2^{10} = 1{,}024 \times 1{,}024$

  c. $2^{10} = 1{,}024$, $2^5 = 32$, $2^{15} = 2^{10} \times 2^5 = 1{,}024 \times 32$

  d. Possible responses are:

$3^4 = 81$, $3^{12} = 3^4 \times 3^4 \times 3^4 = 81 \times 81 \times 81$

$3^2 = 9$, $3^2 \times 3^2 \times 3^2 \times 3^2 \times 3^2 \times 3^2 = 9 \times 9 \times 9 \times 9 \times 9 \times 9$

  e. $3^{12} \times 3^8 = 3^{20}$

NOTE: Encourage students to try fractional or decimal exponents as well.

---

  f. $2^n \times 2^m = 2^{m+n}$

  g. The rule applies to all bases. Exponentiation follows the same patterns regardless of the specific base. To raise any number to the nth power means to use that number n times as a factor; to raise any number to the mth power means to use that number m times as a factor. Therefore, to multiply any number to the nth power times that number to the mth power means that you use that number as a factor $m + n$ times.

Unit 6

Unit 6 Summary

Assessments 231–248

CONSTRUCTING A MATH
TOOLKIT: This Checkpoint
could be used as a guide to
write a unit summary
(Teaching Master 200).

SHARE AND SUMMARIZE full-class discussion

Checkpoint

See Teaching Masters 175a–175b.

ⓐ ■ The patterns in data tables show that the differences in the function values are not constant. If the differences in the x values are constant, then the y values in the table should have a constant *ratio*.

■ The patterns in graphs or scatterplots show curves approaching the x-axis as an asymptote if $0 < b < 1$ or rising quickly if $b > 1$.

■ Exponential models have one of the variables as an exponent. There is a factor increase or decrease in the situation; that is, the amount of change to a *NEXT* value depends on the *NOW* value.

ⓑ ■ $y = a(b^x)$

■ $NEXT = NOW \times b$, starting at a.

■ The a is the starting value and b is the factor increase or decrease.

ⓒ By looking at the rules, you can determine if the exponential model is increasing $(b > 1)$ or decreasing $(0 < b < 1)$. The value of a gives the y-intercept (starting value).

ⓓ Exponential models curve, whereas the linear models are straight lines. Linear models do not have variables as exponents.

ⓔ Responses will vary. Students should mention examples of both increasing and decreasing exponential functions.

JOURNAL ENTRY: Consider all of the various situations that have been modeled with exponential functions, both growth models and decay models. Write a letter to the math department explaining to them your perception of the value of this particular unit to students, to consumers, and to educated citizens.

APPLY individual task

On Your Own

See Unit 6 Summary Masters

Responses will vary. Above all, preparation of this unit summary should be something that is useful to the individual student. You may wish to have students use the unit summary masters for "Exponential Models" to help them organize the information.

See Assessment Resources, pages 231–248.

Checkpoint

Exponential models can be used to solve problems in many different situations.

ⓐ In deciding whether an exponential model will be useful, what hints do you get from

- the patterns in data tables?
- the patterns in graphs or scatterplots?
- the nature of the situation and the variables involved?

ⓑ Exponential models, like linear models, can be expressed by an equation relating x and y values and by an equation relating *NOW* and *NEXT* y values.

- Write a general rule for an exponential model, $y = \ldots$.
- Write a general equation relating *NOW* and *NEXT* for an exponential model.
- What do the parts of the equations tell you about the situation being modeled?

ⓒ How can the rule for an exponential model be used to predict the pattern in a table or graph of that model?

ⓓ How are exponential models different from linear models?

ⓔ What real situations would you use to illustrate exponential change for someone who did not know what those patterns are like and used for?

Be prepared to share your ideas, equations, and examples with the whole class.

▶ On Your Own

Write, in outline form, a summary of the most important mathematical concepts and methods developed in this unit. Organize your summary so that it can be used as a quick reference in future units and courses.

Looking Back, Looking Ahead

▶Reflecting on Mathematical Content

This unit examined properties of a very common and important family of algebraic relations—those that model patterns of compound growth and decay. The symbolic rules for those exponential relations are based on the form $y = a(b^x)$, and those rules produce several fundamental patterns in associated tables and graphs.

By now students should be able to identify situations in which exponential models are appropriate, to construct symbolic rules that match data patterns and given problem conditions, and to use those rules to deduce new information about the related variables. They should recognize the characteristic graph shapes for exponential growth and decay relations, the $NEXT = NOW \times b$ pattern of change in outputs as inputs increase in steps of 1, and the connections among those graph and table patterns and symbolic rules.

In finding exponential models, students should be comfortable using technology-based curve-fitting for given data and reasoning from given problem conditions. In solving problems about those exponential relations, students should be adept at using graphs, tables, and reasoning about the equations involved.

Using graphing calculators or computer software as tools, the rules of formal symbol manipulation are less important for practical applications of exponential relations, so only a few simple properties of exponents were developed. Students' knowledge of the formal properties for exponents and their ability to use them in reasoning will continue to grow throughout this curriculum. In particular, in the "Power Models" unit of *Contemporary Mathematics in Context* Course 2, students will extend rules for operating with exponential expressions to those involving negative and fractional exponents. Students will encounter exponential patterns of change in other units, including "Simulation Models" of Course 1, "Patterns in Chance" of Course 2, "Symbol Sense and Algebraic Reasoning" and "Discrete Models of Change" in Course 3, and are mastered in Course 4 in "Logarithmic Functions and Data Models" and in "Functions and Symbolic Reasoning."

The algebra strand of this curriculum continues to unfold in Course 2. Matrices, matrix operations, and their properties are examined in "Matrix Models." The algebra of coordinate systems and geometric transformations are introduced in "Patterns of Location, Shape, and Size." Direct and inverse variation power models and the full quadratic model are developed in "Power Models." In Course 3, "Multiple-Variable Models" develops methods, including linear programming, for dealing with situations involving several variables and constraints. The unit "Symbol Sense and Algebraic Reasoning" formalizes important ideas of functions and elevates methods of reasoning with symbolic forms themselves. The unit "Families of Functions" reviews and extends students' ability to recognize different function patterns and transformations of those patterns. The "Discrete Models of Change" unit uses recursion to introduce and develop important ideas of arithmetic and geometric sequences. Algebraic representation and symbolic reasoning permeate the Course 4 units where students study rates of change, logarithmic and trigonometric functions and equations, polynomial and rational functions, parametric equations, and complex numbers. Algebraic representation itself is woven into all of the units of the *Contemporary Mathematics in Context* curriculum.

Unit 6 Assessment

Unit 6

Notes continued
from page T420

LAUNCH full-class discussion

If students have trouble understanding the graph, you might want to ask, "What are the variables in this graph?" Students need to articulate that they are tracking the number of people who know the rumor against time. Your students may seem to know which pattern is applicable but still may not be able to say clearly what the pattern means. Be wary of students' answers with phrases like "It grows faster and faster." Maybe they think the actual story is growing (as rumors tend to do), not the number of recipients of the story. Encourage students to make their arguments clearly. For example, for the pattern in Graph II, they should say that the number of people aware of the rumor increases at the same rate every hour.

Think About This Situation

See Teaching Master 162.

ⓐ Graph III indicates that the rumor spreads slowly at first, then increases more quickly as time passes. Graph II shows a constant rate of spread. Graph I suggests that the rumor spreads more quickly initially, but then the rate decreases.

ⓑ Graph I might be a good model for this situation. At 5:00 many people hear the report, but then the rate of spread decreases.

ⓒ Graph III models this situation best, because at first only a few people know, but as time passes the rate of spread increases because the number of people spreading the rumor increases.

Teaching Notes *continued*

Notes continued from page T426

JOURNAL ENTRY: The Checkpoint questions focus on the patterns in the table and the shape of the graph. If you think it appropriate for your students, you may want them to begin to connect the symbols to these ideas. Following is a suggestion for a quick journal entry that can help assess how students are making the connections. Place these diagrams on the board and ask students to complete them, or have the students create similar diagrams with their own ideas.

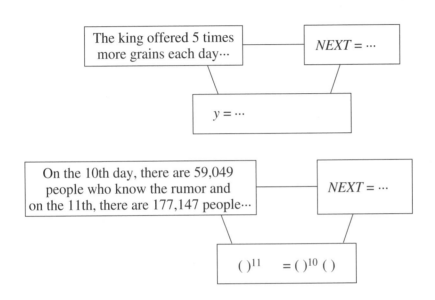

Notes continued from page T428

5. c. Tables and graphs for two starting values, 30 and 100, are shown here. The graphs appear similar because the windows are different.

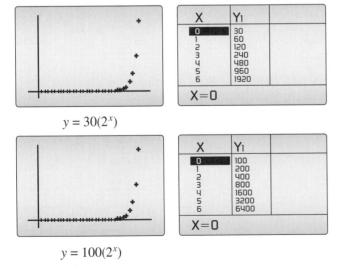

X	Y1
0	30
1	60
2	120
3	240
4	480
5	960
6	1920

X=0

$y = 30(2^x)$

X	Y1
0	100
1	200
2	400
3	800
4	1600
5	3200
6	6400

X=0

$y = 100(2^x)$

Unit 6

Teaching Notes *continued*

Notes continued from page T430

c I $\quad y = 2^x$

II $\quad y = 3(2^x)$

d Each rule is of the form $y = a(b^x)$, where a is the y value when $x = 0$ and b is the rate of growth (in this case, 2). A person with some knowledge of exponential rules would know that because $b = 2$, each successive y value is doubled.

JOURNAL ENTRY: Write a poem that describes exponential growth models. Be creative and imaginative! (You may want to display some of these, with students' permission, of course.)

NOTE: After the Checkpoint answers have been shared, you may want to check understanding by making up a few examples (or having students make up examples) such as

$y = 6^x \qquad\qquad NEXT = NOW \times$ _____, starting at _____

$y = 3 \cdot 2^x \qquad\quad NEXT = NOW \times$ _____, starting at _____

$y =$ _____ $\qquad NEXT = NOW \times 3$, starting at 2

Being wise in the use of the calculator or computer is important, too. This is a good time to ask students to evaluate $3 \cdot 2^2$ and $(3 \cdot 2)^2$. Why does the technology give different answers? Try $3 \cdot 2^0$ and $(3 \cdot 2)^0$. Why are these different?

Notes continued from page T435

Reflecting

1. Strep throat starts by a single bacterium, usually picked up from another individual. The bacterium multiplies rapidly until it affects the health of the individual. The symptoms of the infection are usually a high fever and sore throat. The bacteria are destroyed and eventually wiped out by an oral antibiotic prescribed by a doctor.

2. Responses will vary for this task. Responses should address such issues as the number of people initially called, the number of people each person has to call thereafter, and the total time that all of this will take.

3. **a.** When there is a constant difference between x values, there is a constant ratio between the corresponding y values. The graph curves up, indicating this pattern.

    b. Linear models change at a constant rate while exponential models change at a continually changing rate. Graphs of linear models are straight lines, while graphs of exponential models curve.

4. Responses will vary. Some students may prefer the $NEXT = NOW \times 2$ model because it explains what change is taking place. Others may like the rule $y = 2^x$ because it gives more flexibility and power, especially when using a graphing calculator or computer software.

Teaching Notes *continued*

Notes continued
from page T444

JOURNAL ENTRY: After the Checkpoint, you may wish to ask students to reflect on the different exponential decay situations they have encountered, either in a class discussion or as a journal entry.

Write on the board:

$y = 27 \cdot \left(\frac{2}{3}\right)^x$ the height of the bouncing ball in Investigation 1

$y = 25 \cdot \left(\frac{2}{5}\right)^x$ the height of the bouncing ball in the "On Your Own" following Investigation 1

$y = 1 \cdot \left(\frac{8}{9}\right)^x$ the area remaining in the carpet

Have students answer the following:

How do the symbols relate to the patterns of change? Which graph will show the fastest rate of decay? (Students have to be able to compare fraction sizes to do this.) Choose a different decay factor, write a situation to go with that factor, and explore how the value of y changes.

Notes continued
from page T448

1. **b.** On the fourth bounce the height is less than 1 foot.

L1	L2	L3
0	10	-------
1	5	
2	2.5	
3	1.25	
4	.625	
5	.3125	
6	.15625	

L2={10,5,2.5,1. …

c. $NEXT = \left(\frac{1}{2}\right)NOW$, starting at 10

$y = 10\left(\frac{1}{2}\right)^x$

d. The values in the table will be twice as large. The points will be twice as high but that pattern will have the same shape. The equations will have 20s in place of the 10s.

Teaching Notes continued

Notes continued from page T455

ⓑ Without counting any interest, the first plan will yield $20,000 after 20 years. Students will be wary of choosing this plan, because it is too "obvious." They probably will not know how to calculate interest, but they may well have some idea how this works. Encourage them to talk about interest; who pays it, and why? Ask if anyone knows what is meant by *compound interest*. The best that can be expected at this stage is that students are interested to see if $10,000 invested can grow to be more than $20,000 in the stated period of time.

ⓒ Take any guesses and note them on the board. You can return later to see whose guess was closest. (The correct answer is $21,589.24.)

EXPLORE small-group investigation

INVESTIGATION 1 ▶ Just Like Money in the Bank

Some students will have trouble with the "1" in "1.08," the rate of compounding interest in this activity. They have seen this idea before in Unit 2, "Patterns of Change," but may not remember it. You might want to discuss the introductory paragraph for the investigation with the whole class or with individual students as necessary, and have students express the interest calculation in words:

balance next year = what I start with + 8% of what I start with
or *NEXT* = *NOW* + 8% of *NOW*
or *NEXT* = 108% of *NOW*

Many students see the logic in using 108% as the factor to find how the money is growing, but are less comfortable with 1.08.

Notes continued from page T456

ⓑ A curve that increases at an increasing rate

ⓒ If the interest rate changes, the value of b will be different. For example, if the interest rate was 12%, then b would be 1.12 rather than 1.08. If the initial investment changes, the value of a will change. You may wish to make some numerical problems so that you are sure students can change the rules to match new situations.

ⓓ The increase is larger because you are earning money on the interest as well as the principal.

JOURNAL ENTRY: You may want to follow up student summaries of the Checkpoint with a return to the lottery problem. Start a list describing similar situations:

$10,000 invested at 8%, compounded annually for 10 years
$10,000 invested at 12%, compounded annually for 10 years
$10,000 invested at 1%, compounded monthly for 10 years

Have each group make up a situation to add to the list, varying the rate, or the interest period, or the total time. Then, with a partner, students could investigate and compare two situations from the list, writing in their journals what they find.

Teaching Notes *continued*

Notes continued from page T459

Reflecting

1. In both cases, the amount of increase each year is based on the current amount. Generally speaking, the base rate of increase tends to be somewhat constant.

2. If you wish to maximize your return, the first offer is the better choice. In this savings plan, you earn $20 the first year and this money is then combined with your initial investment of $500 to yield $520. In the second year, you earn 4% of $520, or $20.80. Each subsequent year your earnings grow, as does your balance.

   In the second plan, you also earn $20 the first year. However, this earning is never improved upon. Your balance increases, but the amount you earn does not increase.

Notes continued from page T460

3. **a.** The pattern of change is most likely to be exponential. A car decreases in value very quickly at the beginning and then depreciates at a slower rate as it gets older.

   b. Responses will vary based upon student's choices.

   c. Responses will vary.

   d. Have students discuss their findings and their reasons for choosing one car over another.

   NOTE: For this task it may help if you have a copy of the book of car values for students to use in class. (The Kelly Blue Book is available on the Internet at http://www.kbb.com or may be purchased at a store that has a large selection of magazines.)

See Assessment Resources, pages 219–224.

Notes continued from page T462

1. **Collect Data** Answers will vary; the following is given as a sample.

Stage Number	0	1	2	3	4	5	6	7
Kernels Left	200	146	116	82	61	49	33	25

2. **Display Data** Our sample (*stage number*, *kernels left*) data are displayed below.

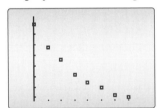

```
WINDOW
Xmin =-1
Xmax =8
Xscl =1
Ymin =20
Ymax =220
Yscl =25
Xres =1
```

3. **Analyze Data** The data table shows that the number of kernels of corn is decreasing, but not at a constant rate. The decreases are greater initially and gradually become smaller with each stage. The graph shows a curve where as x increases, the values for y decrease. The curve drops quickly at first, and then it slowly approaches the x-axis.

   Some students may notice that about 25% of the kernels are being removed each time, which means that 75% remain. This may help them come up with the model $y = 200(0.75)^x$. Many students may find it very difficult to think of the type of model they should start with, but usually they will try some form of exponential function. When they use the calculator, they should find a model similar to $y = 200(0.75)^x$. Students should make the connection between the number of kernels of corn that they started with (which is 200) and a. Also, they should make some connection between 75% and the base b.

Teaching Notes *continued*

Notes continued from page T463

Experiment 3

1. **Collect Data** The following is given as a sample. Please note that it is important to have the different groups use the same type of tacks if they are to compare answers.

Stage Number	0	1	2	3	4	5	6
Number of Tacks	200	84	35	16	6	2	1

2. **Display Data** Our sample (*stage number*, *number of tacks*) data are displayed below.

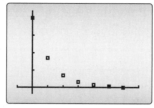
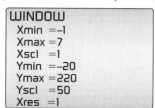

```
WINDOW
Xmin =–1
Xmax =7
Xscl =1
Ymin =–20
Ymax =220
Yscl =50
Xres =1
```

3. **Analyze Data** The data table shows that the number of tacks is decreasing, but not at a constant rate. The decreases are greater initially and then gradually become smaller with each stage. The graph shows a curve where as *x* increases, the values for *y* decrease. The curve drops quickly at first, and then slowly approaches the *x*-axis. The exponential model representing the data is $y = 209(0.41)^x$.

4. **Apply Model** One possible question is:
    What percent of the original tacks is left after 4 stages?

Notes continued from page T464

d If the value of *b* is greater than 1, the problem situations represent exponential growth, such as bacterial growth or money increasing in a savings account.

e ■ Dividing the paper plate differently would cause *b*, and thus the rates of change, to be different. This would mean that the data in the tables and graphs would either be changing faster or slower, but the basic patterns of increase or decrease would be the same.

■ Changing point length would change the likelihood of a tack landing point down. This would cause *b*, and thus the rate of change, to be different. This would mean that the data in the tables and graphs would either be changing faster or slower, but the basic patterns of increase or decrease would be the same.

JOURNAL ENTRY: As an informal assessment or a journal entry, write several equations on the board. For example:

$$y = 10(1.2)^x \qquad y = 10(1.5)^x \qquad y = 10(0.9)^x \qquad y = 10(0.5)^x$$

The students can then write:

■ an interpretation in terms of real objects;

■ which equations represent decay and which growth;

■ what proportion is added each time for the growth equations;

■ which equation represents the fastest growth;

■ what proportion is removed each time from decay equations;

■ which equation represents the fastest decay.

Teaching Notes continued

Notes continued
from page T471

2. Responses will vary. The following are examples.

a.

x	0	1	2	3	4	5	6	7	8
y	5	10	20	40	80	160	320	640	1,280

The initial value is 5, and the common ratio of 2 gives an exponential increase.

b.

x	0	1	2	3	4	5	6	7	8
y	5	15	45	135	405	1,215	3,645	10,935	32,805

The initial value is 5, and the common ratio of 3 gives an exponential increase greater than the one shown in Part a.

c.

x	0	1	2	3	4	5	6	7	8
y	5	8	11	14	17	20	23	26	29

The initial value is 5, and the constant difference of 3 gives a linear increase.

d.

x	0	1	2	3	4	5	6	7	8
y	25	22.5	20.25	18.225	16.403	14.762	13.286	11.957	10.762

The initial value is 25, and the common ratio of 0.9 gives an exponential decrease.

e.

x	0	1	2	3	4	5	6	7	8
y	25	23	21	19	17	15	13	11	9

The initial value is 25, and the constant difference of -2 gives a linear decrease.

3. a.

x	0	1	2	3	4	5
y	10	20	30	40	50	60

$y = 10 + 10x$

b.

x	0	1	2	3	4	5
y	10	20	40	80	160	320

$y = 10(2^x)$

Unit 7 Simulation Models

UNIT OVERVIEW The "Simulation Models" unit introduces students to simulation and to the idea of probability distributions. Important probabilistic concepts explored include the Law of Large Numbers, the geometric distribution, the collector's problem, and the idea of independent events.

Simulation is the modeling of a probabilistic situation using random devices such as coins, spinners, tables of random digits, or computers. Simulation is useful throughout instruction on probability. Setting up a simulation helps students clarify their assumptions about such things as whether trials are independent. Simulation helps develop students' intuition about probabilistic events. And, perhaps most importantly, students who have been introduced to simulation have a feeling of control over probability. They know that they can get the answer to any probability problem that arises.

Unit 7 Objectives

- To design and carry out simulations in order to estimate answers to questions about probability
- To use the Law of Large Numbers to understand situations involving chance
- To use tables of random digits in order to perform simulations and to understand some properties of random digits
- To understand the concept of a probability distribution and how an approximate probability distribution can be constructed using simulation in order to understand situations involving chance

Simulation Models

483

Solving Probability Problems

There are four ways to estimate probabilities, although not all methods work with all problems.

■ Use mathematical formulas or theory.

■ Examine the population.

■ Examine a sample from the population.

■ Simulate the situation using a physically different but mathematically equivalent model; that is, a model whose outcomes have the same probabilities as the outcomes in the situation.

For example, in Investigation 1 (pages 485–489), students will try to discover the probability that a two-child family has one boy and one girl.

■ To solve this problem using mathematical methods, you might list all possible families of two children: older boy and his younger sister, older boy and his younger brother, older girl and her younger brother, older girl and her younger sister. Two out of these four possible families have one boy and one girl. If you can make the assumption that these four possible families occur equally often, then the desired probability is $\frac{2}{4}$ or $\frac{1}{2}$.

■ To solve this problem by examining the population, you could call up the United States Bureau of the Census and ask if they have this information available from the last census of United States families. If so, you would have the best possible answer; in fact, it should give you the exact answer for families in the United States at the time of the Census. You don't need to make any assumptions.

■ To solve this problem by examining a sample, you would take a survey of two-child families and observe the number that have one boy and one girl. If you could observe a large number of families, this would be a very good method of estimating the answer to your question.

■ To solve this problem using simulation, you could write the word "boy" on a card and the word "girl" on another card, place the cards in a hat, and then draw one. If it says "boy," the first child in the family would be a boy. If it says "girl," the first child in the family would be a girl. Replace the card and draw a second card to represent the birth of the second child. After performing many trials of this simulation, you would have a good idea of the percentage of two-child families that have exactly one boy and one girl. This simulation assumes that boys and girls are equally likely and that this probability does not change depending on the gender of the first child (that is, the events are independent).

If you would like to learn how to solve most of the problems in this unit theoretically, see the book "Fifty Challenging Problems in Probability with Solutions" by Frederick Mosteller (Dover, 1989).

See Masters 176a–176c for Maintenance tasks that students can work after Lesson 1.

▶Misconceptions about Probability and the Importance of Simulation

People appear to have unreliable intuition when it comes to many probabilistic events. Many students, and adults as well, believe that a person who has rolled a pair of dice several times without getting doubles is more likely to roll doubles on the next roll. (The person is "due" to get doubles.) Such misconceptions are confronted head-on in this unit. One of the most important lessons we can teach students about probability is that they should be suspicious of their first impulse when analyzing random events.

J. Michael Shaughnessy in "Probability and Statistics" (*The Mathematics Teacher*, Volume 86, March 1993, pages 244–248) gives this "strong recommendation" for the teaching of simulation:

> The technique of simulation is a tremendous problem-solving tool that can help change students' conceptions. It is also reassuring to be able to say, "I don't have any idea what is going on here, but maybe we can simulate it." Even if we have already worked out a theoretical solution to a probability problem, simulation can help us to confirm or challenge our solution. It is important to encourage students to gather data physically or with such concrete-simulation objects as spinners, dice, and random-number charts prior to engaging them in computer simulations. Students must "get a feel" for conducting experiments and simulations themselves before they are dazzled by a computer simulation.

See the following for another good introduction to the research that documents students' misconceptions about probability and what to do about them.

Joan Garfield and Andrew Ahlgren, "Difficulties in Learning Basic Concepts in Probability and Statistics: Implications for Research," *Journal for Research in Mathematics Education* 19 (1988: 44–63).

Unit 7

Probability Distributions

A probability distribution is the complete picture of a probabilistic situation and usually the best way to organize the analysis.

Here is a traditional probability problem:

In a family of six children, what is the probability that exactly five are girls?

When presented with a problem like this, the typical student says something like, "But I do understand probability, I just don't know which formula to use." Even if the student does get the right formula, he or she may make an arithmetic mistake and report an answer like 0.37. The student has no idea that this answer cannot possibly be correct because he or she has no estimation skills in probability.

The probability distribution for the situation of having six children appears below. In this unit, students construct distributions like these by simulating a family of six children (by flipping a coin six times).

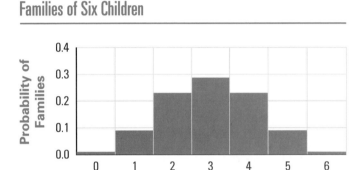

Families of Six Children

Students learn far more from a probability distribution than from the limited question asked above. They build intuition that guides the analysis of future probabilistic situations. Students who develop pictures in their heads like the one above or who are capable of generating probability distributions by simulation will have real power over probabilistic situations.

Overview of Lessons

Lesson 1 is motivated by studying the attempt in China to limit population growth. Students examine various plans that could be adopted and still give parents a reasonable expectation of having a boy. Students learn to simulate situations in which the probability of a given event is 0.5, to construct frequency distributions and to display histograms of these situations. The idea of independent events is reinforced. Students learn that it is impossible to change the percentage of boys in the population by having some clever "stopping rule." For example, if every family has children until they get a boy and then stop, the proportion of boys remains 0.5. This result is contrary to most people's intuition.

Lesson 2 is motivated by the "collector's problem" of how many boxes of cereal one might have to buy in order to get all of the different prizes offered. Students learn to use single random digits to simulate situations, and they explore the nature of random digits.

Lesson 3 is motivated by the problem of the mathematical reasoning that may have lead Major League Baseball to switch from a best-of-five league playoff series to a best-of-seven series. Students learn that the better team is more likely to be the winner of a long series than a short series—a fundamental result in probability related to the Law of Large Numbers. Students expand their ability to use random digits to simulate probabilistic situations.

Unit 7 Planning Guide

Lesson Objectives	MORE Assignments	Suggested Pacing	Materials
Lesson 1 *Simulating Chance Situations* • To simulate situations where the probability of a success is 0.5 • To display the results of a simulation in a frequency table and histogram • To explore the idea of independent events • To explore the waiting-time (geometric) distribution • To explore how the number of trials in a simulation affect the estimated probability	**page 491** **Modeling:** 1 or 2, and 3* (Be sure Task 3 is assigned, because it prepares students for Lesson 3.) **Organizing:** Choice of 1 or 2* **Reflecting:** 1 and choice of 2 or 5* **Extending:** Choose one*	4 days	• Teaching Resources 177–181 • Assessment Resources 249–254 • 1 coin per student • 1 die per student • Each group: Deck of cards, Almanac for World Series records • *Optional*: RAP Book Exercise Set 19
Lesson 2 *Estimating Expected Values and Probabilities* • To use single random digits to simulate probabilistic situations • To explore the nature of random digits • To explore the collector's problem and the binomial distribution • To compare shapes of probability distributions	**after page 502** Students can begin Organizing Task 1 or Reflecting Task 2 from p. 505 <hr>**page 505** **Modeling:** 1 and 2 **Organizing:** 4, and 1 or 3* **Reflecting:** 3 and choice of one* **Extending:** Choose one*	4 days	• Teaching Resources 176a–176c, 182–190 • Assessment Resources 255–260 • COLLECT software • *Optional*: Deck of cards per group, Box of cereal that contains one of a set of prizes
Lesson 3 *Simulation and the Law of Large Numbers* • To use paired random digits to simulate probabilistic situations • To understand that with a larger number of trials the estimated probability tends to be closer to the true probability than with a smaller number of trials (the Law of Large Numbers) • To have more practice simulating binomial situations	**page 519** **Modeling:** 1 and 2 **Organizing:** 1 **Reflecting:** 1 and 2 **Extending:** Choose one*	5 days	• Teaching Resources 191–192 • Assessment Resources 261–266 • *Optional*: RAP Book Exercise Set 20
Lesson 4 *Looking Back* • To review the major objectives of the unit		2–3 days (includes testing)	• Teaching Resource 193 • Unit Summary Master • Assessment Resources 267–282

* When choice is indicated, it is important to leave the choice to the student.
Note: *It is best if Organizing tasks are discussed as a whole class after they have been assigned as homework.*

Simulating Chance Situations

In some cultures, it is customary for a bride to live with her husband's family. Therefore, couples who have no sons and whose daughters all marry will have no one to care for them in their old age.

Customs of a culture and the size of its population often lead to issues that are hard to resolve. China had a population of over 1,200,000,000 in 2000. In an effort to reduce the growth of its population, the government of China instituted a policy to limit families to one child. The policy has been very unpopular among rural Chinese who depend on sons to carry on the family farming.

Think About This Situation

The situation described above raises many interesting mathematical questions as well as societal ones.

a In a country where parents are allowed to have only one child, what is the probability that their one child will be a son? What is the probability they will not have a son? What assumption(s) are you making when you answer these questions?

b If each pair of Chinese parents really had only one child, do you think the population would increase, decrease, or stay the same? Explain your reasoning.

c Describe several alternative plans that the government of China might use to control population growth. For each plan, discuss how you might find the answers to the following questions.

- What is the probability that parents will have a son?
- What will happen to the total population of China?
- What will rural couples think about your plan?

Lesson 1 Simulating Chance Situations

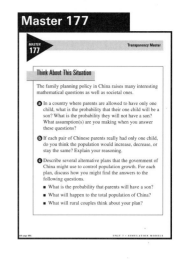

LESSON OVERVIEW In this lesson, students will learn to simulate situations that can be modeled by flipping a coin. As in the rest of this unit, the important thing is for students to learn how to set up a simulation, not for them to perform a large number of trials in order to get results that are highly accurate.

Lesson Objectives

- To simulate situations where the probability of a success is 0.5
- To display the results of a simulation in a frequency table and histogram
- To explore the idea of independent events
- To explore the waiting-time (geometric) distribution
- To explore how the number of trials in a simulation affect the estimated probability

LAUNCH full-class discussion

A good way to begin this lesson is to present the Chinese policy of limiting families to one child, then let your students discuss the "Think About This Situation" questions as an entire class. This will give you an opportunity to assess how much your students know about probability. For Part c, make a list of the plans proposed. At this stage, students are not expected to have the tools to fully investigate their plans.

One result of the Chinese government's policy was reported in a *Washington Post* article on May 29, 2001. China now has 117 boys born for every 100 girls. In rural China, the ratio is even higher (140 boys for every 100 girls). The usual ratio is 105 to 106 boys for every 100 girls. The high ratio in China has been attributed to factors such as underreporting of girls by parents (who hide them so they can have another child). Some reports suggest that more drastic measures, such as abortion, also are being taken. A more recent article about the long-term effects of this policy was reported in *Time* magazine on August 6, 2001.

Students will want to talk a bit about the effect on girls of such a preference. You may want to get them started right away on Reflecting Task 3 (student text page 495). Be sensitive also to the fact that different cultures have different values regarding the number of children a couple should have.

The Chinese overpopulation problem has appeared as a mathematics problem in various publications. One of the first was M. Gnanadesikan *et al.*, *The Art and Techniques of Simulation*, Dale Seymour Publications, Palo Alto, CA, 1987. See also Clifford Konold, "Teaching Probability through Modeling Real Problems," *The Mathematics Teacher* 87, April, 1994, pp. 232–235.

See additional Teaching Notes on page T528C.

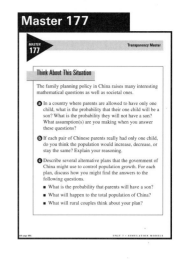

Master 177

Unit 7

INVESTIGATION 1   How Many Children?

In this investigation, all of the probabilities are $\frac{1}{2}$ so that students can use coin flips to do the simulations.

It is important that students understand why they are doing each step in a simulation. Doing the actual coin flipping is deceptively easy, even mindless. But thinking out what to do, what to record, and how to use the results to answer the questions are challenging tasks. (In fact, knowing what question you are trying to answer and stating it clearly is the first step.) So, as you circulate and observe the students doing the simulation, you might inquire,

> "What does that coin flip represent? What does it mean if you get a head? A tail?"

> "What are you recording? And you are trying to find out how frequently . . . (*blank for student to supply*) . . . ?"

Even though the table is already set up for them in Activity 3, students might respond that the trial represents "getting a boy baby" or that they are recording the "number of boy babies" or "families with boy babies." If they give an incorrect response to the meaning of the trial or what they are recording, then you might repeat their own response by saying,

> "So what you are saying is that you are trying to find out how frequently families with boy babies occurred?"

Just hearing this stated clearly is often enough to guide students to rethink.

Teaching Master 183 (Steps in a Simulation), which will help students focus on the steps of a simulation, is provided for use with the Lesson 2 "Think About This Situation" on page 498.

A NOTE ABOUT GENERATING TRIALS QUICKLY: Simulations are fun. Students love to flip coins and they like to observe the fact that unusual events occur if you give them enough opportunities to occur. However, a simulation can get tedious if students must carry out an excessive number of trials. Unfortunately, four hundred trials are needed to be at least 95% sure of estimating a percentage to within 5%. The most important part of the following exercises is having students understand how to set up the simulations. Once students thoroughly understand how to do the simulation, it isn't important to have them do more than a few trials by hand. At that stage, move to the computer if you have one. If not, divide the number of trials among the groups in the class. Then combine the results from all of the groups. You may substitute a smaller number of trials if your class understands that the resulting estimated probabilities may be quite far from the theoretical probabilities.

See additional Teaching Notes on page T528D.

INVESTIGATION 1 How Many Children?

In Part c of the "Think About This Situation" on the previous page, you shared different ways to examine the effects of your policy. In real life, it is hard to gather data that easily show the effects of a policy on the population. It may take several generations to see the long term effects. To estimate these effects you can *simulate* the situation in a way that allows informative data to be gathered more easily and quickly. In this investigation, you will simulate situations by flipping a coin.

1. Suppose China implements a new policy that allows each family to have two children.

    a. Explain how to use a coin to simulate the birth of *one* child. What did a head represent? What did a tail represent? What assumption(s) are you making?

    b. Explain how to use a coin to simulate the births of *two* children to a family. What are the possible outcomes?

    c. When you simulate a family with two children by flipping a coin twice and recording the results, you have conducted one **trial**. To be sure you have a reasonable estimate of what two-child families look like, it is necessary to conduct many trials. Conduct 200 trials simulating two-child families. Share the work among the groups in your class. Make a frequency table like the one below to record the results of your 200 trials.

Type of Family	Frequency
Two Girls	
Older Girl and Younger Boy	
Older Boy and Younger Girl	
Two Boys	
Total Number of Trials	200

d. Use your frequency table to estimate the probability that a family with two children will have *at least one* boy.

e. Estimate the probability that a family with two children will have at least one boy using a mathematical method other than simulation. Explain your other method.

f. Do the four types of families—two girls, older girl and younger boy, older boy and younger girl, two boys—appear to be **equally likely**? Describe the meaning of *equally likely* for a friend who is not in this class.

g. What is the total number of children in the 200 trials in Part c? What is the total number of girls? Of boys?

Here is one plan for reducing population growth that your class may have discussed.

> *Allow parents to continue to have children until a boy is born.*
> *Then no more children are allowed.*

For most of the remainder of this investigation, you will examine this plan. You will begin by making your best prediction about the effects of such a policy. Then you will use simulation techniques to improve your estimates.

2. Suppose that in rural China all parents continue having children until they get a boy. After the first boy, they have no other children. In your group, discuss each question below. Write your best prediction of the answer to each question.

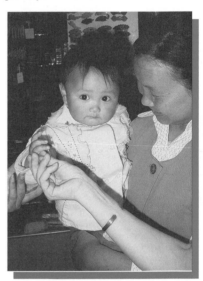

a. Will more boys or more girls be born in rural China?

b. What will be the average number of children per family in rural China?

c. Will the population of rural China increase, decrease, or stay the same?

d. What percentage of families will have only one child?

e. What percentage of families will have four children or more?

f. What percentage of the children in rural China will belong to single-child families?

1. d. Responses may vary. The estimate from the second column of the typical table above is $\frac{149}{200} = 0.745$.

   e. Responses may vary. For example, there are four equally likely families: two girls, an older girl and younger boy, an older boy and younger girl, and two boys. Thus, the probability of at least one boy is $\frac{3}{4}$. Some students may think there are three equally likely families: no boys, one boy, and two boys. If so, spend some time on Part f and generate more "families" until the pattern is clear.

   f. They are equally likely, but the results of the simulation may not make that entirely clear. Point out to students that we expect some variation from "perfect" results. Perform more trials until the simulation resembles the actual probabilities. For example, a typical table showing the results of 1,000 trials is shown here. The probabilities are each converging to 0.25.

Type of Family	Frequency	Relative Frequency
Two Girls	222	0.222
Older Girl and Younger Boy	299	0.299
Older Boy and Younger Girl	221	0.221
Two Boys	258	0.258
Total Number of Trials	1,000	1.000

   Note that the frequencies, however, are diverging from the expected frequency. In the table in Part c, the expected frequency in each row is 50. The deviations from 50 are 1, 5, −12, and 6. In the table above with a larger number of trials, the expected frequency in each row is 250. The deviations from 250 are −28, 49, −29, and 8. Notice that while these numbers are greater in magnitude than the first group of numbers, they represent a smaller percentage of the expected frequency for the simulation than the first group does for its simulation. This is an important idea for students to learn— that as you are flipping a coin, for example, the *percentage* of heads tends to get closer and closer to 50% as the number of flips increases, while the *number* of heads tends to get further and further from half the number of tosses. If students don't understand this, they will believe that the coin must balance out in the future by changing the probability that it will be a head. This idea comes up again in the MORE set with Reflecting Task 1 (student text page 523).

   g. There are 200(2) or 400 children. The number of girls and the number of boys will vary. To find the number of girls, for example, double the frequency on the first line and add it to the frequency on the second line. Then add the result to the frequency on the third line. So for the typical table in Part c above there are 2(51) + 55 + 38 or 195 girls.

2. Responses will vary to all of these questions. Note especially how your students answer Parts a and b. For your information, theoretical values are given in Activity 6, Part e of this investigation.

NOTE: Part f is not the same question as Part d, because it is calculated from the point of view of an individual, rather than a family. See the fourth and sixth bullets of Activity 4 on page T487 as well as Organizing Task 3 on page 494 of the student text.

Unit 7

NOTE: This situation is an example of a geometric or "waiting-time" distribution.

3. Let tails represent a boy, and toss the coin until tails appears. Count the number of tosses needed.

   a. A typical table will look like this, but there will be wide variation in the tables students produce.

Number of Tosses to Get a "Boy"	Frequency
1	25
2	10
3	8
4	3
5	2
6	1
7	1
8	0
9	0
10	0
Total Number of Trials	50

   b. Responses may vary for the first and third bullets.
   - For our sample data, seven families had four children or more.
   - 50 boys, since each family had one boy
   - For our sample data, 54 girls were born. From the frequency table,
     $10 + 2 \cdot 8 + 3 \cdot 3 + 4 \cdot 2 + 5 \cdot 1 + 6 \cdot 1 = 54$

4. Responses may vary. According to our sample data, the estimates are as follows:
   - The number of boys was 50, and the number of girls was 54. In this simulation, there were more girls than boys. The number of boys and girls should be about the same. (Keep students focused on the results of their simulation.)
   - There was a total of 104 children in the 50 families. So the average number of children per family is $\frac{104}{50}$ or 2.08.
   - The population will stay about the same, since $2.08 \approx 2$.
   - $\frac{25}{50}$ or 50% of the families will have only one child.
   - $\frac{7}{50}$ or 14% of the families will have four or more children.
   - Using the typical table from Activity 3, there are 25 boys who have no siblings. The total number of children is $25 + 2(10) + 3(8) + 4(3) + 5(2) + 6 + 7 = 104$. Thus, the percent of children with no siblings is $\frac{25}{104}$ or approximately 24%.

   a. Responses will vary.

   b. Many students will believe that there will be more boys than girls since each family must have a boy. Other students will visualize the long string of girls that some families will have before they have a boy and so think that there will be more girls than boys. Almost everyone believes the average family size is greater than 2, and so the population of rural China will increase.

To get a good estimate of the answers to the questions in Activity 2, your group could simulate the situation. To do this, design a **simulation model** that imitates the process of parents having children until they get a boy.

3. Explain how to use a coin to conduct one trial that models a family having children until they get a boy.

   a. Carry out one trial for your simulation of having children until a boy is born. Make a table like the following one. Make a tally mark (/) in the frequency column opposite the number of tosses it took to get a "boy."

Number of Tosses to Get a "Boy"	Frequency	Number of Tosses to Get a "Boy"	Frequency
1		7	
2		8	
3		9	
4		10	
5		⋮	
6		**Total Number of Trials**	50

   b. Continue carrying out trials of having children until a boy is born. Stop when you have a total of 50 "families." Divide the work among the members of your group. Record your results in the frequency table. Add as many additional rows to the table as you need.

     ■ How many of your 50 families had four children or more?

     ■ How many boys were born in your 50 families?

     ■ How many girls were born in your 50 families?

4. Now use your frequency table to estimate answers to the six questions posed in Activity 2.

   a. Compare your estimates with your original predictions. For which questions did your initial prediction vary the most from the simulation estimate? (If most of your original predictions were not accurate, you are in good company. Most people aren't very good at predicting the answers to probability problems.)

   b. Write several misconceptions that you or others in your group originally had about this situation.

Unit 7

5. Make a histogram of your group's frequency table on a graph like the one shown below or on your calculator or computer.

a. Describe the shape of this distribution.

b. What is the largest family size? The smallest?

c. On the histogram, locate the median and the lower and upper quartiles of the distribution.

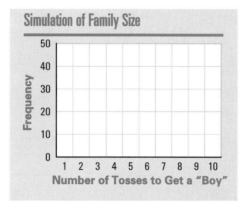

6. Each group should reproduce their histogram on a sheet of paper or on the chalkboard.

a. Describe any similarities in the histograms.

b. Describe any differences in the histograms. Explain why the differences occurred.

c. Combine the frequency tables from all of the groups in your class into one frequency table on the overhead projector or chalkboard.

d. Make a histogram of the combined frequency table. How are the histograms from the individual groups similar to this one? How are they different?

e. Reproduced below are the questions from Activity 2. Estimate the answers to these questions using the combined frequency table of Part c above.

- Will more boys or more girls be born in rural China?

- What will be the average number of children per family in rural China?

- Will the population of rural China increase, decrease, or stay the same?

- What percentage of families will have only one child?

- What percentage of families will have four children or more?

- What percentage of the children in rural China will belong to single-child families?

f. Should you have more confidence in the estimates from Part e or in the estimates from your group? Explain your reasoning.

5. The following TI-82 Calculator Tip is a review of how to use a frequency distribution to make a histogram on the TI-82. The TI-83 works similarly.

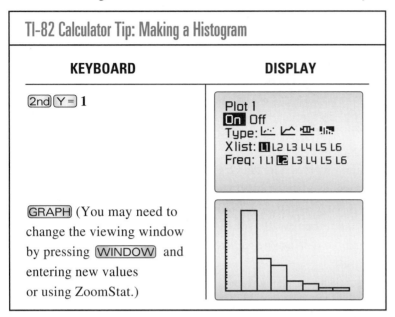

For the sample frequency data, the histogram would look like the one in the technology tip above.

a. The frequency decreases as the family size increases. The graph is strongly skewed right. The smallest family size is one child, and that is the most common family size.

b. Responses may vary. In our sample data, the largest family had seven children, and the smallest families had one child.

c. Since this distribution is skewed right so strongly, measures of center and spread can be misleading. In our sample data, $Q_1 = 1$, Med $= 1.5$, $Q_3 = 3$.

6. **See Teaching Master 178.**

a–d. Responses will vary. As students will learn in Course 2, a histogram for a geometric (waiting-time) distribution has the tallest bar on the left with the height of the bars gradually decreasing. For this situation, each bar should be about half the height of the one to its left.

e. The answers given here are the theoretical ones. The data combined from all groups should give answers that are close to these theoretical ones. (Note: You may wish to refer to the Technology Tip provided as Teaching Masters 180a–180b.)

■ There will be equal numbers of boys and girls born.

■ The average number of children per family in rural China will be 2.

■ The population will stay the same if each adult marries and has children.

■ 50% of the families will have only one child.

■ 12.5% of families will have four children or more.

■ 25% of the children will belong to single-child families. Only first-born boys will have no brothers or sisters.

f. Students should understand that as the number of trials increases, the estimated probability tends to get closer to the theoretical probability. This is the Law of Large Numbers. Some students like to use the phrase, "It's more accurate." Try to get them to explain what they mean by that vague expression.

NOTE: This would be a good time to remind students that they can visually estimate the mean of a histogram.

NOTE: Retain the data from Part d to use in the MORE set for Organizing Task 1 (student text page 494).

NOTE: Most people are surprised at first to find that half of all babies born will be boys and half will be girls in the have-children-until-you-get-a-boy plan. However, since the probability of a baby being a boy is $\frac{1}{2}$ for each birth, the proportion of boys in the population also must be $\frac{1}{2}$.

Unit 7

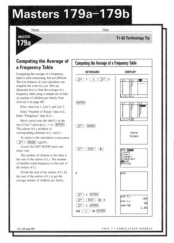

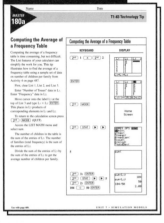

Unit 7

EXPLORE *continued*

7. See Teaching Masters 179a–180b.

a–d. Responses will vary. Be sure that students can see how the plan they have chosen is modeled by their simulation. It is important that they can articulate clearly what constitutes one trial before they begin work on gathering the data in Part b.

SHARE AND SUMMARIZE   full-class discussion

Checkpoint

See Teaching Master 181.

ⓐ A simulation involves a model of a real-life probabilistic situation that is mathematically equivalent to that situation. A simulation consists of a series of trials. By observing a large number of trials, you can estimate the answers to probabilistic questions about the real-life situation. A simulation is a way to model a situation so that informative data can be gathered more quickly and easily than by observing the situation itself.

As the number of trials increases, the estimated probability tends to get closer to the theoretical probability.

ⓑ A histogram is a complete picture of the relative likelihood of the possible outcomes of a probabilistic situation. From the histogram, you can estimate shape, center, and spread. (As students will see in this unit, the histograms fall into families of characteristic shapes. Eventually a student's intuition will become strong enough that he or she will be able to "see" the results of some simulations before actually running the simulation.)

ⓒ One could use a die, letting the numbers 1, 2, and 3 represent the birth of a girl and the numbers 4, 5, and 6 represent the birth of a boy. Students also may suggest spinners or drawing slips of paper from a hat.

ⓓ Neither. This is one of the main points of this investigation. Since the probability of getting a head is $\frac{1}{2}$ on *each* flip of a coin, the proportion of heads in a large number of flips should be close to $\frac{1}{2}$ no matter how clever our scheme for starting and stopping. For example, if each person in a large group flips a coin until they get a head and then stops, the proportion of heads will remain $\frac{1}{2}$.

See additional Teaching Notes on page T528D.

7. In the "Think About This Situation" on page 484, your class proposed several alternative plans for reducing population growth in China.

a. As a class, choose a plan different from the one in which parents have children until they get a boy, and design one trial of your plan.

b. Perform at least 200 trials, sharing the work among groups in the class. Place your results in a frequency table.

c. Under your plan, what is the probability that parents will have a son? How did you calculate the probability?

d. Will the population of China increase, decrease, or remain the same under your plan? Explain your reasoning.

Checkpoint

In this lesson, you learned how to design simulations.

a Describe, in your own words, what a *simulation model* is. Why is it important to conduct a large number of trials?

b Why is it always a good idea to make a histogram of the results of a simulation?

c Describe a way to simulate the have-children-until-you-get-a-boy plan that does not use coins.

d If you flip a coin until you get a head and then repeat this many times, will you tend to have a larger proportion of heads or of tails?

Be prepared to share your descriptions and thinking with the class.

Unit 7

Simulation is a good way to estimate the answer to a probability problem. The greater the number of trials, the more likely it is that the estimated probability is close to the actual probability. In our complex world, simulation is often the only feasible way to deal with a problem involving chance. Simulation is an indispensable tool to scientists, business analysts, engineers, and mathematicians.

"I've had it! Simulated wood, simulated leather, simulated coffee, and now simulated probabilities!"

STATISTICS: CONCEPTS AND CONTROVERSIES by Moore © 1979 by W.H. Freeman and Company. Used with permission.

On Your Own

When asked in what way chance affected her life, a ninth-grader in a very large Los Angeles coeducational city high school noted that students are chosen randomly to be checked for weapons. Suppose that when this policy was announced, a reporter for the school newspaper suspected that the students would not be chosen randomly, but that boys would be more likely to be chosen than girls. The reporter then observed the first search and found that all 10 students searched were male.

a. If a student is in fact chosen randomly, what is the probability that the student will be a boy?

b. Write instructions for conducting one trial of a simulation that models selecting 10 students at random and observing whether each is a boy or a girl.

c. What assumptions did you make in your model?

d. Perform 20 trials using your simulation model.

e. Report the results in a frequency table showing the number of boys selected.

f. Write an article for a school paper describing your simulation, its results, and your conclusion. Include a histogram in your article.

▶On Your Own

a. We will assume that the coeducational high school has an equal number of boys and girls. The probability a randomly selected student will be a boy is 0.5.

b. Use a coin and let a head represent the event of a male being selected and a tail represent the event of a female being selected. Flip the coin ten times and count the number of males (or females) selected to be searched. (Students might choose to use a spinner or a die. In that case, be sure the probability of "searching a male" is 0.50.) It may be difficult for students to understand that one trial will consist of ten flips. If this is the case, get them to verbalize what each flip represents and then, how many students the reporter observed.

c. We assumed that there are the same number of males as females in the school and that the choices of who is to be searched are independent of each other. For example, we assume the students aren't selected in a group as they are walking together into the school. Such a group might tend to have all males or all females. We also are assuming that the high school is large enough that the probability of a boy remains about 0.5 on each trial.

NOTE: This situation is an example of a binomial distribution. A binomial distribution results when we count the number of "successes" in a *fixed* number of trials where the probability of a "success" on each independent trial remains the same.

d-e. Results will vary. A typical table might look like this:

Number of Boys Selected	Frequency
0	0
1	0
2	1
3	3
4	4
5	5
6	3
7	2
8	1
9	1
10	0
Total Number of Trials	20

f. Responses will vary. Students should realize that it is very unlikely to get all males in the search if the students really were selected randomly. The theoretical probability is $\left(\frac{1}{2}\right)^{10}$, which is $\frac{1}{1,024}$ (approximately 0.0009765, or 0.10%). The theoretical histogram is symmetric about 5, but a typical one is shown below. Twenty trials is not very many, and so there will be great variability among the histograms.

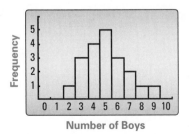

ASSIGNMENT *pp. 491–497*

Modeling: 1 or 2, and 3*
(Be sure 3 is
assigned because it
prepares students for
Lesson 3.)
Organizing: 1 or 2*
Reflecting: 1, and 2 or 5*
Extending: Choose one*

*When choice is indicated, it is important
to leave the choice to the student.
NOTE: It is best if Organizing tasks are discussed as a whole class after they have
been assigned as homework.

Modeling

1. a. Responses may vary. Some possible simulations are:
- For each birth, flip a coin letting heads represent a boy and tails represent a girl. Flip the coin until a head appears, but no more than three times.
- For each birth, draw a ball from a bag containing equal numbers of two different colored balls. One color represents a boy and one color represents a girl. Draw with replacement until you get the "boy" color, but not more than three tries.
- Use a die or spinner, designating half the numbers as "boys" and half the numbers as "girls." Spin the spinner until you get a "boy," but not more than three times.

b. A typical table appears below.

Type of Family	Frequency
First Child is a Boy	97
Second Child is a Boy	53
Third Child is a Boy	27
Three Girls and no Boy	23
Total Number of Trials	200

c. Responses will vary. For the table above, it is $\frac{23}{200}$ or 11.5%. The theoretical percentage is 12.5%.

d. Responses will vary. Following is the bar graph for the table above.

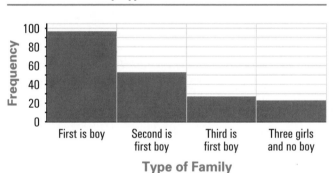

Simulation of Family Type

e. The first three bars should be about the same height as in the other plan, because those bars represent families who first got a boy with the first, second, and third child. The "three girls and no boy" frequency should be about the same as the sum of the rest of the frequencies in the have-children-until-you-get-a-boy simulation. In both cases, those represent the families who had three girls in a row for the first three children.

See additional Teaching Notes on page T528E.

MORE

Modeling

1. A new plan to control population growth in rural China is proposed. Parents will be allowed to have *at most three* children and must stop having children as soon as they get a boy.

   a. Describe how to conduct one trial that models one family that follows this plan.

   b. Conduct 5 trials. Copy the following frequency table which gives the results of 195 trials. Add your results to the frequency table so that there is a total of 200 trials.

Type of Family	Frequency
First Child is a Boy	97
Second Child is a Boy	50
Third Child is a Boy	26
Three Girls and No Boy	22
Total Number of Trials	

   c. Estimate the percentage of families that would not have a son.

   d. Make a histogram of the results in your frequency table.

   e. How does the shape of this histogram differ from that of the have-children-until-you-get-a-boy plan? Explain why you would expect this to be the case.

   f. What is the average number of children per family? Will the total population increase or decrease under this plan or will it stay the same?

   g. In the long run, will this population have more boys or more girls or will the numbers be about equal? Explain your reasoning.

2. Jeffrey is taking a 10-question true-false test. He didn't study and doesn't even have a reasonable guess on any of the questions. He answers "True" or "False" at random.

   a. With your group, decide how to conduct one trial that models the results of a true-false test.

   b. Conduct 50 trials. Share the work. Record your results in a frequency table that gives the number of questions Jeffrey got correct in each trial.

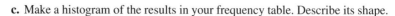

c. Make a histogram of the results in your frequency table. Describe its shape.

d. Use your frequency table to estimate, on average, the number of questions Jeffrey will get correct. Theoretically, what is the number of questions that he should expect to get correct using his random guessing method?

e. If 70% is required to pass the test, what is your estimate of the probability that he will pass the test?

3. The winner of the World Series of baseball is the first team to win four games.

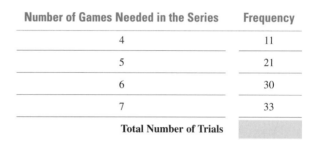

a. What is the fewest number of games that can be played in the World Series? What is the greatest number of games that can be played in the World Series? Explain.

b. Suppose that the two teams in the World Series are evenly matched. Describe how to conduct one trial simulating a World Series.

c. Use your simulation model to determine the probability that the series lasts seven games. Conduct 5 trials. Construct a frequency table similar to the one shown below and add your 5 results so that there is a total of 100 trials.

Number of Games Needed in the Series	Frequency
4	11
5	21
6	30
7	33
Total Number of Trials	

d. Make a histogram of the results in your frequency table.

e. What is your estimate of the probability that the series will go seven games?

4. According to the U.S. Department of Education report, *The Condition of Education 2000* (page 42), about 50% of high school seniors say they like mathematics.

2. **c.** Responses will vary. Theoretically, the histogram will be symmetric with the highest bar at 5, and the bars tapering off from there. Following is the histogram for the table on page T528E.

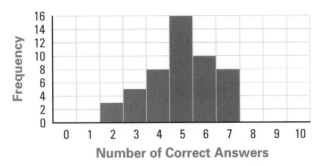

d. Responses will vary. In the 50 trials above, Jeffrey answered a total of 249 of the 500 questions correctly, for an average of 0.498. Theoretically, he would expect to get half of the ten questions correct.

e. Responses will vary. A score of 70% or better would be the same as 7 or more correct. In the example above, Jeffrey passed the test only 8 times out of the 50, for a probability of 0.16. Theoretically, the probability he gets 70% or more correct is about 0.17.

3. **a.** If one team wins the first four games, the series is over in four games. The greatest number of games is seven, because, if there are seven games, one of the two teams must have won at least four of them.

b. Responses may vary. Students may choose any random device that has two equally likely events such as two colored balls, even number vs. odd number on a six-sided die, or coins. For example, let the flip of a coin represent a game. If the flip is heads, team A wins the game. If the flip is tails, team B wins the game. Flip the coin until there are either four heads or four tails. Count the number of flips required.

NOTE: The assumption that the teams are evenly matched on every game is certainly not true in the real World Series. It is a convenient simplifying assumption that allows us to begin to analyze the situation. More sophisticated simulation models can be designed that use more realistic assumptions. The situation with unevenly matched teams will be explored in Lesson 3 of this unit.

---

c. Responses will vary. A typical table appears below. (The theoretical probabilities are 0.125 for 4 games, 0.25 for 5 games, 0.3125 for 6 games, and 0.3125 for 7 games.)

Number of Games Needed in the Series	Frequency
4	11
5	22
6	32
7	35
Total Number of Trials	100

3. **d.**

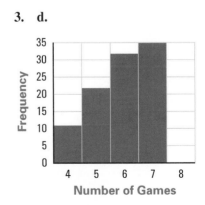

d. Responses will vary. The histogram for the table in Part c appears at the right.

e. For the example above, the estimated probability is $\frac{35}{100}$ or 0.35.

Unit 7

4. **This situation is an example of a binomial distribution.**

   a. Responses may vary. Students may choose any random device that has two equally likely events such as two colored balls, even number vs. odd number on a six-sided die, or coins. For example, let the flip of a coin represent whether the seniors like mathematics (heads) or not (tails). Flip the coin 30 times and count the number of seniors who like mathematics (the number of heads). Be sure students can explain why one trial is composed of 30 flips.

   b. Responses will vary. A typical table appears below.

Number of Seniors Who Like Mathematics	Frequency	Number of Seniors Who Like Mathematics	Frequency
6	1	15	29
7	0	16	19
8	1	17	25
9	6	18	13
10	5	19	7
11	9	20	5
12	19	21	3
13	30	22	1
14	27	**Total Number of Trials**	200

   c. ■ No. From the sample results above, the estimate of the probability that 12 or fewer seniors like mathematics is $\frac{41}{200} = 0.205$. Thus, "only" 12 isn't unusual. That number or even fewer happens about 20% of the time in a random sample of 30 seniors. (The theoretical probability is 0.18.)

      ■ Yes. This didn't happen at all in 200 trials. (The theoretical probability is $\left(\frac{1}{2}\right)^{30} \approx 9 \times 10^{-10}$.)

   d. **The concept of a rare event is an important one. It is formalized and expanded in Course 2, "Patterns in Chance," and Course 3, "Modeling Public Opinion."**
      Student opinions on whether the number is unusual will vary. Some possible explanations for an unusually large or small number are:

      ■ Your students didn't get a random sample of 30 seniors at the high school. For example, they may have surveyed a precalculus, calculus, or physics class.

      ■ Your high school isn't typical. Either more or fewer students than average for the United States like mathematics.

      ■ The percentage of seniors in the high school who like mathematics is about 50%, but the class just happened to get a sample with quite a different percentage. An unusual number is possible even though unlikely.

   e. The class might be an advanced mathematics or science class. Finding that all students in one class like math is unusual, but it is possible.

a. Describe how to conduct one trial of a simulation to answer the following questions.

- Would it be unusual to find that only 12 seniors of a randomly selected group of 30 said they liked mathematics?
- Would it be unusual for all 30 randomly selected seniors to say they like mathematics?

b. Conduct five trials using your simulation model. Copy the frequency table below that shows the results of 195 trials. Add your results to the table.

Number of Seniors Who Like Mathematics	Frequency
6	1
7	0
8	1
9	6
10	5
11	9
12	19
13	29
14	26

Number of Seniors Who Like Mathematics	Frequency
15	28
16	18
17	24
18	13
19	7
20	5
21	3
22	1

c. Use your results to estimate answers to the questions in Part a.

d. Select 30 seniors at your school and survey them to determine how many like mathematics. Is the number unusual? If so, what are possible reasons for this?

e. Suppose you survey a classroom of seniors selected at random in your school and find that all 30 of the students in the class like mathematics. List as many reasons as you can why this could occur.

Organizing

1. Refer to your class frequency table from Part c of Activity 6 (page 488).

   a. Make a scatterplot of the (*number of tosses to get a "boy", frequency*) data.

   b. Would a line be a reasonable model of the relationship between number of tosses and frequency? Why or why not?

2. In 2000, China had a population of approximately 1,250,000,000. Assume parents were not following the one-child-per-family policy and the population of China continued to grow at about 1% per year.

   a. At that rate, how many people would have been added to the population of China in 2001? Compare this number to the population of your state.

   b. Assume the growth rate of 1% per year continues. Make a table of the year-end populations of China from 2000 to 2010.

   ■ Is the relationship a linear one? Explain your reasoning on the basis of your table.

   ■ What is the percent increase in China's population from 2000 to 2010?

   c. Make a scatterplot of the data in your table.

   ■ Find an equation that fits this data well.

   ■ Use your equation to predict when the population of China will exceed 1.5 billion people.

3. Suppose that during first period, Central High School has 95 classes of 30 students each and 5 classes of 100 students each.

   a. What is the average first period class size as reported by the high school?

   b. Suppose each student records the size of his or her first period class. What is the average class size from the students' point of view?

   c. How are these questions similar to Activity 2, Parts d and f of Investigation 1?

4. You can use random devices other than coins to simulate the birth of a child.

   a. How could a cube be used to simulate the birth of a child—either boy or girl?

   b. Could you use a regular tetrahedron to simulate the birth of a child? Explain your procedure.

   c. Identify other geometric shapes that could be used as the basis for a simulation model of births.

5. A circle with radius 6 inches is inscribed in a square as a model of a dartboard. Suppose a randomly thrown dart hits the board.

   a. What is a reasonable estimate of the probability the dart will land in the circle? Explain your reasoning.

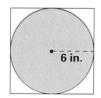

6 in.

Organizing

1. a. The plot from our sample data of 50 trials (from Activity 3) follows.

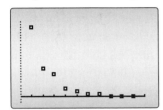

b. No. The frequencies decrease, but not at a constant rate, so a line is not a reasonable model. (The relationship follows an exponential model: $y = (0.5)^n$, where n is the total number of trials.)

2. a. The population of China would have increased by $0.01(1,250,000,000)$ or about 12,500,000 people.

This is more people than lived in any state in 2000 except California, Florida, New York, and Texas.

b.

Year	Population	Year	Population
2000	1,250,000,000	2006	1,326,900,188
2001	1,262,500,000	2007	1,340,169,190
2002	1,275,125,000	2008	1,353,570,882
2003	1,287,876,250	2009	1,367,106,591
2004	1,300,755,013	2010	1,380,777,657
2005	1,313,762,563		

■ When you study the rate of change from the table, you notice that the rate of change is not constant (it's always increasing), so it is not a linear relationship.

■ In 2010, the population of China will be approximately 1,380,777,657. The percent increase is $\frac{1,380,777,657 - 1,250,000,000}{1,250,000,000}$, or approximately 10.5%.

c.

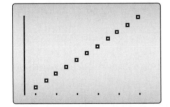

■ The relationship is exponential: $P = 1,250,000,000(1.01)^t$, where t is the number of years after 2000 and P is the population of China.

■ The population of China will exceed 1.5 billion when approximately 18.3 years have passed. Thus, the population will exceed 1.5 billion people in the year 2019.

See additional Teaching Notes on page T528F.

5. **b.** Responses may vary. Possible solutions follow.
- Have a blindfolded person face the board and throw darts. If a dart misses the square entirely, it should not be counted. Then compute the proportion of throws that are in the circle.
- Place the diagram on a coordinate axis. Simulate a throw by randomly picking numbers for *x*- and *y*-coordinates. Then decide if the (*x*, *y*) point is inside the circle.

c. Throwing darts involves skill on the part of the thrower, so it is not a random happening. A skilled thrower would hit the circle every time even if blindfolded.

d. Your estimated probability *P* from Part b is approximately equal to the ratio of the area of the circle to the area of the square:

$$P \approx \frac{\text{area of circle}}{\text{area of square}} = \frac{\pi r^2}{(2r)^2} = \frac{\pi}{4}$$

Thus, an estimate of π is $4P$.

Reflecting

1. The answers to the questions are:
   a. 50%   **b.** 0.5   **c.** 0.5

   There is no real difference in the three questions.

2. **a.** The probability that you will get heads on the fifth toss is $\frac{1}{2}$.

   b. The probability will be $\frac{1}{2}$ as long as births are independent. The answer to Part a is clearly $\frac{1}{2}$ since the coin has no memory of what happened before. However, the answer to this part about births depends on whether the sex of a child is independent of the sexes of the previous children in the family. If boys (or girls) tend to "run" in some families, the probability won't be $\frac{1}{2}$. If there has been a long string of girls, say, then the parents may be more likely to produce girls. To find the answer, we would have to examine real families that had had four boys in a row and then had a fifth child.

3. Responses may vary. Be sure students don't just offer their own opinions here. Their statements should be supported with references.

4. Jason's simulation model is probably not a reasonable one. The probability that a person will buy a magazine isn't likely to be exactly $\frac{1}{2}$. Also, some people may buy more than one magazine.

5. In this particular problem, which amounts to counting the number of heads and tails in two flips of a fair coin, the order of the heads and tails isn't important. It doesn't matter if you flip one coin twice or flip two coins once. In the first method, the student would flip a coin, note whether it was heads or tails, and then flip the coin again and note whether it was heads or tails. At the end, all the student records is the number of heads and the number of tails in the two flips. In the second method, the student flips two coins at the same time and records the number of heads and the number of tails in the two flips.

   Students may convince themselves that the two methods are equivalent by imagining that in the two-coin situation, one coin has a big "1" written on it and the other has a big "2" written on it. Coin "1" corresponds to the first flip of a single coin and coin "2" corresponds to the second flip of a single coin.

   However, many students will be reluctant at this point to believe that there are two different ways to simulate the same situation. It is quite reasonable for them to be cautious until they are more proficient at designing simulations.

b. Describe a simulation that could be used to estimate the probability.

c. Why might throwing darts at the board not be a good simulation?

d. How could you use the results of your simulation in Part b to estimate π?

Reflecting

1. Is there any difference in the following three questions? Explain your position.

   a. In a country where parents are allowed to have only one child, what percentage of couples will have a daughter?

   b. In a country where parents are allowed to have only one child, what is the probability that a couple, selected at random, will have a daughter?

   c. In a country where parents are allowed to have only one child, what fraction (proportion) of couples will have a daughter?

2. In future work in *Contemporary Mathematics in Context*, you will have to decide if trials are *independent*—past events don't change the probabilities.

   a. Suppose you toss a penny four times and get heads each time. What is the probability you will get a head on the fifth toss?

   b. If a family has four boys in a row, what is the probability the next child will be a girl? How is this question different from the one in Part a? How could you find the answer to this question?

3. Do some library research to find information about one of the following questions. Prepare a brief written report on your findings.

   a. In what cultures of the world is there a strong preference for male children? For female children? What effect does this have on children of the opposite gender in these cultures?

   b. Does a preference for male or female children exist in the United States? How do we know whether or not this is the case? If there is a preference for a particular gender in the United States, what might be some possible reasons for this preference?

4. A school is selling magazine subscriptions to raise money. A group wants to simulate the situation of asking ten people if they will buy a magazine. Jason proposes that the group flip a coin ten times and count the number of heads since a person either buys a magazine (heads) or doesn't buy a magazine (tails). Is Jason's simulation model a reasonable one? Explain your position.

5. In Part c of Activity 1 of Investigation 1 (p. 485), you simulated the situation of counting the number of girls and boys in a family that has two children. Does it matter if you flip *one* coin twice or flip *two* coins once? Explain your reasoning.

Extending

1. You have studied four plans in this lesson for population planning.
   - Each family has only one child.
   - Each family has exactly two children.
   - Each family has children until they have a boy (or girl).
   - Each family has at most three children, stopping when they get a boy (or girl).

   Suppose that all people marry at the age of 20 and have children immediately. Assume the first generation consists of an imaginary population of 32 twenty-year-old men and 32 twenty-year-old women. How many children can we expect to be in the fifth generation under each one of the four plans above? (Assume that in every generation there are equal numbers of males and females.)

2. If a student guesses on every question of a 10-question true-false test, how many questions would you expect that student to get correct? What percentage is this? Devise a method of scoring a true-false test so that a student who guesses on every question would expect to get a 0% on the test and a student who knows all of the answers gets 100%.

3. In 1974, 48 male bank supervisors were each given one personnel file and asked to judge whether the person should be promoted or the file held and other applicants interviewed. The files were identical except that half of them indicated that the file was that of a female and half indicated that the file was that of a male. Of the 24 "male" files, 21 were recommended for promotion. Of the 24 "female" files, 14 were recommended for promotion. (B. Rosen and T. Jerdee, "Influence of Sex Role Stereotypes on Personnel Decisions," *Journal of Applied Psychology*, Volume 59, 1974, pages 9–14.) Design and carry out a simulation to evaluate how likely it is that a difference this large could occur just by chance. After conducting your simulation, do you believe that the bank managers were discriminating or do you believe the different numbers of people promoted could reasonably have happened just by chance?

4. Look up the records of the number of games actually played in past World Series.
   a. Make a histogram of the number of games actually played per series.
   b. How does the shape of the histogram of the real data compare to the one of your simulated data in Part d of Modeling Task 3?
   c. Does it appear to you that the teams tend to be evenly matched?

Extending

1. *Assuming* that an equal number of boys and girls are born each generation:

Plan	Number of 5th Generation Children
Each family can have only one child	4
Each family has exactly two children	64
Each family can have children until they have a boy	64
Each family can have at most three children	38 (approximately)

For the fourth situation, the theoretical average number of children per family is 1.75. (See Modeling Task 1, Part f.) This leads to the following expected number of children:

2nd generation: $1.75(32) = 56$ children

3rd generation: $1.75(28) = 49$ children

4th generation: $1.75\left(\frac{49}{2}\right) = 42.875$ children

5th generation: $1.75\left(\frac{42.875}{2}\right) = 37.515625$ children

So there are approximately 38 children in the fifth generation.

2. We would expect the student to get 5 or 50% of the questions correct.

   A common method for scoring true-false tests is "right minus wrong." For example, if a student gets 6 questions right and 4 wrong, the student would get a score of 2 out of 10 or 20%. The justification is that since the student missed four questions, he or she probably got another four questions correct just by luck. Thus, there were probably only two questions that the student really knew.

3. **This situation is an example of a *hypergeometric* distribution. A hypergeometric distribution results when (1) we select *r* items at random and without replacement from a group of items consisting of "successes" and "failures," and (2) we count the number of "successes" among the *r* items selected.**
   One way to do the simulation is to remove the four aces from a deck of cards. Of the 48 remaining cards, 24 are red (female) and 24 are black (male). Shuffle the 24 red cards and 24 black cards. (Statisticians have found that at least seven shuffles are necessary in order to mix up a deck of cards thoroughly.) Count off the top 35 cards to represent those recommended for promotion. Then count the number of red cards (women) that were recommended. The probability of getting 14 or fewer females recommended for promotion is about 0.025. This situation could have happened by chance, but it is quite unlikely to have done so.

See additional Teaching Notes on page T528G.

Unit 7

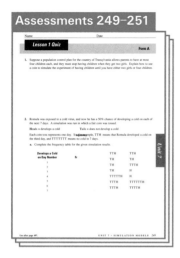

Assessments 249–251

Assessments 252–254

5. **This situation is an example of a hypergeometric distribution.**

   a. The sample of 10 people is being chosen from a small group of only 50 people rather than from a large group. This means that the probability of choosing a male does not remain the same as the people are chosen.

   b. One model is to take 25 cards with the word "female" written on them (or 25 red cards) and 25 cards with the word "male" written on them (or 25 black cards). Shuffle the cards. Deal out the top ten to represent the people chosen to be searched. Count the number of "male" cards out of the ten. This time we did not make the assumption that the probability that a male is chosen is $\frac{1}{2}$ on each selection. That wouldn't be the case with a small population. With the first draw, the chance of a male being selected is $\frac{25}{50}$ or $\frac{1}{2}$. But if the first student is a male, the probability that the next student selected is a male is only $\frac{24}{49}$ because one of the males has been removed from the group of possible students. We still must assume that the people are selected independently of one another. That is, the people aren't selected in groups (which might consist of all males or all females).

   c. Responses will vary.

   d. The probability that all ten people chosen to be searched are male is less in this situation than in the case of the large high school.

6. **a.** Responses may vary. Make sure that students have reasons for their choices.

   b. Responses will vary.

   c. Have students count the longest sequence of heads in their sequence of 200 flips. They should realize quickly that the first sequence is the real one. Initially, most people think it is the second sequence because they don't realize how long the runs of heads and tails will be. In 200 flips of a fair coin, we would expect that the longest run of heads would be 7 heads long, more like the first sequence than the second. When people write down a sequence that they think looks like tossing a fair coin, they invariably make the runs of heads and tails too short. See Mark F. Schilling, "The Longest Run of Heads," *The College Mathematics Journal* 21, May 1990, 196–207.

   This situation has an application to sports where fans, and players, seek to attribute reasons to so-called "streaks" and "slumps." A statistician understands that streaks and slumps occur naturally in any random process.

See Assessment Resources, pages 249–254.

5. For some rock concerts, audience members are chosen randomly to be checked for cameras, food, and other restricted items. Suppose that you observe the first 25 boys and 25 girls to enter a concert, and all 10 people chosen to be searched were male.

  a. How is this situation mathematically different from the one in the "On Your Own" on page 490?

  b. Describe a simulation model for this situation. What assumptions did you make in your model?

  c. Conduct at least 20 trials of your simulation. Record the results in a frequency table showing the number of boys selected.

  d. Is your conclusion different from your conclusion in the "On Your Own" task? Explain.

6. One of the sequences below is the result of actual flips of a coin. The other was written by a student trying to avoid doing the actual flips.

Sequence I

THHHHTTTTH	HHHTHHHHH	HHTTTHHTTH	HHHHTTTTTT
HHTHHTHHHT	TTHTTHHHHT	HTTTHTTTHH	TTTTHHHHHH
TTTHHTTHHH	THHHHHTTTT	THTTTHHTTH	TTHHTTTHHT
TTHHTHHTHH	TTTTTHHTHH	HHHTHTHTHT	HTHTTHHHTT
HHTHTHHHHH	HHHTTHTTHH	HHTTHTTTHH	TTTHHHTHHH

Sequence II

THTHTTTHTT	HTTHTHTTTH	TTHHHTHHTH	THTHTTTTHH
TTHHTTHHHT	HHHTTHHHTT	THHHTHHHHT	TTHTHTHHHH
THTTTHHHTH	HTHTTTHHTH	HHTHHHHTTH	THHTHHHTTT
HTHHHTHHTT	THHHTTTTHH	HTHTHHHHTH	TTHHTTTTHT
HTHTTHTHHT	THTTTHHTTT	HHHHTHTHHH	TTHHTHTTHH

  a. Which sequence do you think is the real one? Why did you select this one?

  b. Flip a coin 200 times, being sure each time that the coin spins many times in the air. Record the sequence of results.

  c. Does your sequence of actual coin flips look more like the first sequence or more like the second sequence?

Unit 7

Estimating Expected Values and Probabilities

In trips to a grocery store, you may have noticed that boxes of cereal often include a surprise gift such as one of a set of toy characters from a current movie or one of a collection of stickers. Cheerios®, a popular breakfast cereal, once included one of seven magic tricks in each box.

Collect All 7 and Put On Your Own Magic Show!

MONEY CLIP TRICK
Make two clips magically join together!

MIND-READING TRICK
Guess the color your friend secretly picked!

VANISHING CARD TRICK
Make a card magically disappear!

MAGIC ROPE TRICK
Make the rope magically pass through solid tube!

DISAPPEARING COIN TRICK
Make a coin magically disappear and reappear!

SURPRISE 4'S
Turn two blank cards into two 4's!

MULTIPLYING COIN TRICK
Turn two coins into three!

Think About This Situation

This practice of cereal manufacturers raises interesting mathematical questions as well as marketing questions.

a Why do manufacturers include "surprises" in the packages with their product? How do you think they determine the number of different "gifts" to include?

b What is the least number of boxes you could buy and get all seven magic tricks?

c What is your prediction of the average number of boxes of Cheerios a person would have to buy to get all seven magic tricks?

d How could you simulate this situation?

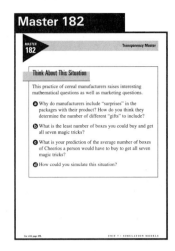

Master 182

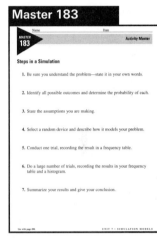

Master 183

Lesson 2 Estimating Expected Values and Probabilities

LESSON OVERVIEW In this lesson, students will learn to use single digits taken from their calculator or computer or from a table of random digits to simulate probabilistic situations. Students will extend their ability to simulate chance situations.

The introductory situation concerns the number of boxes of Cheerios® one would expect to have to buy to get a complete collection of seven magic tricks. This problem is an example of what is called "the collector's problem" or "the coupon collector's problem." You may want to continue to ask students to explain each step in their simulation. Encourage students to use their words carefully. ("And you are answering a question about how frequently . . . ?")

The basic steps in a simulation are as follows:

1. Be sure you understand the problem—state it in your own words.
2. Identify all possible outcomes and determine the probability of each.
3. State the assumptions you are making.
4. Select a random device and describe how it models your problem.
5. Conduct one trial, recording the result in a frequency table.
6. Do a large number of trials, recording the results in your frequency table and a histogram.
7. Summarize your results and give your conclusion.

These steps are listed on Teaching Master 183, "Steps in a Simulation." It may be best to give this handout to students after they have discussed the "Think About This Situation."

Lesson Objectives

- To use single random digits to simulate probabilistic situations
- To explore the nature of random digits
- To explore the collector's problem and the binomial distribution
- To compare shapes of probability distributions

LAUNCH full-class discussion

Think About This Situation

If you prefer, bring in a different box of a cereal that has one of a set of prizes in it and design a simulation for that set of prizes.

See Teaching Master 182.

a "Surprises" may prompt consumers to buy one brand of a product over another. If there are a large number of prizes, a customer will probably have to buy a larger number of boxes to get a desired prize or to get the complete set.

b 7

See additional Teaching Notes on page T528G.

INVESTIGATION 1 Simulation Using a Table of Random Digits

When using a table of random digits, each student should start at a randomly selected spot on the table and go across or down. If students all start at the same spot, they might get identical results. After the first simulation is finished, students should take up where they left off in the table rather than starting again at a randomly selected spot.

A table of random digits is supplied as Teaching Master 184. You may need additional tables of random digits. They can be found in most introductory statistics books, or you can use the final four digits of phone numbers torn out of an old phone book. (The first three digits aren't random as each locality will have only a few prefixes.)

NOTE: A set of random digits has several important characteristics: (1) you cannot predict with greater than a 10% success rate what the next digit is; and (2) each digit occurs, in the long run, with a probability of $\frac{1}{10}$. It is these characteristics that make random digit tables so valuable for simulation.

---

1. **a.** There are 112 digits in the table. Because 6 should occur about $\frac{1}{10}$ of the time, you would expect to find about 11 6s. In this table, the digit 6 occurs 14 times.

   b. Since half of the digits from 0 through 9 are even (zero is even) and half are odd, about 50% of the digits in a large table will be even.

   c. Since 10 equally likely digits could follow the 1, there is a 1 in 10 or 10% chance that the digit will be a 2.

   d. Once a digit is chosen, the probability that the following digit will be the same digit is 1 in 10. So about 10% of the digits in a large table will be followed by the same digit.

2. **a.** Start at a random spot in the table. If the first digit is odd, it represents the birth of a boy. If it is even, it represents a girl. A second way would be to let the digits 0, 1, 2, 3, and 4 represent the birth of a boy and the digits 5, 6, 7, 8, and 9 represent the birth of a girl. A third way would be to let the digit 0 represent a boy and the digit 1 represent a girl. All other digits would be disregarded as if they weren't there.

   b. Start at a random spot in the table. If the first digit is 1, 2, 3, 4, 5, or 6, let it represent the corresponding face on a die. If the digit is 7, 8, 9, or 0, ignore it and go on to the next digit until a 1, 2, 3, 4, 5, or 6 appears.

   c. An example is to start at a random spot in the table. If the digit is a 1, it represents the money clip trick; if it is a 2, it represents the mind-reading trick; … if it is a 7, it represents the multiplying coin trick. If the digit is an 8, 9, or 0, ignore it and go to the next digit. You need to ignore three of the digits since there are seven different magic tricks and ten digits.

INVESTIGATION 1 ▸ Simulation Using a Table of Random Digits

In the first lesson, you flipped a lot of coins to simulate situations. Calculators and computers can do this work for you. You can get strings of **random digits** either from your calculator or from a random digit table produced by a computer.

1. Examine this table of random digits between 0 and 9 inclusive generated by a computer.

2	4	8	0	3	1	8	6	5	6	4	2	0	0
7	6	8	6	3	0	5	6	8	2	5	0	7	5
0	9	5	8	1	7	3	0	9	9	8	7	7	7
0	2	6	8	6	2	5	5	4	1	5	9	8	0
4	1	2	9	0	8	6	7	0	3	3	8	2	1
1	5	8	0	9	5	7	3	5	6	5	0	2	3
9	7	6	2	5	9	2	6	3	5	0	3	1	3
2	1	0	9	6	0	1	8	5	5	2	2	6	6

a. How many digits are in the table? About how many 6s would you expect to find? How many are there? Choose another digit and determine its frequency.

b. About what percentage of digits in a large table of random digits from 0 to 9 will be even?

c. About what percentage of the 1s in a large table of random digits from 0 to 9 will be followed by a 2?

d. About what percentage of the digits in a large table of random digits from 0 to 9 will be followed by that same digit?

2. Refer to the table of random digits in Activity 1 when describing simulation models for the situations below.

a. Explain how you could use the random digits to simulate whether a newborn baby is male or female. Describe a second way of using random digits for the same simulation.

b. Explain how you could use the random digits to simulate tossing a die. (Disregarding particular digits won't affect the results.)

c. Explain how you could use the random digits to simulate checking a box of Cheerios for which of seven magic tricks it contains. Does your plan require that you disregard some digits? Why or why not?

d. Explain how you could use the random digits to simulate spinning the spinner shown here.

e. Explain how you could use the random digits to simulate selecting three students at random out of a group of ten students. What does it mean to select students "at random"?

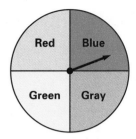

3. Obtain a table of one thousand random digits from your teacher or produce one using a calculator or computer.

a. Explain how you could use this table of random digits to simulate the random selection of three students from a group of seven students. Perform one trial.

b. Explain how you could use the table to simulate the experiment of rolling a die until you get a six. Perform one trial.

c. Explain how you could use the table to simulate tossing two coins until both tosses are heads. Perform one trial.

4. Refer back to the description of magic tricks in Cheerios at the beginning of this lesson.

a. If you buy one box of Cheerios, what is the probability that you will get a multiplying coin trick? To get your answer, what assumptions did you make about the tricks?

b. Suppose you want to find the number of boxes of Cheerios you will have to buy before you get all seven magic tricks. Describe a simulation model for this. Describe how to conduct one trial using a table of random digits.

c. Compare your group's simulation model with that of other groups. Then as a class, decide on a simulation model that all groups will use.

d. Have each member of your group perform one trial using the agreed upon simulation model. How many "boxes" did each person in your group have to buy? Put these numbers in a frequency table such as the one below.

Number of Boxes to Get All 7 Tricks	Frequency	Number of Boxes to Get All 7 Tricks	Frequency
7		13	
8		14	
9		15	
10		16	
11		⋮	
12		**Total Number of Trials**	200

2. **d.** Start at a random spot in the table. If the digit is a 1 or 2, it represents red; if it is a 3 or 4, it represents blue; if the digit is a 5 or 6, it represents gray; and if it is a 7 or 8, it represents green. If the digit is a 9 or 0, ignore it and go to the next digit.

   e. Assign a digit to each one of the students. Start at a random spot in the table. If the first digit is a 4, for example, then the student who has been assigned 4 is the first student selected. Go to the second digit. If it is a 4, ignore it and go to the next digit. Keep on in this way until three different students have been selected. "At random" means that each student has the same chance of being selected, and the students are chosen independently of each other.

3. **A table of random digits is supplied as Teaching Master 184.**

   a. To perform a trial, assign the students the digits 1, 2, 3, 4, 5, 6, and 7. Start at a random spot in the table. If the first digit is an 8, 9, or 0, go to the next digit. If the first digit is, say, a 3, then student number 3 will be selected. Go to the next digit that isn't a 3, 8, 9, or 0. Continue in this way until three students have been selected. For example, starting on the fifth line of the random digit table, 6 6 0 4 1 ..., students with numbers 6, 4, and 1 would be selected.

   b. Start at a random spot in the table. If the first digit is 1, 2, 3, 4, 5, or 6, let it represent the corresponding face on a die. If the digit is 7, 8, 9, or 0, ignore it and go on to the next digit. Keep going until a 6 appears. For example, starting on the third line of the random digit table, 5 1 5 8 4   7 2 3 0 5   4 6 ..., nine rolls would be required to get a 6. (The 8, 7, and 0 are ignored.)

   c. One way is to associate even numbers in the table with heads and odd numbers with tails. Then consider the digits in the table two at a time. Keep going until you arrive at a pair in which both digits are even. For example, in the string

   $$25 \quad 85 \quad 17 \quad 54 \quad 08 \quad 55 \quad 11$$

   five two-coin tosses would be required to get the desired two heads.

4. This situation is an example of the collector's problem.

   a. Assuming the prizes are randomly and equally distributed, the probability you will get a multiplying coin trick is $\frac{1}{7}$.

   b. To perform one trial: start at a random spot in the table. If the digit is a 1, it represents the money clip trick; if it is a 2, it represents the mind-reading trick; ... if it is a 7, it represents the multiplying coin trick. If the digit is an 8, 9, or 0, ignore it and go to the next digit. Keep going until all of the digits 1, 2, 3, 4, 5, 6, and 7 have appeared. For example, starting on the sixth line of the random digit table, 6 4 7 8 3 0 5 3 2 0   7 7 8 5 9   7 4 6 9 3   6 3 6 8 0   2 1 ..., 19 boxes would have to be purchased before getting all seven tricks.

   c. Models will vary but should be equivalent to the model outlined above.

   d. Responses will vary.

NOTE: For the subsequent trials, tell students to continue in the random digit table where they left off previously.

CONSTRUCTING A MATH TOOLKIT: Students should keep a copy of the Table of Random Digits (Teaching Master 184) in the Probability and Statistics section of their Math Toolkits.

Unit 7

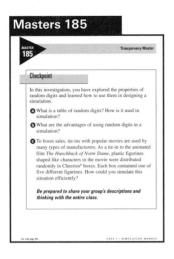

4. e. A typical table might look like this one:

Number of Boxes to Get All 7 Tricks	Frequency
7	1
8	3
9	4
10	11
11	13
12	18
13	22
14	13
15	9
16	8

Number of Boxes to Get All 7 Tricks	Frequency
17	10
18	11
19	13
20	12
21	4
22	8
23	3
24	0
25	0
26 or more	37
Total Number of Trials	**200**

f. Multiply the number of boxes purchased by the frequency. Add these products and then divide the sum by 200.

(The theoretical average number of boxes purchased is about 18. In general, the theoretical waiting time to get n equally likely prizes is

$$\frac{n}{n} + \frac{n}{n-1} + \frac{n}{n-2} + \cdots + \frac{n}{3} + \frac{n}{2} + \frac{n}{1}$$

This formula is based on the observation that if the probability of an event is p, the average or expected number of trials before it occurs is $\frac{1}{p}$. For example, suppose we have 3 of the 7 magic tricks already. The probability of getting a new trick in the next box purchased is $\frac{4}{7}$. So, on the average, we would have to purchase $\frac{7}{4} = 1\frac{3}{4}$ additional boxes to get a new magic trick.)

g. Without simulation, you could buy boxes of Cheerios® to estimate the average number of boxes needed. But obviously simulation is faster, more practical, and less expensive. Actually buying the boxes is better if the assumptions in Part a can't reasonably be made.

h. Responses may vary. However, the balance point of the histogram should be at the computed average.

i. The histogram is skewed right and is not the same shape as any other histogram so far in this unit. The shape of the histogram is roughly this:

See additional Teaching Notes on page T528H.

e. Complete a total of 200 trials of this simulation by sharing the work among the groups in your class. Complete a frequency table for the class data. Add additional rows if they are needed.

f. Find the average number of boxes purchased to obtain a complete set of the seven tricks. Use the frequency table and your calculator as needed. How does this estimate compare with the prediction you gave in Part c of the "Think About This Situation" on page 498?

g. If you didn't use simulation, how else could you estimate the average number of boxes needed? Which method is preferable? Why?

h. Make a histogram of the information in your frequency table. Explain how your histogram verifies that your answer to Part f is reasonable.

i. Describe the shape of your histogram. Is the shape of this distribution similar to any others you have constructed in this unit? If so, identify the situations related to those histograms.

Checkpoint

In this investigation, you have explored the properties of random digits and learned how to use them in designing a simulation.

ⓐ What is a table of random digits? How is it used in simulation?

ⓑ What are the advantages of using random digits in a simulation?

ⓒ To boost sales, tie-ins with popular movies are used by many types of manufacturers. As a tie-in to the animated film *The Hunchback of Notre Dame*, plastic figurines shaped like characters in the movie were distributed randomly in Cheerios boxes. Each box contained one of five different figurines. How could you simulate this situation efficiently?

Be prepared to share your group's descriptions and thinking with the entire class.

▶ On Your Own

A teacher notices that of the last 20 single-day absences in her class, 10 were on Friday. She wants to know if this can be attributed reasonably to chance or if she should look for another explanation.

a. Assuming that absences are equally likely to occur on each day of the school week, describe how to conduct one trial simulating the days of the week for 20 single-day absences using a table of random digits.

b. Conduct 10 trials. Place the results in a frequency table showing the number of absences that are on Friday.

c. Based on your simulation, what is your estimate of the probability of getting 10 or more absences out of 20 on Friday just by chance? What should the teacher conclude?

d. What is your estimate of the average number of absences on Friday, assuming that the 20 absences are equally likely to occur on each day of the week?

e. How could you get better estimates for Parts c and d?

INVESTIGATION ▶ 2 Simulation Using a Random Number Generator

A table of random digits is a convenient tool to use in conducting simulations. Playing cards and regular polyhedra models with numbered faces, such as dice, are sometimes useful. However, a more versatile tool is a calculator or computer software with a *random number generator*.

1. Investigate the nature of the numbers produced by the random number generator on your calculator or computer software. On some calculators, the generator is abbreviated "rand."

    a. How many decimal places do the numbers usually have? Do some have one fewer place? If so, why?

    b. Between what two whole numbers do all the random numbers lie?

    c. Generate random numbers of the form "6 rand" (or "6 × rand"). Between what two whole numbers do all the random numbers lie?

    d. Between what two whole numbers do the random numbers lie when "rand" is multiplied by 10? By 36? By 100?

On Your Own

This situation is an example of a binomial distribution.

a. For example, assign the digits 0 and 1 to Monday, 2 and 3 to Tuesday, 4 and 5 to Wednesday, 6 and 7 to Thursday, and 8 and 9 to Friday. Begin at a random point in the table and look at the following 20 digits. The number of 8s and 9s will correspond to the number of absences that occurred on Friday.

b. To conduct 10 trials, students will need to consider 10 sets of 20 digits. The table below is close to the theoretical one.

Number of Absences

on Friday	Frequency
0	0
1	1
2	1
3	2
4	2
5	2
6	1
7	1
8	0
Total Number of Trials	10

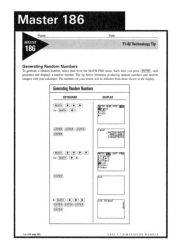

Master 186

Master 187

c. According to the table above, if absences are equally likely to occur on each day of the week then the probability that 10 or more absences out of 20 will be on Friday is 0. This is found by evaluating

$$\frac{\text{number of trials with ten or more absences on Friday}}{10}$$

The theoretical probability is 0.0026. The absences on Friday in the teacher's class cannot reasonably be attributed to chance. The teacher should look for another explanation for the large number of Friday absences.

d. Responses will vary. According to the table above, the average number of absences on Friday is 4. This is also the theoretical answer. Because only 10 trials were done, there may be a lot of variation from student to student in this response. Make sure each student's response agrees with his or her simulation.

e. You could get better estimates by performing more trials.

MORE
ASSIGNMENT   pp. 505–512

Students can now begin Organizing Task 1 or Reflecting Task 2 from the MORE assignment following Investigation 2.

EXPLORE small-group investigation

INVESTIGATION 2 Simulation Using a Random Number Generator

See Teaching Masters 186–187.

Random number generators speed up the work of performing trials. However, students still should go through all of the *steps* in a simulation.

> See additional Teaching Notes on page T528I.

Unit 7

1. e. ■ The integers {0, 1, 2, 3, 4, 5} are generated by the command "int 6 rand".

■ It truncates or cuts off the part of the number to the right of the decimal point.

f. ■ Use "int 6 rand + 1".

■ The lists of random numbers will vary.

2. a. The integers from 1 to 10 inclusive are generated by the command "int 10 rand + 1".

b. ■ int 23 rand + 1   ■ int 100 rand + 1

■ int 52 rand + 1   ■ int 7 rand

3. Responses may vary. A sample simulation model is given for each situation.

a. Use "int 2 rand" and associate 0 with heads and 1 with tails.

b. Assign each student a unique number between 1 and 7, inclusive. Then generate numbers using "int 7 rand + 1" until three different digits have been given.

c. Assign each student a unique number between 1 and 50, inclusive. Generate numbers using "int 50 rand + 1" until six different digits have been given.

d. Using "int 6 rand + 1", press ENTER until a 6 occurs.

e. Associate a digit between 1 and 7 with each magic trick available, then use "int 7 rand + 1" and press ENTER once.

f. Two possible simulations are described here.

Since there are 52 cards and 4 aces, the probability of drawing an ace is $\frac{1}{13}$. Let the number 13 represent an ace and, using "int 13 rand + 1", press ENTER and see if a 13 occurs.

Use "int 52 rand + 1" and assign 1, 2, 3, and 4 as aces.

NOTE: When students use software the mechanics are hidden from sight, and this may cause students to think less clearly about what a trial would be, what would be recorded, and what question is going to be answered. In Activity 4, students may use the *Collections* (COLLECT) software. This program runs trials where random numbers (1 through 7) are generated, and the length of the wait-time for all seven numbers to appear is noted. The software then creates a frequency table from these trials, and finally displays a histogram. You will want to talk this through with your students before they use the software. You could ask:

"What is a trial? What would be recorded? What would the labels be on the frequency table?"

You also will want to check for understanding of the output. As you listen to the students answering the questions in this activity, have them compare and interpret results. If it seems to you that their answers to the questions in the activity are superficial or vague, you can push them for specifics. You could ask:

"Where is the highest bar on Jane's graph? What does it mean? Where is the highest bar on Tony's graph? What does that mean?"

"Is it likely that we'd get all 7 tricks in the first seven boxes? What does the bar above the 7 look like in Jane's graph? On Tony's graph?"

"Can you say whether it is likely or not that we'd have to buy 30 boxes to complete the collection?"

"Are all the graphs the same shape? What is that shape? What does that shape tell you?"

---

e. Generate several numbers using the command "int 6 rand."

- What random numbers are generated by this function?

- What is the effect of the "int" function?

f. To simulate rolling a die, you need a random digit selected from the set 1, 2, 3, 4, 5, 6. In Part e, you generated random digits from the set 0, 1, 2, 3, 4, 5.

- How could you modify the command "int 6 rand" to produce the numbers on the faces of a die? Try it.

- Generate a list of 10 digits randomly selected from the set 1, 2, 3, 4, 5, 6.

2. Now explore how to generate random digits from other sets of numbers.

a. What random digits are generated by the command "int 10 rand + 1"?

b. Modify the command in Part a to generate random digits from the set:

- 1 to 23 inclusive   ■ 1 to 100 inclusive

- 1 to 52 inclusive   ■ 0 to 6 inclusive

Test your modified commands.

3. Next, consider some of the possible contexts in which a random number generator might be useful.

a. Explain how you could use the random number generator to simulate the flips of a fair coin.

b. Explain how you could use the random number generator to select three students at random from a group of seven students. Perform one trial of this simulation.

c. Explain how you could use the random number generator to select six students at random from a group of 50 students. Perform one trial of this simulation.

d. Explain how you could use the random number generator to simulate the experiment of rolling a die until you get a six. Perform one trial of this simulation.

e. Explain how you could use the random number generator to simulate checking a box of Cheerios for which magic trick it contains. Perform one trial of this simulation.

f. Explain how you could use the random number generator to simulate the experiment of drawing a card from a well-shuffled deck of 52 playing cards and checking if it is an ace. Perform one trial of this simulation.

Unit 7

4. Software for computers and calculators has been developed to help you quickly conduct many trials of a simulation. This activity will illustrate how you can use such software to implement your simulation model for the Cheerios problem. The calculator software *Collections* (COLLECT) is an example.

a. Use such software to conduct 25 trials of collecting the seven magic tricks.

b. Study a histogram of the results of your 25 trials. What do the bars in the display represent?

c. Compare your histogram with those of other members of your group. Are they the same? If not, what accounts for the differences?

d. With the COLLECT program, you can use the arrow keys to explore the histogram. What do the "min =," "max =," and "n =" mean? (Remember that the number between two bars belongs in the bar to the right of the number.)

e. What is your estimate of the average number of boxes of cereal you would have to buy before you obtained all 7 tricks? (With COLLECT, press ⟨ENTER⟩ from the histogram screen. This information will be displayed.)

f. Have each member of your group use the software to conduct different numbers of trials (for example, 50, 75, or 99). Record and compare your results.

g. Suppose the cereal manufacturer modified its marketing scheme. It randomly packaged one of six differently colored pens in each box of cereal. Use the software to help you estimate the average number of boxes of Cheerios you would have to purchase in order to get a complete set of the six pens.

Checkpoint

When using a calculator or computer to generate random numbers,

ⓐ how can you control the size of these numbers?

ⓑ how can you ensure they will be integers?

Be prepared to share your group's thinking with the class.

4. **a.** Results of the trials will vary.

b. A sample histogram is shown here. Each bar represents the number of trials in which it took the "min" value of boxes to get all 7 tricks.

c. The histograms will vary since the numbers are generated randomly.

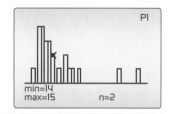

NOTE: The bars are each 1 unit in width, as can be seen by the trace key. They may appear different in size because the display is based on pixels which are not continuous.

d. "Min" refers to the number of boxes of cereal that were required to obtain all 7 tricks in the bar being considered. "Max" refers to the number of boxes required in the bar to the right. Finally, "$n =$" refers to the frequency, or the number of times collecting all 7 tricks took "min" boxes of cereal.

e. Responses will vary. The theoretical average is about 18 boxes. The average for the histogram above is 15.28 boxes.

f. Responses will vary.

g. Have students use COLLECT with $I = 6$ and various numbers of trials. The theoretical average with six colors is 14.7 boxes. One sample of 50 trials using COLLECT gave an average of 15.06 boxes to collect all 6 pens.

SHARE AND SUMMARIZE   full-class discussion

Checkpoint

See Teaching Master 188.

ⓐ You can control the size of the random numbers generated by multiplying by a constant. If you want to generate numbers between 0 and n, exclusive, use the command "n rand".

ⓑ You can ensure these numbers are integers by using the "int" command: "int n rand" generates integers from 0 to $(n - 1)$.

CONSTRUCTING A MATH TOOLKIT: Students should add the random number generating process to their Math Toolkits for future reference (Teaching Master 199).

JOURNAL ENTRY: Write two questions that can be answered using the COLLECT software. Then describe what input you would need to provide and how you would interpret the output from the software to answer your question.

▶**On Your Own**

This situation is an example of a binomial distribution.

a. Lynn has $\frac{1}{4}$ chance of getting each question right. We need to pick a random digit from 1, 2, 3, and 4 using the calculator or computer. If the digit is, say, a "1," Lynn selected the right answer. Repeat this ten times and count the number of 1s.

b. A typical table may look like this one.

Number of Correct Answers	Frequency
0	0
1	3
2	4
3	6
4	3
5	3
6	1
7	0
8	0
9	0
10	0
Total Number of Trials	20

c. To estimate this probability students need to evaluate

$$\frac{\text{number of trials with seven or more correct answers}}{20}$$

The estimate from the frequency table above is 0. The theoretical answer is 0.0035.

Modeling: 1 and 2
Organizing: 4, and 1 or 3*
Reflecting: 3 and choice of one*
Extending: Choose one*

*When choice is indicated, it is important to leave the choice to the student.
NOTE: *It is best if Organizing tasks are discussed as a whole class after they have been assigned as homework.*

Modeling

1. This situation is an example of the collector's problem.

　a. Responses may vary. There are five different prizes. Assume that the chance of getting any specific prize is $\frac{1}{5}$ each time a box of Cracker Jack® is purchased. Use the numbers 1, 2, 3, 4, and 5 to represent the prizes, and go through the random digit table until you get all of 1, 2, 3, 4, and 5, ignoring the digits 6, 7, 8, 9, and 0.

On Your Own

Lynn is taking a 10-question multiple-choice test. Each question offers four possible choices for the answer. She didn't study and doesn't even have a reasonable guess on any of the questions. For each question, Lynn selects one of the four possible answers at random.

a. Describe how to conduct one trial simulating a 10-question test. Use the random number generator on your calculator or a computer.

b. Conduct 20 trials and place the results in a frequency table.

c. What is your estimate of the probability that Lynn will pass the test with a score of 70% or more?

MORE
Modeling • Organizing • Reflecting • Extending

Modeling

1. Cracker Jack®, the caramel corn-peanut snack, traditionally gives a prize in each box. At one time, it offered five different prizes.

   a. Describe how to conduct one trial of a simulation for estimating the number of boxes of Cracker Jack® you would have to buy before you get all five prizes. What assumptions are you making?

   b. Conduct five trials. Copy the following frequency table, which has the results from 195 trials. Add the results from your five trials to the table.

Number of Boxes Purchased	Frequency
5	6
6	15
7	23
8	18
9	21
10	18
11	15
12	15
13	11
14	11
15	10

Number of Boxes Purchased	Frequency
16	6
17	6
18	8
19	1
20	2
21	4
22	0
23	0
24	1
25	2
26	0

Number of Boxes Purchased	Frequency
27	1
28	0
29	0
30	0
31	0
32	0
33	0
34	0
35	0
36	1

c. What is the average number of boxes purchased in the 200 trials to get all five prizes?

d. Make a histogram of the (*number of boxes purchased, frequency*) data. Describe the shape of the histogram.

e. Explain how you can use the histogram to verify the average you found in Part c.

2. Toni doesn't have a key ring and so just drops her keys into the bottom of her backpack. Her four keys—a house key, a car key, a locker key, and a key to her bicycle lock—are all about the same size.

a. If she reaches into her backpack and grabs the first key she touches, what is the probability it is her car key?

If the key drawn is not her car key, she holds onto it. Then, without looking, she reaches into her backpack for a second key. If that key is not her car key, she holds on to both keys drawn and reaches in for a third key.

b. Do the chances that Toni will grab her car key increase, decrease, or remain the same on each grab? Explain your reasoning.

1. **b.** Responses will vary. For example, in this simulation a 1 was added to the frequency for the numbers 5, 7, 8, 16, and 27.

Number of Boxes Purchased	Frequency	Number of Boxes Purchased	Frequency
5	7	21	4
6	15	22	0
7	24	23	0
8	19	24	1
9	21	25	2
10	18	26	0
11	15	27	2
12	15	28	0
13	11	29	0
14	11	30	0
15	10	31	0
16	7	32	0
17	6	33	0
18	8	34	0
19	1	35	0
20	2	36	1

c. Using the simulation above, $5(7) + 6(15) + 7(24) + \cdots = 2{,}271$. The average number of boxes purchased is $\frac{2{,}271}{200}$ or 11.355. The theoretical average number of boxes is 11.4.

d. The histogram has a minimum at 5 and a maximum at 36. It is strongly skewed to the right, with gaps at 22, 23, 26, and 28 through 35. (With a larger number of trials, these gaps would fill in and the tail would get longer.)

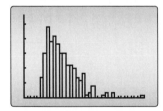
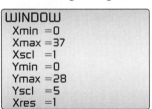

e. The average number of boxes is 11.355, so the histogram should "balance" at about 11.

2. **a.** The probability that the first key she touches is her car key is $\frac{1}{4}$.

b. The chances that Toni will grab her car key increase on each grab. For example, if she grabs her house key first, then the chance she will get her car key on the next (second) draw is $\frac{1}{3}$.

2. c. Let the digit 1 represent the house key, the digit 2 represent the car key, the digit 3 represent the locker key, and the digit 4 represent the bicycle key. Ignore all other digits. Start at a random spot in the random digit table and count the number of digits required until "2" appears. This time, do not count repeats of the digits 1, 3, and 4. For example, starting on the third line of the random digit table,

$$5\ 1\ 5\ 8\ 4\ \ 7\ 1\ 2\ ...$$

Toni gets her car key on the third draw.

Alternatively, with a calculator use the instruction "int 4 rand + 1" and count the number of digits until a 2 appears, ignoring repetitions of the digits 1, 3, and 4.

d. Responses will vary. Our simulation resulted in the numbers 1, 1, 1, 2, 2, 2, 2, 3, 3, 3, so 3 was added to the frequency for 1, 4 was added for 2, and 3 was added for 3.

Number of Keys Toni Needs to Grab to Get Her Car Key	Frequency
1	256
2	254
3	236
4	254
Total Number of Trials	1,000

e. The estimate from the table above is $\frac{254}{1,000}$ or about 25%.

f. Theoretically, all of these outcomes are equally likely. There is no reason why Toni's car key should appear first, for example, more often than fourth.

3. a. One description follows. There are 16 different items. Assume that the chance of getting any specific item is $\frac{1}{16}$ each time a box of cereal is purchased. Use the numbers 01, 02, 03, and 04 to represent the yellow items; 05, 06, 07, and 08 to represent the pink items; 09, 10, 11, and 12 to represent the blue items; and 13, 14, 15, and 16 to represent the lavender items. Go through the random digit table in pairs until you get all of 13, 14, 15, and 16. Ignore all pairs of digits other than 01 through 16. This is a case where simulating this using a random number generator along with the command "int 16 rand + 1" will be more efficient than using a table of random digits.

b. Responses may vary. For example, the following numbers of boxes have been added to the stem-and-leaf plot: 25, 33, 49, 22, 15.

```
1 | 0 4 4 5 6 6 8 8 9
2 | 0 1 2 2 2 3 4 4 5 6 6 7 7 8 8 9 9
3 | 1 3 3 3 3 4 4 5 7 8
4 | 0 1 4 5 6 9
5 | 0 0 1 6 7 8 8
6 | 6                        2|4 represents 24.
```

c. According to the data above, $\frac{\text{needed more than 15 boxes}}{\text{total number of trials}}$ is $\frac{46}{50}$ or 92%. So 92% of the time we would expect to need to purchase more than 15 boxes of cereal to get a complete set all in lavender.

d. According to the data above, the estimate of the average number of boxes to be purchased is 32.3.

e. Since the plot is skewed right, the median should be less than the mean. The median for the above data is 29, which indeed is lower than the mean.

c. Describe how to conduct one trial of a simulation to estimate the probability that Toni has to grab all four keys before she gets her car key. Use a table of random digits, a calculator, or computer software to conduct the trial.

d. Conduct 10 trials. Copy the frequency table below and add your results so that there is a total of 1,000 trials.

Number of Keys Toni Needs to Grab to Get Her Car Key	Frequency
1	253
2	250
3	233
4	254
Total Number of Trials	

e. What is your estimate of the probability that Toni has to grab all four keys before she gets her car key?

f. From the frequency table, it appears that the numbers of keys needed are equally likely. Explain why this is the case.

3. One cereal promotion offered one of four items for little girls: a comb, a mirror, a barrette, or a bracelet. The catch was that each item came in four colors: yellow, pink, blue, and lavender. Suppose that María wants a complete set, all in lavender.

a. Describe how to use a table of random digits or a random number generator to conduct one trial simulating the number of boxes María's family will have to buy. What assumptions are you making?

b. Conduct five trials. Add your results to a copy of the stem-and-leaf plot at the right. There will be a total of 50 trials.

c. What is your estimate of the probability that more than 15 boxes of cereal must be purchased to get a complete set all in lavender?

1	04466889
2	012234466778899
3	133344578
4	01456
5	0016788
6	6

2|4 represents 24

d. What is your estimate of the average number of boxes that must be purchased?

e. Will the median number of boxes be more or less than the average? Find the median to check your prediction.

LESSON 2 • ESTIMATING EXPECTED VALUES AND PROBABILITIES **507**

4. Suppose Whitney also knows about the promotion described in Modeling Task 3. She wants a complete set in one color, but any color is okay.

a. Describe how to use a table of random digits or a random number generator to conduct one trial simulating the number of boxes Whitney's family will have to buy. What assumptions are you making?

b. Conduct 10 trials. Combine your results with those from other members of your group. Place the results in a frequency table.

c. What is your estimate of the probability that more than 15 boxes of cereal must be purchased to get a complete set all in the same color?

d. What is your estimate of the average number of boxes that must be purchased?

5. The card below shows a McDonald's-Atari Asteroids® scratch-off game. All of the asteroids were originally covered. The instructions say:

Start anywhere. Rub off silver asteroids one at a time. Match 2 identical prizes BEFORE a "ZAP" appears and win that prize. There is only one winning match per card.

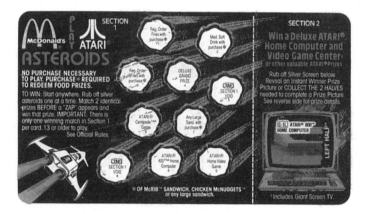

a. Describe how to conduct one trial of a simulation to determine the probability of winning the prize in the scratch-off game. Share your instructions for how to perform a trial with your group. Modify the sets of instructions to reach a consensus on the model.

b. Exchange your instructions with another group. Conduct 20 trials using the other group's model.

c. Combine the results from all of the groups in your class and estimate the probability of winning the prize.

4. a. There are 16 different items. We will assume that the chance of getting any specific item is $\frac{1}{16}$ each time a box of cereal is purchased. We will use the numbers 01, 02, 03, and 04 to represent the yellow items; 05, 06, 07, and 08 to represent the pink items; 09, 10, 11, and 12 to represent the blue items; and 13, 14, 15, and 16 to represent the lavender items. We will go through the random digit table in pairs until we get all of either 01, 02, 03, 04; or 05, 06, 07, 08; or 09, 10, 11, 12; or 13, 14, 15, 16. We will ignore 00, 17, 18, ... , 99. (That's a lot of pairs to ignore. Your students may come up with a more efficient way to use the table.)

Alternatively, with a calculator use the instruction "int 16 rand + 1". Look for all four of 01–04, 05–08, 09–12, or 13–16. This is a much more efficient simulation than the one described above.

b. Responses will vary. One simulation of 10 trials follows.

Number of Boxes Needed to Get One Complete Set in any Color	Frequency	Number of Boxes Needed to Get One Complete Set in any Color	Frequency
8	1	15	1
9	0	16	1
10	1	17	1
11	0	18	1
12	1	19	0
13	2	20	0
14	1	21	0

c. Responses may vary. For the above data, our estimate of the probability that more than 15 boxes of cereal would be required to get a complete set is $\frac{3}{10}$ or 30%.

d. Responses may vary. For the above data, our estimate of the average number of boxes needed to get one complete set in any one color is

$$\frac{8(1) + 10(1) + 12(1) + 13(2) + \cdots + 18(1)}{10} = \frac{136}{10} = 13.6$$

5. a. One easy way to do the simulation is to number the 10 asteroids from 1 to 10. Shuffle ten playing cards, the ace through ten, and turn them over one at a time to represent scratching off the asteroids.

b–c. Combine the results from all groups to get a good estimate. The theoretical probability of winning the prize (fries with purchase) is $\frac{1}{6}$. There are only four asteroids that matter, the two Zaps and the two matching fries. The probability of scratching off the two fries before either Zap is (*probability of scratching off fries from the 4 asteroids*) · (*probability of scratching off fries from the remaining 3 asteroids given one fries has been scratched off*), which is $\left(\frac{2}{4}\right)\left(\frac{1}{3}\right)$ or $\frac{1}{6}$.

Unit 7

Organizing

1. **a.** Box plots will vary depending on the data from the simulation. The right part of the box and the right whisker should be longer than their counterparts on the left, reflecting the fact that the distribution is skewed right.

   b. This question is asking for the median number of boxes. For the typical distribution given in Activity 4, Part e, of Investigation 1 (page 501), the median occurs between the 100th and 101st values, which is 16 boxes. The median is less than the mean, which is typical of distributions which are skewed right.

2. Responses will vary. Box plots for Modeling Tasks 1, 3, and 4 should have the same basic shape as the one made in Organizing Task 1.

3. Responses to Parts a through f will vary. The response that is provided here is based on the theoretical averages.

   a. 3 boxes

   b. 5.5 boxes

   c. 11.42 boxes

   d. 21.74 boxes

   e. 71.95 boxes

   f. The data lie approximately on a straight line.

   The equation for the regression line is approximately $y = 3.9x - 7.8$. Adding one prize results in about 3.9 additional boxes that need to be purchased.

   (In fact, the relationship isn't linear. For n prizes, the average number of boxes purchased is approximately $n(\ln n) + 0.577n + \frac{1}{2}$.)

4. **a.** The "words" are in alphabetical order—called *lexicographic order* in combinatorics.

   b. AB
   BA
   There are two permutations.

Organizing

1. Make a box plot of the data from the 200 trials simulating the Cheerios problem in Part e of Activity 4 (page 501).

   a. How does the shape of the box plot reflect the shape of the histogram you prepared for Part h of that activity? In which direction are the plots skewed?

   b. Complete this sentence about the distribution of boxes purchased to get all 7 magic tricks: *Half of the time, a person who wanted all seven magic tricks would have to buy at least _____ boxes of Cheerios.* Does this statement refer to the average number of boxes or the median number of boxes?

2. Make a box plot of the distribution in one of the Modeling tasks you completed. Compare this box plot to the one you made in Organizing Task 1. Do the two plots have the same basic shape? Explain.

3. Suppose different cereal companies have packaged in their boxes the number of different prizes given below. Carry out simulations to estimate the average number of boxes that would have to be purchased to get all of the prizes in each case. (The software you used for Activity 4, Investigation 2 on page 504 would be helpful.)

   a. 2 different prizes   b. 3 different prizes

   c. 5 different prizes   d. 8 different prizes

   e. 20 different prizes

   f. Create a table with column headings "Number of Prizes" and "Average Number of Boxes Purchased." Fill the table with your responses to Parts e and g of Activity 4, Investigation 2 (page 504) and your data for this task (Parts a–e above). Make a scatterplot of the (*number of prizes, average number of boxes purchased*) data.

   ■ Does a linear model fit these data reasonably well? If so, find the regression line. If not, describe the shape of the graph.

   ■ About how many additional boxes must be purchased if one more type of prize is added to the boxes?

4. Toni's key selection problem (Modeling Task 2) is one that depends on *order*—the order in which she chooses the keys. One way to model the problem would be to list all the possible orders in which the keys could be selected. An ordering of a set of objects is called a **permutation** of the objects. For example, the permutations of the letters A, B, and C are:

   ABC   ACB   BAC   BCA   CAB   CBA

   a. In what special sequence are the permutations above listed?

   b. List all of the permutations of the letters A and B. How many are there?

Unit 7

c. List all of the permutations of the letters A, B, C, and D. How many are there?

d. Look for a pattern relating the number of permutations to the number of letters.

e. How many permutations do you think there are of the letters A, B, C, D, and E? Check your conjecture by listing all of the permutations or by using the permutations option on your calculator or computer software. (For most calculators, you need to enter "5 nPr 5". This means the number of permutations of 5 objects taken 5 at a time.)

f. How many permutations are there of Toni's four keys? What is the probability that all four keys have to be drawn before Toni gets her car key?

Reflecting

1. You have conducted simulations by coin flipping and by using random digits from a table, calculator, or computer.

  a. Which of these simulation tools is easiest for you to understand?

  b. Which tool is the most flexible in simulating a variety of situations?

  c. Which tool do you find easiest to use?

2. A deck of playing cards can be used to simulate some situations.

  a. How could you use cards to conduct one trial in a simulation of collecting Cheerios tricks?

  b. How could you use cards to generate a table of random digits?

3. Consider the calculator command "int 12 rand + 1".

  a. What random numbers are generated by this command?

  b. Give an example of a real-life situation which might lead to a simulation model involving use of this calculator or computer command.

4. Do you think it is faster to do a simulation using a table of random digits or using a calculator to generate random digits? Design and carry out an experiment to answer this question. Write a brief summary describing your experiment and findings.

5. The COLLECT program will conduct up to 99 trials of certain simulations. Suppose you need 200 trials simulating a collecting problem. How could you use the program to help you?

4. c.

ABCD	BACD	CABD	DABC
ABDC	BADC	CADB	DACB
ACBD	BCAD	CBAD	DBAC
ACDB	BCDA	CBDA	DBCA
ADBC	BDAC	CDAB	DCAB
ADCB	BDCA	CDBA	DCBA

There are 24 permutations.

d. The number of permutations of n objects is $n(n - 1)(n - 2) \cdots 3 \cdot 2 \cdot 1$ or $n!$. Students probably will not know the factorial notation but should be able to find this pattern if they organize the results of Parts a–c in a table.

e. See Teaching Masters 189–190.

There are 120 permutations.

f. There are 24 orders for Toni's four keys. (Label the keys A, B, C, and D. As figured in Part c above, there are 24 ways of permuting the 4 letters.) The probability that the car key is the last one drawn is

$$\frac{\text{number of favorable outcomes}}{\text{number of possible outcomes}} = \frac{6}{24} = \frac{1}{4}$$

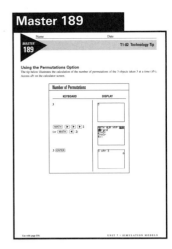

Reflecting

1. Responses will vary.
2. Responses may vary.
    a. Use seven different cards. Let each card represent a particular trick and then shuffle the cards and pick one.
    b. Use the ace through 10 only and let the 10 stand for zero. Shuffle the cards and pick them one by one and put the number in a table. Be sure to replace the card and shuffle after each card is drawn.
3. **a.** There are 12 integers randomly generated. The "+1" means the numbers begin at 1 and go to 12.
    b. Responses will vary. The 12 numbers could represent the months of the year, years in school (first through twelfth), signs of the zodiac, *etc.*
4. Responses will vary. Responses will depend on the student's ability to use the table and the calculator, and on the situation that is being simulated.
5. Responses may vary. Students may choose to do two sets of 99 trials plus one set of two more trials, 4 sets of 50 trials, or some other combination that gives a total of 200 trials.

Unit 7

MORE *continued*

Extending

1. Simulations will vary. For example, suppose that four times as many disappearing coin tricks are put into the boxes as each of the other six tricks. Using a random digit table, let the digits 0, 1, 2, 3, 4, and 5 represent the other tricks and 6, 7, 8, 9 represent the disappearing coin trick.

   For example, suppose the random digits begin like this:

28918	69578	88231	33276	70997	79936
56865	05859	00106	31595	0154	

   Then one trial of this simulation took 54 boxes to get all seven tricks.

   If the tricks aren't equally likely to get, the average number of boxes purchased will be larger. Think of the extreme situation such as one of those scratch-off games where the grand prize winner must collect, say, each of the letters YOU WIN from the inside wrappers of a candy bar. It's very hard to get all six letters because only one or two of the wrappers has, say, the letter W.

2. This situation is sometimes called the hat check problem or the secretary's problem.

   a. One way to simulate this is to start at a random place on the random digit table, and let the first digit represent the card selected by the first person. If that digit is a 3, for example, then person number 1 is assigned the gift brought by person number 3. The next digit represents the card selected by the second person. If it's a 3, ignore it and go to the next digit. For example, starting at line ten of the random digit table:
   3 5 5 6 5 3 5 6 9 0 3 6 8 9 9 9 7 1 2 2 8 9 3 1 2 3 2 0 8 6 2 3 7 3 0 9 4 …
   Person number 1 gets the gift brought by person number 3.
   Person number 2 gets the gift brought by person number 5.
   Person number 3 gets the gift brought by person number 6.
   Person number 4 gets the gift brought by person number 9.
   Person number 5 gets the gift brought by person number 0.
   Person number 6 gets the gift brought by person number 8.
   Person number 7 gets the gift brought by person number 7.
   Person number 8 gets the gift brought by person number 1.
   Person number 9 gets the gift brought by person number 2.
   Person number 0 gets the gift brought by person number 4.
   Person number 7 gets her or his own name.

   With a calculator, use the instruction "int 10 rand". It is easier and much faster to do this problem with ten playing cards, the ace through ten. Shuffle them and count them out. Notice the above simulation assumes a class size of 10. Students should tailor their simulation to reflect the number of students in their class.

   b. Responses will vary.

   c. The theoretical probability that at least one person will draw his or her own name in a gift exchange involving n people is almost independent of n and is roughly 0.63.

See additional Teaching Notes on page T528I.

Unit 7

Extending

1. There is some evidence that either there were more of some of the Cheerios magic tricks than others, or the magic tricks weren't put into the boxes randomly. (This might happen, for example, if all of the boxes containing the disappearing coin trick were sent to California.) Suppose you are more likely to get some magic tricks than others. Will the average number of boxes purchased in order to get all seven magic tricks be more, the same, or less than if each trick is equally likely? Design and carry out a simulation to answer this question.

2. Suppose your class is having a holiday gift exchange. The name of each student is written on a card. The cards are placed in a hat, mixed up, and each student draws one. One of your classmates wonders how many students will draw their own names.

   a. Describe one trial of a simulation of this situation. Use cards or a table of random digits.

   b. Conduct 50 trials. Place the results in a table that shows the number of students who got their own name.

   c. What is your estimate of the probability that at least one student will get his or her own name?

   d. What is your estimate of the average number of students who will get their own names?

3. In Extending Task 2, you answered these two questions:

   ■ What is the probability that at least one student will get his or her own name?

   ■ What is the average number of students who will get their own names?

   Will the answers to these two questions change with larger or smaller class sizes than yours? Design and carry out simulations to test your prediction. Write a summary of your findings.

4. One type of CD player will hold five CDs. The player can be set so that it selects a CD at random and plays a song on that CD. It then continues selecting CDs at random from all five CDs and playing songs. Describe one trial of a simulation to estimate the probability that there is at least one song from each of the five CDs among the first ten songs played.

Unit 7

5. Imagine 10 people in a room.

   a. What is your estimate of the probability that two of them have the same birthday?

   b. Describe a simulation model to determine the probability that two people out of a group of 10 people have the same birthday. What assumptions are you making?

   c. Conduct 100 trials, sharing the work with other members of your class.

   d. From your simulation, what is your estimate of the probability? Are you surprised?

   e. Investigate the probability that two people will have the same birthday if there are 20 people in the room. Repeat for cases when there are 30, 40, 60, and 80 people in the room.

   f. People often make too much of coincidences. Write an explanation of the following Drabble cartoon for a child who doesn't "get it."

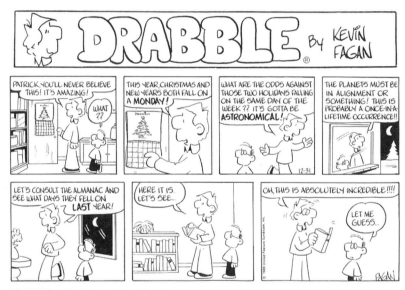

DRABBLE reprinted by permission of United Feature Syndicate, Inc.

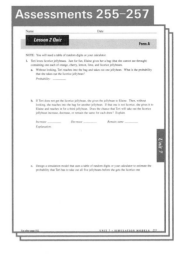

5. This situation is called the birthday problem.

    a. Responses will vary. Most estimates probably will be lower than the theoretical probability of 0.12. Do not reveal the theoretical probability at this point.

    b. Start at a random spot in a random digit table. Take the digits three at a time. If the three digit number is 000 or 367 to 999, ignore it. (The three-digit number gives the day of the year the person was born.) After looking at ten triples, see if any are the same. For example, starting at the eighth line of the random digit table, we have these triples:

        030 600 139 672 035 593 880 488 470 800 011
        019 125 247 330 400 699 275 235 …

    and there are no repeated birthdays.

    Alternatively, use the instruction "int 366 rand + 1" on the calculator, and generate 10 random numbers. (December 31 is represented by 366 so that February 29 can have a number. This presents a slight and insignificant problem as the probability of a birthday of February 29 is only $\frac{1}{4}$ that of other dates. It would perhaps be better to ignore the possibility of February 29.)

    This simulation assumes that all birthdays are equally likely and that the 10 people are a random sample of people.

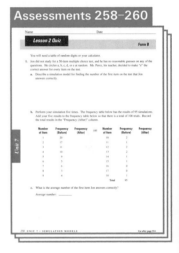

    c. Responses will vary.

    d. The theoretical probability is about 0.12, which students probably will find higher than they estimated.

    e. Here are the theoretical probabilities:

Number of People	Probability of At Least One Matching Birthday
20	0.41
30	0.71
40	0.89
60	0.99
80	0.9999

    f. Christmas and New Year's Day are always on the same day of the week since they are always seven days apart.

> **See additional Teaching Notes on page T528J.**

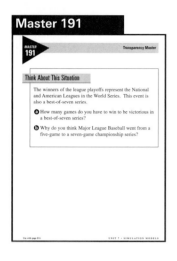

Lesson 3 *Simulation and the Law of Large Numbers*

LESSON OVERVIEW The purpose of this lesson is to help students understand the Law of Large Numbers. That is, as a trial is repeated more and more times, the estimated probability tends to approach the theoretical probability. The setting for this idea is a championship series in sports. By the end of the lesson, students should see that the better team is more likely to win a longer series than a shorter one. (See also E. Lee May, Jr.: "Are seven-game baseball playoffs fairer?" *The Mathematics Teacher* 85, 1992, 528–531.)

Lesson Objectives

- To use paired random digits to simulate probabilistic situations
- To understand that with a larger number of trials the estimated probability tends to be closer to the true probability than with a smaller number of trials (the Law of Large Numbers)
- To have more practice simulating binomial situations

LAUNCH full-class discussion

Think About This Situation

NOTE: You may need to have a student explain how the World Series is played.

See Teaching Master 191.

ⓐ To win a best-of-seven series you must win four games.

ⓑ Responses will vary. One obvious reason is that it should result in more ticket sales and revenue from concessions and television. Encourage students to think of mathematical reasons.

  Some students may already have some sense that a longer series is more "fair" than a shorter series, but will have difficulty giving a reason. An insightful reason at this stage might be: "Because a longer series gives us a better chance to estimate a team's 'true' ability."

NOTE: Before students begin work on this investigation, you may wish once again to discuss the steps involved in a simulation on Teaching Master 183, "Steps in a Simulation." This will help the students when they are working on the more complicated simulations in this lesson.

EXPLORE small-group investigation

INVESTIGATION 1 How Many Games Should You Play?

1. **a.** The probability that the Cyclones would win is 0.6.
   b. The Cyclones would be expected to win about 6 games and the Hornets would be expected to win about 4 games. This is because the Cyclones should win about 60% of the time, or 6 games out of 10.

Simulation and the Law of Large Numbers

In 1985, Major League Baseball switched from a best-of-five league playoff series to a best-of-seven league playoff series. In a best-of-five series, the team that first wins three games wins the series.

Think About This Situation

The winners of the league playoffs represent the National and American Leagues in the World Series. This event is also a best-of-seven series.

a How many games do you have to win to be victorious in a best-of-seven series?

b Why do you think Major League Baseball went from a five-game to a seven-game championship series?

INVESTIGATION ▶ 1 How Many Games Should You Play?

In this investigation, you will explore playoff series of various lengths. You will begin with the simplified situation in which the probability a team wins stays the same from game to game.

1. The Cyclones are playing the Hornets for the softball championship. Based on their history, the Cyclones have a 60% chance of beating the Hornets in any one game.

   a. Suppose the championship series were only one game long. What is the probability that the better team (Cyclones) would win?

   b. Suppose the Cyclones and the Hornets were to play 10 games. About how many games would you expect the Cyclones to win? The Hornets? Explain your reasoning.

c. Describe how you would design one trial of a simulation model for a one-game series. Use a table of random digits or a random number generator. How will you split the numbers so that the Cyclones have a 60% chance of winning and the Hornets have a 40% chance of winning?

d. Why isn't it appropriate to use a coin flip in your model to determine which team wins a game?

2. Should an even number of games be used for a playoff series? Explain your reasoning.

3. Suppose the Cyclones and the Hornets play a three-game series. A three-game series ends after one team wins two games.

a. Describe how to conduct one trial of a simulation model for a three-game series.

b. Describe how you could use 200 trials of your simulation model to estimate the probability that the better team (Cyclones) will win a best-of-three series.

c. Conduct 200 trials. Share the work among the groups in your class. Record your data in a frequency table like the one below.

Number of Games Won by the Cyclones in a Best-of-Three Series	Frequency
0	
1	
2	
Total Number of Trials	200

d. Which rows represent a win of the championship series by the Cyclones? By the Hornets?

e. What is your estimate of the probability that the Cyclones will win a best-of-three series?

4. Next, explore the idea of a five-game series between the same two teams.

a. Describe how to conduct one trial of a simulation model for a best-of-five series.

b. Describe how you could use your simulation model to estimate the probability that the Cyclones will win a best-of-five series.

c. Conduct 200 trials by sharing the work among the groups in your class. Record your data in a frequency table where the number of games won by the Cyclones goes from 0 to 3. Why do you only need numbers up to 3?

1. **c.** Since the Cyclones have a 60% chance of winning, the numbers need to be assigned so that, theoretically, 60% of them will represent a win by the Cyclones. For example, assign the digits 0, 1, 2, 3, 4, and 5 to the Cyclones and the digits 6, 7, 8, and 9 to the Hornets. Start at a random spot in the random digit table or use the instruction "int 10 rand" on the calculator. If the digit is a 0, 1, 2, 3, 4, or 5, that represents a Cyclone win; if the digit is a 6, 7, 8, or 9, that represents a Hornet win.

   d. It's not appropriate to flip a coin because that would give both teams a 50% chance of winning the game.

2. No, because at the end of an even number of games the series might be split evenly and there would be no winner.

3. **a.** Responses may vary. One method for simulating this situation is described here. Assign the digits 0, 1, 2, 3, 4, and 5 to the Cyclones and the digits 6, 7, 8, and 9 to the Hornets. Start at a random spot in the random digit table or use the instruction "int 10 rand" on the calculator. If the first digit is a 0, 1, 2, 3, 4, or 5, that represents a Cyclones win in the first; if the digit is a 6, 7, 8, or 9, that represents a Hornets win. Keep looking at digits until one team has won two games. (Students also may use "int 1000 rand" and examine the three digits as separate games. They must realize that if the Hornets win the first two games, there is no third game and the Cyclones win zero games even if the third digit is a 0, 1, 2, 3, 4, or 5.)

> NOTE: Remind students that we are making the simplifying, but unrealistic, assumption that the Cyclones' chance of winning each game is 0.6. More sophisticated simulations can be designed that use more realistic assumptions.

   b. The trial described in Part a needs to be done 200 times. On a random digit table, you may continue reading three-digit groups of numbers, ignoring the third digit if one team wins the first two games. The estimated probability that the Cyclones will win is the ratio of the number of series won (which is the number of two-game wins) to the total number of series played.

   c. A table with frequencies close to the theoretical one follows.

Number of Games Won by the Cyclones in a Three-Game Series	Frequency	Theoretical Probability
0	32	0.16
1	38	0.192
2	130	0.648
Total Number of Trials	200	

   d. The last row represents a win of the playoff series by the Cyclones. The first two rows represent a win of the playoff series by the Hornets.

   e. The estimate from the table in Part c is $\frac{130}{200} = 0.65$. (The theoretical probability is 0.648.)

4. **a.** One example is to assign the digits 0, 1, 2, 3, 4, and 5 to the Cyclones and the digits 6, 7, 8, and 9 to the Hornets. Start at a random spot in the random digit table or use the instruction "int 10 rand" on the calculator. If the first digit is a 0, 1, 2, 3, 4, or 5, that represents a Cyclones win in the first game; if the digit is a 6, 7, 8, or 9, that represents a Hornets win. Go to the second digit to see who wins the second game. Keep looking at digits until one team has won three games.

   b. Perform many trials of the simulation. The probability of the Cyclones winning would be the ratio of the number of three-game wins to the total number of trials.

See additional Teaching Notes on page T528J.

Unit 7

4. **d.** Responses will vary. The estimate from the table in Part c is $\frac{137}{200} = 0.685$. (The theoretical probability is about 0.683.)

5. **a.** One example is to assign the digits 0, 1, 2, 3, 4, and 5 to the Cyclones and the digits 6, 7, 8, and 9 to the Hornets. Start at a random spot in the random digit table or use the instruction "int 10 rand" on the calculator. If the first digit is a 0, 1, 2, 3, 4, or 5, that represents a Cyclones win in the first game; if the digit is a 6, 7, 8, or 9, that represents a Hornets win. Go to the second digit to see who wins the second game. Keep looking at digits until one team has won four games.

   b. Run many trials of the simulation. The probability of the Cyclones winning would be the ratio of the number of 4-game wins to the total number of trials.

   c. A table with frequencies close to the theoretical ones follows.

Number of Games Won by the Cyclones	Frequency	Theoretical Probability
0	5	0.0256
1	12	0.06144
2	18	0.09216
3	22	0.110592
4	143	0.710208
Total Number of Trials	200	

   d. Responses will vary. The estimate from the table in Part b is $\frac{143}{200} = 0.715$. (The theoretical probability is about 0.710.)

6. These are the theoretical probabilities. The results from the students' simulations may not be this clear cut.

Type of Series	Estimate of Probability that Cyclones Win
One game	0.60
Best of three	0.65
Best of five	0.68
Best of seven	0.71

See additional Teaching Notes on page T528K.

Unit 7

d. What is your estimate of the probability that the Cyclones will win a best-of-five series?

5. Now explore the idea of a seven-game series for the same teams.

   a. Describe how to conduct one trial of a simulation for a seven-game series.

   b. Describe how you could use your simulation to estimate the probability that the Cyclones will win a best-of-seven series.

   c. Conduct 200 trials. Share the work among the groups in your class. Place your results in a frequency table showing the number of games won by the Cyclones.

   d. What is your estimate of the probability that the Cyclones will win a best-of-seven series?

6. Complete the table below using the results from Activity 1 Part a and Activities 3, 4, and 5.

Type of Series	Estimate of Probability the Cyclones Win
One game	
Best-of-three	
Best-of-five	
Best-of-seven	

   a. What pattern do you observe in the table? Which team, the Cyclones or the Hornets, would have the better chance to win a best-of-nine series? Estimate the probability of their winning.

   b. Improve your estimate in Part a by carrying out a simulation.

   c. From a mathematical point of view, why do you now think that Major League Baseball went from a five-game to a seven-game championship series?

7. Make histograms of your frequency tables from Activities 3–5. How are these histograms alike? How are they different?

8. Tennis players have two chances to make a legal serve. Monica makes about 50% of her *first* serves. If she has to try a *second* serve, Monica makes about 80% of those.

   a. Describe how to use a table of random digits to conduct one trial simulating this situation.

   b. Describe how to use a random number generator to conduct one trial simulating this situation.

c. Conduct one trial of your simulation model and record the result in a frequency table. Your frequency table should have three rows: Makes First Serve, Misses First Serve and Makes Second Serve, and Double-Faults (misses both serves).

d. Conduct 50 trials.

e. Estimate the probability that Monica double-faults.

In the previous situations, the percentages of *success*—winning a game or making a serve—were multiples of 10. In those cases, you may have used single digits from your random digits table or from your calculator. Often, as in the next two situations, the percentages are not as "nice."

9. A survey of high school seniors found that 29% had seen a movie in the previous two weeks.

a. Describe how to conduct one trial of a simulation to estimate the number of recent movie-goers in a randomly selected group of 20 seniors.

b. Conduct 10 trials, placing the results on a number line plot that shows the number of recent movie-goers in each group of 20 randomly selected students.

10. In the 50-year history of National Basketball Association finals, the home team has won about 71% of the games. Suppose that the Los Angeles Lakers are playing the Philadelphia 76ers in the NBA finals. The two teams are equally good, except for this home team advantage. The finals are a best-of-seven series. The first two games will be played in Philadelphia, the next three (if needed) in Los Angeles, and the final two (if needed) in Philadelphia.

a. What is the probability that the 76ers will win a game if it is at home? What is the probability that the 76ers will win a game if it is played in Los Angeles? What is the probability the 76ers will win the first game of the series? The second game? The third game? The fourth game? The fifth game? The sixth game? The seventh game?

b. Describe how to conduct one trial to simulate a finals series.

c. Conduct 200 trials by sharing the work among the groups in your class. Place the results in a frequency table like the one on the next page.

8. c. Responses will vary.

  d. Responses will vary. One possible response is given below.

Type of Serve	Frequency
Makes First Serve	24
Misses First Serve and Makes Second	21
Misses Both	5

  e. The theoretical probability that Monica double-faults is $(0.5)(0.2) = 0.10$. Student estimates should be the number of double-faults divided by 50.

9. This situation is an example of a binomial distribution.

  a. Responses may vary. Start at a random place in the table of random digits. Look at the first 20 pairs of digits. Let the pairs 01 through 29 represent movie-goers and the other pairs represent non-movie-goers. Count the number of "movie-goer" pairs.

  b. A typical line plot might look like this:

10. a. We are assuming that the only difference between the teams is the home court advantage. Thus, the probability the 76ers will win a home game is 0.71 and an away game is 0.29. The probabilities that the 76ers will win each game are 0.71, 0.71, 0.29, 0.29, 0.29, 0.71, and 0.71.

  b. Responses will vary. One possibility is to use the "int" and "rand" functions as follows: Randomly generate integers 1 to 100, inclusive, using the "int 100 rand + 1" command. For the games played in Philadelphia (the first, second, and sixth and seventh if needed), let the numbers 1 through 71 represent a win by the 76ers. For the games played in Los Angeles, let the numbers 72 through 100 represent a win by the 76ers. These different representations account for the home court advantage.

Unit 7

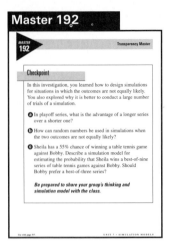

EXPLORE *continued*

10. c. Results will vary. The frequencies in the table below are close to the theoretical.

Number of Games Won by the 76ers	Frequency	Theoretical Probability
0	9	0.042
1	34	0.172
2	22	0.109
3	21	0.102
4	115	0.575
Total Number of Trials	200	

d. Students should look at the ratio of the number of times the 76ers won four games to the total number of games played. The theoretical probability is about 0.575.

e. Results will vary. Again students could use the "int 100 rand + 1" to generate the integers 1 to 100, inclusive. This time, for the games played in Los Angeles (games 1 through 3), let the integers 72 through 100 represent a 76ers win. For the games in Philadelphia (if necessary), let the integers 1 through 71 represent a 76ers win. The frequencies in the table below are close to the theoretical values.

Number of Games Won by 76ers	Frequency	Theoretical Probability
0	21	0.104
1	22	0.110
2	22	0.109
3	20	0.102
4	115	0.575
Total Number of Trials	200	

The theoretical probability that the 76ers win this series is also 0.575, which will surprise most students.

f. The proposed scheme would still give the 76ers the same chance of winning, but probably would be perceived to be unfair. Moving between the cities also gives the players a chance to rest and may build excitement in the two cities. It doesn't matter in what order the four Philadelphia and three Los Angeles games are scheduled, which is a counterintuitive result.

SHARE AND SUMMARIZE full-class discussion

Checkpoint

CONSTRUCTING A MATH TOOLKIT: After completing the Checkpoint, have students add the "Steps in a Simulation" handout (Teaching Master 183) to their Math Toolkits.

See Teaching Master 192.

ⓐ Because a longer series contains more "trials" than a shorter series, the percentage of games won by the better team is more likely to be closer to the overall percentage for that team. (Notice that this is the percentage of games won, not the probability that the better team wins the series.) Therefore, the better team is more likely to win in a longer series.

See additional Teaching Notes on page T528K.

Number of Games Won by the 76ers	Frequency
0	
1	
2	
3	
4	
Total Number of Trials	200

d. What is your estimate of the probability that the 76ers win the finals?

e. Suppose that, to cut travel costs, the NBA schedules three games in Los Angeles followed by four in Philadelphia.

- Design a simulation to determine the probability that the 76ers win the finals in this situation.

- Conduct 200 trials by sharing the work with other groups.

- What is your estimate of the probability that the 76ers win this series?

f. Compare the probabilities in Parts d and e. What is your conclusion?

Checkpoint

In this investigation, you learned how to design simulations for situations in which the outcomes are not equally likely. You also explored why it is better to conduct a large number of trials of a simulation.

ⓐ In playoff series, what is the advantage of a longer series over a shorter one?

ⓑ How can random numbers be used in simulations when the two outcomes are not equally likely?

ⓒ Sheila has a 55% chance of winning a table tennis game against Bobby. Describe a simulation model for estimating the probability that Sheila wins a best-of-nine series of table tennis games against Bobby. Should Bobby prefer a best-of-three series?

Be prepared to share your group's thinking and simulation model with the class.

The simulations in this unit were based on a variation of the **Law of Large Numbers**. The Law of Large Numbers says, for example, that if you roll a die more and more times, the proportion of fives tends to get closer to $\frac{1}{6}$. The

Cyclones have a 60% chance of winning each game. For a very long series, the Law of Large Numbers says that the percentage of games the Cyclones win tends to be close to 60%. (So the Cyclones are almost sure to win a very long series.)

▶ **On Your Own**

Recall that in Major League Baseball, the World Series is a best-of-seven-games series. In Modeling Task 3 on page 492, you estimated the probability that the World Series will go seven games if the teams are equally matched. That probability is actually 0.3125.

a. Suppose the two teams aren't evenly matched. Do you think the World Series is more likely to go seven games or less likely to go seven games than if the teams are evenly matched? Why?

b. Suppose that the teams are not evenly matched and that the American League team has a 70% chance of winning each game. Describe how to conduct one trial of a best-of-seven series for this situation.

c. Conduct 5 trials. Add your results to a copy of the frequency table below so that there is a total of 100 trials.

Number of Games Needed in the Series	Frequency
4	24
5	30
6	24
7	17
Total Number of Trials	

d. What is your estimate of the probability that the series will go seven games in this case? Is this probability of a seven-game series more or less than when the teams are evenly matched?

On Your Own

a. If the teams aren't evenly matched, the series is less likely to go the full seven games. Think of the extreme situation where one team is almost sure to win each game. The series will probably be over in four games.

b. Responses will vary. One example is to assign the digits 0, 1, 2, 3, 4, 5, and 6 to the American League team and the digits 7, 8, and 9 to the National League team. Start at a random spot in the random digit table or use the instruction "int 10 rand" on the calculator. If the first digit is a 0, 1, 2, 3, 4, 5, or 6, that represents an American League win in the first game. If the digit is a 7, 8, or 9, that represents a National League win. Look at the second digit to see who wins the second game. Keep looking at digits until one team has won four games.

c. The table below is close to the theoretical one.

Number of Games Needed in the Series	Frequency	Theoretical Probability
4	25	0.2482
5	31	0.3108
6	26	0.25578
7	18	0.18522
Total Number of Trials	100	

d. The theoretical probability that the series will go seven games is about 0.185. This is less than when the teams are evenly matched, which has a probability of 0.31.

Unit 7

MORE
ASSIGNMENT *pp. 519–525*

Modeling: 1 and 2
Organizing: 1
Reflecting: 1 and 2
Extending: Choose one*

*When choice is indicated, it is important to leave the choice to the student.
NOTE: *It is best if Organizing tasks are discussed as a whole class after they have been assigned as homework.*

Modeling

1. **This situation is an example of a binomial distribution.**

   a. To model this situation, you could let the digits 1, 2, 3, 4, 5, and 6 represent a student who took chemistry or physics. The digits 7, 8, 9, and 0 could represent a student who did not take chemistry or physics.

   b. Responses will vary. In our simulation, a 1 was added to the frequency for rows 6, 7, 9, 10, and 11.

Number Who Took Chemistry or Physics	Percentage Who Took Chemistry or Physics	Frequency
6	30	4
7	35	3
8	40	17
9	45	40
10	50	52
11	55	54
12	60	80
13	65	66
14	70	39
15	75	29
16	80	13
17	85	3
Total Number of Trials		400

   c. Responses may vary. This histogram below matches the data in Part b.

   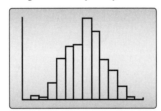 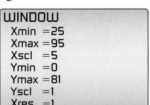

   d. Responses may vary. In our simulation, the probability that fewer than half of 20 randomly selected students took chemistry or physics is 0.16 or 16% (40 + 17 + 3 + 4 = 64, out of 400). The theoretical probability is about 0.13 or 13%.

MORE
Modeling • Organizing • Reflecting • Extending

Modeling

1. About 60% of high school transcripts in the United States show that the student has taken a chemistry or physics course.

   a. Describe how to conduct one trial of a simulation to estimate the number of students who took a high school chemistry or physics course in a randomly selected group of 20 high school graduates.

   b. Conduct 5 trials. Add your results to a copy of the frequency table below so there is a total of 400 trials.

Number Who Took Chemistry or Physics	Percentage Who Took Chemistry or Physics	Frequency
6	30	3
7	35	2
8	40	17
9	45	39
10	50	51
11	55	53
12	60	80
13	65	66
14	70	39
15	75	29
16	80	13
17	85	3
Total Number of Trials		

   c. Make a histogram of these results. Place "Percentage Who Took Chemistry or Physics" on the horizontal axis.

   d. When 20 students are randomly selected, what is your estimate of the probability that fewer than half took chemistry or physics in high school?

2. The following histogram shows the result of 400 trials of a simulation. The situation modeled is the same as in Task 1 except that 80 students were randomly selected.

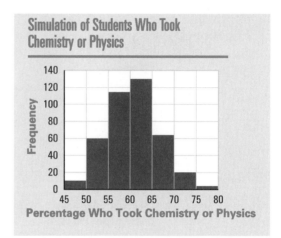

Simulation of Students Who Took Chemistry or Physics

a. Estimate the probability that fewer than half of 80 randomly selected students took chemistry or physics.

b. Why do you think the probabilities in Part d of Modeling Task 1 and Part a above are different?

c. Describe how the histograms from Modeling Tasks 1 and 2 are different. Why would you expect this to be the case? How do these histograms illustrate the Law of Large Numbers?

d. Estimate the probability that fewer than half of a random selection of 320 students took chemistry or physics in high school. Explain your reasoning.

3. Several years ago, a survey found that 25% of American pet owners carry pictures of their pets in their wallets.

a. Assume this percentage is true. Describe how to simulate determining if a randomly chosen American pet owner carries a picture of his or her pet. Use a calculator, computer, or table of random digits in your simulation.

b. Describe how to conduct one trial that models how many people in a random sample of 20 American pet owners carry pictures of their pets.

c. Perform 10 trials of your simulation. Add your results to a copy of the following frequency table so that there is a total of 100 trials.

2. **This situation is an example of a binomial distribution.**
   a. From the histogram, the estimated probability is 10 out of 400, or 0.025.
   b. As the sample size increases, the percentage in the sample tends to get closer to the theoretical probability. Since the probability that a student took chemistry or physics is 60%, in a larger sample we would expect close to 60% of that sample of students took chemistry or physics. Thus, as the sample size increases, the probability that fewer than half of the sample took chemistry or physics decreases, which explains the difference in responses for Modeling Task 1, Part d, and Modeling Task 2, Part a.
   c. Modeling Task 1 has a larger spread and the tails are longer on each side. For Modeling Task 2, the distribution varies less from 60%. We expect this to be the case from the Law of Large Numbers because of the larger sample size in Modeling Task 2.
   d. Responses will vary. Students should estimate the probability is very, very close to 0, which it is.

3. **This situation is an example of a binomial distribution.**
   a. Responses may vary. Start at a random spot in the random digit table. Look at the first digit. If the digit is a 0, the person carries a picture of his or her pet. If the digit is a 1, 2, or 3, the person doesn't. If the digit is a 4, 5, 6, 7, 8, or 9, ignore it and go to the next digit.

   Alternatively, use "int 4 rand" on the calculator to generate numbers from 0 to 3, and proceed as described above.
   b. Follow the procedure in Part a, looking at 20 digits randomly selected (more if some digits are ignored).

Unit 7

3. c. Responses may vary. Our simulation gave the following result: 3, 7, 5, 3, 6, 1, 2, 5, 4, and 9.

Number of People With a Picture of Their Pet	Frequency
0	0
1	3
2	7
3	14
4	18
5	20
6	16
7	11
8	5
9	4
10	1
11	1
Total Number of Trials	100

d. Responses will vary. If the survey of 20 people finds one or zero people with pictures of pets, or 10 or more people with pictures of pets, that would be a rare event that would need explaining.

4. This situation is an example of a binomial distribution.

a. The library expects 80% or 24 people to show up. However, it certainly is possible that all will show up.

b. $(0.80)x = 25$, so $x = 31.25$ or 31 people. The library should take 31 reservations so that 25 are expected to show up. Certainly more than 25 people could show up.

c. Responses may vary. Start in a random spot in the random digit table. Look at the first digit. If the digit is a 0, the person doesn't show up. If the digit is a 1, 2, 3, or 4, the person shows up. Ignore the digits 5, 6, 7, 8, and 9 and go on to the next digit. Record the results for the 30 digits.

Or, instead of reducing 20% to $\frac{1}{5}$, students may choose to use the digits 0 and 1 to represent a no-show and the digits 2, 3, 4, 5, 6, 7, 8, and 9 for those who show up. There would be no need to ignore any digits. Record the results for 30 digits.

Alternatively, use the following instructions on the calculator:

"int 5 rand + 1"　(for numbers generated from 1 to 5)

"int 10 rand + 1"　(for numbers generated from 1 to 10)

Then proceed as described in the similar situation above.

See additional Teaching Notes on page T528L.

Number of People with a Picture of Their Pet	Frequency
0	0
1	2
2	6
3	12
4	17
5	18

Number of People with a Picture of Their Pet	Frequency
6	15
7	10
8	5
9	3
10	1
11	1
Total Number of Trials	

d. Take a survey of 20 American pet owners to see how many carry pictures of their pets in their wallets. Do you have any reason to doubt the reported figure of 25%?

4. A library has 25 computers which must be reserved in advance. The library estimates that people will decide independently whether or not to show up for their reserved time and that for each person there is an 80% chance that he or she will show up.

a. If the library takes 30 reservations for each time period, how many are expected to actually show up? Is it possible that all 30 will show up?

b. How many reservations should the library take so that 25 are expected to show up? Is it possible that if the library takes this many reservations, more than 25 people will show up?

c. Suppose the library decides to take 30 reservations. Describe one trial in a simulation of this situation.

d. Conduct 5 trials. Add your results to a copy of the frequency table below so that there is a total of 55 trials.

Number of People Who Show Up	Frequency
19	0
20	1
21	2
22	3
23	5
24	8

Number of People Who Show Up	Frequency
25	9
26	9
27	7
28	4
29	2
30	0
Total Number of Trials	

LESSON 3 • SIMULATION AND THE LAW OF LARGE NUMBERS   **521**

e. Make a histogram of the results of this simulation. Describe the shape of your histogram.

f. Suppose the library takes 30 reservations. Based on your simulation, estimate the probability that more than 25 people show up. Is 30 a reasonable number of reservations to take? Should the library take fewer or could it get away with taking more?

g. What assumption made in this simulation is different from the real-life situation being modeled?

Organizing

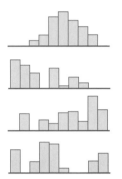

1. Examine all of the histograms that you have made in this unit. Group them according to their general shape. What observations can you make about the shapes and kinds of probability situations associated with them? For example, which kinds of situations give distributions that have line symmetry?

2. Explain why it is important to conduct as many trials as you can in a simulation.

3. Suppose you want to be at least 95% sure that a probability estimate from a simulation is within a certain *margin of error* of the actual probability. The formula gives the number of trials n needed in order to estimate within a margin of

$$n = \frac{1}{E^2}$$

error E.

For example, suppose you want to estimate the probability that a bent coin comes up heads. You want to be at least 95% sure your estimated probability is within $E = 0.1$ (10%) of the actual probability. You need to perform trials of the simulation.

$$n = \frac{1}{(0.1)^2} = \frac{1}{0.01} = 100$$

Being "at least 95% sure" means that out of every 100 simulations you perform, you expect that in 95 or more of them your estimated probability is within E of the actual probability.

a. Suppose you want to estimate a probability in a simulation and be at least 95% sure that your estimated probability is within 5% of the actual probability. How many trials should you perform?

b. In some of the simulations in this unit, you performed 200 trials. What is the margin of error associated with 200 trials of a simulation?

c. What is the margin of error associated with 1,000 trials of a simulation?

4. e. The histogram has a minimum of 20 and a maximum of 29. It is almost symmetric, and is centered around 25.

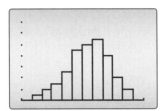 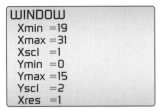

f. Responses may vary. Given the sample data, the probability that more than 25 show up is 0.45 or 45% $\left(\frac{11 + 8 + 4 + 2}{55} = \frac{25}{55}\right)$. Since there is a 45% chance that more than 25 people will show up if 30 people have reservations, the library probably should take fewer reservations. A more reasonable number of reservations would be 27 or 28.

g. This simulation assumes that each person decides independently whether or not to keep their reservation. However, for a real situation, people probably won't decide independently whether or not to show up. For example, some people may plan to drive together.

Organizing

1. The collector's problems, such as the Cheerios® and Cracker Jack® problems, have histograms that are skewed to the right.

   In geometric or waiting-time situations such as "having a child until you have a boy," the distribution has the highest bar at the left, the next highest to the right of that, and so on.

   In binomial situations such as the True-False tests and selecting students for a weapons search, the distributions are more symmetrical in shape. When $p = 0.5$, the distributions are symmetrical. When p is farther from 0.5, the distribution is more skewed.

2. The larger the number of trials, the closer you can expect the estimated probability to be to the theoretical probability.

3. a. $n = \frac{1}{0.05^2} = \frac{1}{0.0025} = 400$

   You should perform at least 400 trials to be at least 95% sure that the estimated probability is within 5% of the actual probability.

b. $200 = \frac{1}{E^2}$ or $E^2 = \frac{1}{200}$, so $E \approx 0.0707$ or 7.07%.

   The margin of error associated with 200 trials is approximately 7%.

c. $1{,}000 = \frac{1}{E^2}$ or $E^2 = \frac{1}{1{,}000}$, so $E \approx 0.0316$ or 3.16%.

   The margin of error associated with 1,000 trials is approximately 3.16%.

Unit 7

4. **a.** Since $n = \frac{1}{E^2}$, let y represent the number of trials n and let x represent the margin of error E.

   b. A reasonable choice for Xscl is 0.01. By using Xmin = 0.01 and Xmax = 0.15, we get y values from 44.44 to 10,000. Good choices for Ymin and Ymax are 0 and 10,000, respectively. Reasonable choices for Yscl are 500 or 1,000.

   c. The graph shown below is not linear; it is a curve.

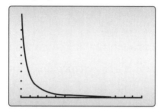

   d. Responses may vary, depending on whether students zoom in or not. At 2%, the number of trials needed is 2,500. At 3%, approximately 1,111 trials are needed. At 8%, approximately 156 trials are needed.

   e. The table-building capacity can be used with 0.01 increments to get values for y when $x = 0.01$, 0.02, and 0.08.

x	y
0.03	1,111.1
0.02	2,500.0
0.08	156.25

5. **a.** In Organizing Task 3, Part a, we saw that if we want E to be 5% then we need to do 400 trials.

   b. In Organizing Task 4, Part d, we saw that if we want E to be 0.02 then we need to perform 2,500 trials.

   c. In general, to cut a margin of error in half, the number of trials must be quadrupled. To show this algebraically, suppose $n = \frac{1}{E^2}$. Now let n^* be the number of trials needed to cut the margin of error in half: $n^* = \frac{1}{\left(\frac{1}{2}E\right)^2} = 4 \cdot \frac{1}{E^2} = 4n$.

Reflecting

1. **a.** Yes it does. As the number of tosses increases, the percentage of heads tends to get closer to 50%.

   b. Even though the percentage of heads is getting *closer* to 50%, the actual number of heads is getting *further* from the expected number of heads. Before seeing this problem, most students do not believe that this could happen.

2. Since you are the best player, you are more likely to be the winner of a long series than a short series. So you would want to play as many games as possible. (This assumes that losing a single game does not disqualify you.)

4. Use your graphing calculator or computer software to investigate the graph of the *number-of-trials* function given in Organizing Task 2.

   a. Should *x* or *y* represent the number of trials? What does the other variable represent?

   b. Set Xmin = 0.01 and Xmax = 0.15. What are reasonable choices for Xscl, Ymin, Ymax, and Yscl?

   c. Describe the shape of the graph of this function, including any symmetry.

   d. Use the trace function to estimate the number of trials needed for a margin of error of 2%, 3%, and 8%.

   e. How could you answer Part d using the table-building capability of your calculator or computer software?

5. In this task, you will investigate the number of trials of a simulation needed to cut the margin of error in half.

   a. In Organizing Task 3, you saw that with 100 trials, there is a margin of error of 10%. How many trials would you need to cut this margin of error in half?

   b. With 625 trials there is a margin of error of 4%. How many trials would you need to cut this margin of error in half?

   c. In general, to cut a margin of error in half, how must the number of trials change?

Reflecting

1. The Law of Large Numbers tells you that if you flip a coin repeatedly, the percentage of heads tends to get closer to 50%.

   a. Does the table below illustrate the Law of Large Numbers? Why or why not?

   b. Do you see a surprising result in the table? Explain why you find it surprising.

Number of Flips	Number of Heads	Percentage of Heads	Expected Number of Heads	Excess Heads
10	6	60%	5	1
100	56	56%	50	6
1,000	524	52.4%	500	24
10,000	5,140	51.4%	5,000	140

2. Suppose your class is planning a checkers tournament and you are sure you are the best player in the class. What kind of tournament rules would you propose? Explain your reasoning.

3. One simulation method, called the *Monte Carlo method*, was developed during World War II at Los Alamos, New Mexico, to solve problems that arose in the design of atomic reactors. The method is once again an area of active research, this time with applications to ecology, genetics, sociology, political science, and epidemiology (the study of the prevalence and spread of disease). Investigate the history of the Monte Carlo method and prepare a brief report.

4. You have now used simulation extensively to estimate answers to problems involving chance.

  a. What advantages do you see in using simulation?

  b. What disadvantages do you see in using simulation?

5. The mathematician Pierre Simon, Marquis de Laplace (1749–1827), once said:

  > *"It is remarkable that a science which began with the consideration of games of chance should have become the most important object of human knowledge. ... The most important questions of life are, for the most part, really only problems of probability."*

  a. What do you think Laplace meant by the last statement?

  b. Do you agree with him? Why or why not?

Pierre Simon, Marquis de Laplace

Extending

1. **Acceptance sampling** is one method that industry uses to control the quality of the parts they use. For example, a recording company buys blank cassette tapes from a supplier. To ensure the quality of these tapes, the recording company examines a sample of the tapes in each shipment. The company buys the shipment only if 5% or fewer of the tapes in the sample are defective. Assume that 10% of the tapes actually are defective.

"By a small sample we may judge the whole piece."
Miguel de Cervantes

3. Reports will vary. This information can be found in an encyclopedia.

4. **a.** By this time, students may realize that simulation is a technique that they can always use to get an approximate answer to a probability problem. With a large number of trials, the approximation can become as accurate as they wish. Many probability problems are too hard for students to solve theoretically, or so tricky that students aren't sure if they have solved it correctly. Even if they think they can work the problem theoretically, it is a good idea if they do a simulation to check their work.

   Simulation is a good technique for students to use because the process of modeling the probabilistic situation means that they must thoroughly understand the problem and clarify their assumptions.

   b. Some students will say that to get an accurate answer, a large number of trials are needed. Thus, simulation can be time-consuming and boring to carry out by hand. To avoid this, one would have to know how to program a computer. Other students will find the process of setting up a simulation quite difficult. These students should realize that once they thoroughly understand the problem, they will be able to set up a simulation.

5. Responses will vary. Look for student responses that are well thought out and that indicate some understanding of the role that probability plays in our lives.

Extending

1. **This situation is an example of a binomial distribution.**
   First note that the percentage of defective tapes is actually higher than the recording company wants. The shipments *should* be rejected. The point of this exercise is to show that in a larger sample, the proportion of defective tapes tends to be closer to 10% than in a smaller sample. Larger samples, then, tend to result in rejected shipments more often than smaller samples.

Assessments 261–263

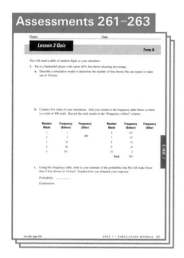

Assessments 264–266

MORE *continued*

1. **a.** Let the digit 0 represent a defective tape and the digits 1 through 9 represent good tapes. Look at 20 random digits and count the zeroes. Repeat the simulation many times. The shipment is acceptable if there are no defective tapes or only one defective tape. (Since 5% of 20 is 1, then 1 or 0 defective tapes is acceptable.) The theoretical probability that the shipment will be accepted is approximately 0.39, or 39%.

    b. The simulation will be similar to the one in Part a, but you must look at 100 digits instead of 20. The shipment is acceptable if 5 or fewer tapes are found defective. The theoretical probability that the shipment is accepted is about 0.06, or 6%.

2. **This situation is an example of a binomial distribution.**

    Look at 10 pairs of random digits to simulate the 10 seeds. Let 01, 02, … , 06 represent the event that the seed fails to germinate, and let 07, … , 98, 99, 00 represent the event that the seed does germinate. If *one or more* of the ten pairs is 01, 02, … , 06, count the trial as having at least one failed germination. Alternatively, use the random function on a calculator. Press ENTER twice and look at the digits two at a time, ignoring the decimal points. Repeat the simulation 100 times. Students should make a frequency table as shown below.

Number of Failed Germinations	Frequency
0	
1 or more	
Total Number of Trials	100

    The theoretical probability of at least one failed germination is $1 - (0.94)^{10} \approx 0.46$.

    The same simulation can be done for the 1% rate, except that 01 is the only pair of digits that would represent a failed germination. The theoretical probability of at least one is $1 - (0.99)^{10} \approx 0.096$.

3. **a.** A player who wins on the first try will be ahead $1. On the third try the player has bet a total of $1 + $2 + $4 or $7 and won $8, so is $1 ahead. On the tenth try the player has bet $1 + $2 + $4 + $8 + $16 + $32 + $64 + $128 + $256 + $512 or $1,023 and won $1,024, so is $1 ahead.

    b. The gambler is taking the chance of losing a large amount of money in order to win $1 since it's possible that the gambler will run out of money before the single win occurs. A further problem is that some casinos limit the amount a person can bet on each spin of the wheel.

    c. Responses will vary.

    d. Responses will vary.

See Assessment Resources, pages 261–266.

a. Suppose the recording company examines a sample of 20 tapes from each shipment. Design and carry out a simulation of this situation. What is your estimate of the probability that the shipment will be accepted?

b. Suppose the recording company examines a sample of 100 tapes from each shipment. Design and carry out a simulation of this situation. What is your estimate of the probability that the shipment will be accepted?

2. Laboratory tests indicate that when planted properly, 6% of a particular type of seed fail to germinate. This means that out of every 100 seeds planted according to instructions, on the average 6 do not sprout. The laboratory has been developing a new variety of the seed in which only 1% fail to germinate. Suppose that in an experiment, 10 seeds of each of the two types are planted properly.

a. For each type of seed, make a prediction of the probability that *at least one* seed out of the 10 will fail to germinate.

b. Design and carry out a simulation to estimate the chance that if 10 of the seeds with the 6% rate are planted, *at least one* will fail to germinate.

c. Design and carry out a simulation to estimate the chance that if 10 of the new variety of the seed are planted, *at least one* will fail to germinate.

d. Compare the estimates from your simulations to your predictions in Part a. What have you learned?

3. The Martingale is an old gambling system. At first glance, it looks like a winner. Here's how it would work for a player betting on red in roulette. The roulette wheel has 38 spaces; 18 of these spaces are red. On the first spin of the wheel, Tom bets $1. If red appears, he collects $2 and leaves. If he loses, he bets $2 on red on the second spin of the wheel. If red appears,  he collects $4 and leaves. If he loses, he bets $4 on red on the third spin of the wheel, and so on. Tom keeps doubling his bet until he wins.

a. If Tom wins on his first try, how much money will he be ahead? If he wins on his third try, how much money will he be ahead? If Tom finally wins on his tenth try, how much money will he be ahead?

b. From a gambler's point of view, what are some flaws in this system?

c. Design and carry out a simulation to test the Martingale system on roulette.

d. Write a report on this system for a newspaper.

Looking Back

In this unit, you have used simulation models to help solve problems involving chance. An important feature of all your models was the use of coins, dice, or random numbers to produce random outcomes. In each case, the outcomes had the same mathematical characteristics as those in the original problem.

Almost any problem involving probability or an expected value can be solved using simulation models. This final lesson of the unit provides three more such problems to help you pull together the ideas you have developed and increase your confidence in using simulation methods.

1. About 10% of the adult population of the United States are African-American.

a. Jurors are selected for duty in their city or town. Consider a city which has an African-American population representative of the U.S. population. Design a simulation model to determine the probability that a randomly selected jury of 12 people would have no African-American members. Write instructions for performing one trial of your simulation. Exchange instructions with another group.

b. Do the other group's instructions model the situation well? If necessary, modify the instructions and then conduct 5 trials. Add your results to a copy of the following frequency table so that there is a total of 200 trials.

Number of African-Americans on the Jury	Frequency	Number of African-Americans on the Jury	Frequency
0	56	3	16
1	73	4	4
2	45	5	1
		Total Number of Trials	

c. Make a histogram of the results in your frequency table.

d. What is your estimate of the probability that a randomly selected jury of 12 people would have no African-American members?

Before you and your students start the "Looking Back" lesson, you might want to refer back to the initial "Think About This Situation" on page 484 of the student text and consider the following:

How have you been able to get estimated answers for how likely an event is (such as having three girls before having a boy, or getting all 7 tricks in fewer than 10 purchases, or getting at least 75% on a True-False quiz) without any formulas?

Describe a method for solving probability problems (such as finding the probability that a couple has a son if one of the suggested alternative plans is adopted).

This should focus students on the main point, which is the power of simulation to estimate the answers to previously inaccessible problems. (Later in the curriculum, students will apply theoretical formulas to waiting-time distributions.)

1. This situation is an example of a binomial distribution.
   a. Responses may vary. For example, let the digit 4 represent an African-American. Let the other nine digits represent a person who isn't an African-American. Look at the first twelve digits in a randomly selected place in the random digit table or repeat "int 10 rand" 12 times on the calculator. Count the number of 4s. For example, starting on line ten of the random digit table, we get the digits 3 5 5 6 5 3 5 6 9 0 3 6 .... There are no African-Americans on this jury.
   b. Responses will depend on the results of each simulation. The frequencies in the table below are close to the theoretical ones.

Number of African-Americans on the Jury	Frequency	Theoretical Probability
0	57	0.282
1	75	0.3765
2	46	0.230
3	17	0.0852
4	4	0.0213
5	1	0.0038
Total Number of Trials	200	

   c. Responses will vary and will depend on the frequency table in Part b. The histogram for the frequency table above is shown at the right.
   d. In the above example, *P(no African-Americans on the jury)* $\approx \frac{57}{200}$. The theoretical probability is $(0.9)^{12} \approx 0.28$.

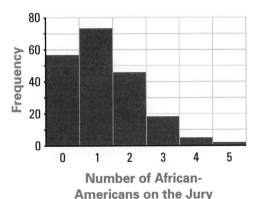

LESSON 4 • LOOKING BACK   **T526**

e. The probability is much less because there are twice as many people on a grand jury. Therefore there is a greater chance that an African-American *will* be on the jury.

f. As in Part a, let 4 represent an African-American and let the other 9 digits represent a person who is not an African-American. Repeat "int 10 rand" 24 times and count the number of 4s. Students' frequency tables will vary, but the probability that a randomly selected grand jury would have no African-American members is relatively low. The theoretical probability that the grand jury will have no African-American members is $(0.9)^{24} \approx 0.08$.

2. **This situation is an example of a binomial distribution.**

Student estimates will vary, as will their explanations.

a. Each time, the probability is $\frac{1}{7}$. Yes, because she has 10 chances at something that happens 1 time out of 7. The theoretical probability she sits in the front seat at least once is $1 - \left(\frac{6}{7}\right)^{10}$ or approximately 0.79.

b. Responses may vary. For example, choose 1 to mean that Ranjana sits in the front car, 2 to mean she sits in the second car, and so on. Since the roller coaster has only 7 cars, disregard the digits 8, 9, and 0. For each trial, look at the first 10 digits that are not 8, 9, or 0 to see how many 1s appear. The number of 1s represents the number of times she sits in the front car.

c. Responses may vary. One simulation resulted in the following table:

Number of Times in the Front Car	Frequency
0	5
1	7
2	2
3	1

d. Responses may vary. In the example simulation, Ranjana sat in the front car at least once in 10 of the 15 trials, so the estimated probability is $\frac{10}{15}$ or approximately 0.67.

e. For better estimates, perform more trials.

3. a. Responses may vary. Students should recall that as the number of trials increases, the estimated probability approaches the theoretical probability (in this case, $\frac{1}{2}$). Therefore, the number of days in which 60% or more of the babies born were boys should be smaller in the larger hospital.

b. Responses may vary. With coins, use heads for girls and tails for boys. With a table, use even digits for girls and odd digits for boys. With the calculator, use "int 2 rand + 1" and use 1s for girls and 2s for boys. The small hospital delivers only five babies per day, so one trial would consist of looking at five digits (or tossing the coin five times) and counting the number of girls. The large hospital delivers 20 babies per day, so one trial would consist of looking at 20 digits (or coin tosses) and counting the number of girls.

NOTE: This situation is an example of a binomial distribution. The problem is from the work of two psychologists, Daniel Kahneman and Amos Tversky, who did pioneer work in misconceptions about probability.

Unit 7

e. A *grand jury* decides whether there is enough evidence against a person to bring him or her to trial. A grand jury generally consists of 24 people. Do you think the probability that a randomly selected grand jury would have no African-American members is more, less, or the same as your answer to Part d? Why?

f. Describe a simulation to find the probability that a randomly selected grand jury would have no African-American members. Conduct 5 trials of your simulation model.

2. This roller coaster has 7 cars. Ranjana stands in a long line to get on the ride. When she gets to the front, she is directed by the attendant to the next empty car. No one has any choice of cars, but must take the next empty one in the coaster. Ranjana goes through the line 10 times. She likes to sit in the front car.

a. Each time she goes through the line, what is the probability Ranjana will sit in the front car? Do you think Ranjana has a good chance of sitting in the front car at least once in her 10 rides? Explain your reasoning.

b. Describe how to conduct one trial simulating this situation. Use your calculator or computer or a table of random digits.

c. Perform 15 trials. Place the results in a frequency table that lists the number of times out of the 10 rides that Ranjana sits in the front car.

d. From your simulation, what is your estimate of the probability that Ranjana will sit in the front car at least once?

e. How could you get a better estimate for Part d?

3. The chance that a newborn baby will be a girl is about $\frac{1}{2}$. Suppose that in one large hospital, 20 babies are born each day. In a smaller hospital nearby, 5 babies are born each day.

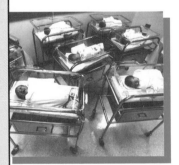

a. Do you think the size of the hospital affects the number of days in which 60% or more of the babies born are girls? If so, do you think this would happen more often in the large hospital or the small one? Explain your reasoning.

b. Describe how to conduct one trial of a simulation model to find the number of girls born on one day in the large hospital. Describe a similar model for the small hospital.

c. Conduct 20 trials of a simulation for both the large and the small hospital to test the conjecture you made in Part a. Be sure to make a histogram of your results.

d. Are the results of your simulations different from your conjecture? What should you conclude?

e. Shown below are responses to the question in Part a by a group of college undergraduates.

Small Hospital	Large Hospital	No Difference
17	15	48

Why do you think so many undergraduates believed the size of the hospital would not make a difference?

f. How is this problem related to your work in the previous lesson on the best length for a playoff series?

Checkpoint

In this unit, you learned how to model situations involving chance using simulations.

a Summarize the steps involved in using a simulation model to solve a problem involving chance.

b Will a simulation give you an "exact" answer? Explain your reasoning.

c What does the Law of Large Numbers say about how many trials should be done in a simulation?

d A letter to the *Washington Post* on May 11, 1993, suggested that China has more boys born than girls because if the first child is a boy then the parents tend to stop having children. Based on your work in this unit, do you think this is likely to be the case? Write a response to the author of this letter explaining your reasoning.

Be prepared to share your summary and explanations with the entire class.

On Your Own

Write, in outline form, a summary of the important mathematical concepts and methods developed in this unit. Organize your summary so that it can be used as a quick reference in your future work.

3. c. The results of simulations will vary. The results of one simulation (20 trials) for each hospital are summarized in the tables below.

Small Hospital
(5 births per day)

Number of Girls Born	Frequency
0	0
1	2
2	9
3	7
4	1
5	1

Large Hospital
(20 births per day)

Number of Girls Born	Frequency	Number of Girls Born	Frequency
5	1	11	2
6	0	12	1
7	3	13	3
8	4	14	1
9	0	15	1
10	4	16	0

There were 9 days in the small hospital and 6 days in the large hospital in which 60% or more of the babies born were girls.

d. The results of the 20 trials may or may not corroborate the students' conjectures.

e. Perhaps the undergraduates did not realize that the larger the number of trials, the closer the estimated probability tends to be to the theoretical probability.

f. In both cases, the larger the number of trials (either births or games), the closer the estimated probability should be to the theoretical probability.

SHARE AND SUMMARIZE full-class discussion

Checkpoint

See Teaching Master 193.

ⓐ Responses may vary. See Teaching Master 183, "Steps in a Simulation."

ⓑ A simulation usually will not give an exact answer. This is because probability experiments don't always come out exactly like we expect them to. For example, if we flip a coin 10 times we don't always get exactly 5 heads. However, the more trials that are performed, the closer we can expect the estimated answer to be to the theoretical answer.

ⓒ The Law of Large Numbers says that with more trials of the simulation, we can expect the estimated probability to be closer to the theoretical probability.

ⓓ The author of the letter is mistaken. We learned in Investigation 1 (pages 485–489) that the percentage of boys should still be 50%. There must be another reason for the large percentage of boys.

NOTE: Following the final Checkpoint of the Capstone, there is a note regarding the importance of retaining the students' Math Toolkits for next year.

Master 193

Unit 7 Summary

Assessments 267–282

Unit 7

CONSTRUCTING A MATH TOOLKIT: Following a class discussion, a summary of this Checkpoint or the unit should be included in the students' Toolkits (Teaching Master 199).

See additional Teaching Notes on page T528L.

Looking Back, Looking Ahead

▶ **Reflecting on Mathematical Content**

The fundamental concept in the statistics and probability units of this curriculum is that of distribution. In "Patterns in Data" and "Simulation Models," distributions have been represented by a graph or a table (or both) that displays all outcomes with their associated frequencies or probabilities. Students have learned that probability distributions, like histograms of data, have shapes, centers, and spreads. To develop their intuition about probability, it is important that students learn to anticipate these shapes, centers, and spreads. They will receive more practice with this in future courses.

In "Simulation Models," students learned to use simulation to construct approximate probability distributions. Simulation methods are very powerful and often provide the only approach possible to probability questions in the real world. In the Course 2 unit "Patterns in Chance," students will learn how to construct the geometric distribution exactly using mathematical theory. Geometric distributions sometimes are called "waiting-time" distributions. They model situations like the one in Lesson 1, where students simulated the situation of having children until a boy is born. In "Patterns in Chance," students will discover that this probability distribution also can be represented by a formula.

The situations studied in "Simulation Models" and in most of "Patterns in Data" were univariate (single variable). The next unit in the probability and statistics strand is "Patterns of Association" in Course 2. In that unit, students will learn more about regression, and they will be introduced to correlation. These techniques are useful with bivariate (two variable) data such as those introduced in the scatterplot lesson of "Patterns in Data."

The development of students' understanding of statistics and probability continues in two units in Course 3. In Unit 2, "Modeling Public Opinion," students will study surveys, samples, sampling distributions, the relationship between a sample and a population, confidence intervals, margin of error, and critical analysis of surveys. In Unit 5, "Patterns in Variation," students use the normal distribution as a model of variation and study the standard deviation and its properties. Students use the addition rule of probability and mutually exclusive events along with the normal distribution to understand statistical process control as used in business and industry.

In Course 4, data analysis continues to be a central idea. In Unit 3, "Logarithmic Functions and Data Models," students learn how to linearize data and fit models using log and log-log transformations. In Unit 5, "Binomial Distributions and Statistical Inference," students extend their understanding of the binomial distribution (introduced in the "Counting Models" unit) and learn how the normal approximation to the binomial distribution is used in statistical inference to test a single proportion and to compare two treatments in an experiment.

Upon completion of seven units from this strand, students will be well prepared for additional work in statistics at the college level or to take an Advanced Placement Statistics course.

▶Reflecting on Instruction

You may wish to spend a few minutes discussing with your students perceptions of their experiences in your mathematics classroom. Possible journal prompts or questions to initiate the discussion follow.

- Compare your approach to learning mathematics now to your approach at the beginning of this course.
- When I begin a new investigation, I expect that ...
- When you read a question for which the solution method is not immediately clear, what do you do?

You have been gathering much information about students' levels of understanding and disposition toward mathematics. Some of the information was used to make decisions about instruction and some for student evaluation. The Capstone, Planning a Benefits Carnival, will provide a comprehensive extended assessment. This may be used, along with selected exam tasks, as an end-of-course assessment.

Unit 7 Assessment

Lesson Quizzes	Assessment Resources
Lesson 1 *Simulating Chance Situations*	pp. 249–254
Lesson 2 *Estimating Expected Values and Probabilities*	pp. 255–260
Lesson 3 *Simulation and the Law of Large Numbers*	pp. 261–266
In-Class Exams	
Form A	pp. 267–272
Form B	pp. 273–276
Take-Home Assessments	pp. 277–278
Unit 7 Projects	
Simulating for All	pp. 279–280
Keep the Line Moving	pp. 281–282

Teaching Notes continued

Notes continued
from page T484

Think About This Situation

See Teaching Master 177.

ⓐ For our purposes, 0.5 is a close-enough estimate. (The actual probability is closer to 0.52.) The probability they won't have a son is also 0.5. The assumptions are that the probability of having a boy is the same for each set of parents and that the probability of having a boy is 0.5.

ⓑ If each family had only one child, the population would decrease rapidly, halving each generation.

ⓒ Students may offer several different plans, varying in their complexity, to solve the problem. For some of their suggestions, students will not have the facts or the ability to work out the answers for the questions. This may lead to some frustration or to disagreement. One way to take advantage of the inevitable difficulty involved in such a complex situation might be to encourage brainstorming of alternate plans, and then to assign several groups to discuss the same plan for a limited time, say 5 minutes. This highlights the disagreements about the impact of these plans, and allows you, the teacher, to say encouragingly that this unit will provide a single powerful method that works for analyzing many different complex situations. Encouraging a longer debate than usual should pay dividends in motivating the search for a strategy, and in clarifying how difficult it is to think about probability problems if the situation is at all complex.

Plans suggested by students may include:

■ Limit each couple to two children, so that they "replace" themselves. This could result in GG, GB, BG, or BB. So couples still have a $\frac{3}{4}$ chance of having at least one boy. Students may not get correct probabilities at this stage. (They may say the probability of at least one boy is 50%.) The population will stay constant with this plan, but one quarter of rural couples won't be happy.

■ Allow couples to have children until they have a boy, then no more children will be allowed. This could result in B, GB, GGB, GGGB, and so on. There is an almost 100% chance of getting a boy. Students probably will think that this results in a population increase, as they imagine all those large families of girls. In fact, if we start by analyzing 100 families and track the number of children expected under such a system, we will arrive at a total of 200 children, the number necessary to replace the population. Again, students probably will not analyze this correctly. Tell students that the situation is difficult to analyze, but that they will soon have a method of doing it.

Students may suggest educating people to value the work girls can do, before deciding on any other plan.

NOTE: Students may have heard reports that some women in the United States are combining ultrasound scans with abortion to assure the gender of their unborn child. This may come up in the students' discussion, so you may want to give some thought as to how you might deal with this topic.

Teaching Notes continued

1. a. You can simulate the birth of one child by flipping a coin. If it lands heads, the baby is a girl. If it lands tails, the baby is a boy. The assumption is that boys and girls are equally likely. When students use a coin to simulate the birth of a child, they are assuming that the probability that a baby is a boy is 0.50.

Notes continued from page T485

b. Flipping the coin twice will simulate the births of two children. The possible outcomes are: two girls, older girl and younger boy, older boy and younger girl, two boys. This simulation assumes that boys and girls are equally likely and that this probability does not change depending on the sex of the first child.

c. A typical table might look like this one:

Type of Family	Frequency
Two Girls	51
Older Girl and Younger Boy	55
Older Boy and Younger Girl	38
Two Boys	56
Total Number of Trials	200

Notes continued from page T489

JOURNAL ENTRY: There is so much to absorb in this first lesson that students should take time to reflect. This may be as straightforward as elaborating on the Checkpoint answers in their own words. Or you may want to ask students to consider other questions for which they could estimate the answers by using simulation.

■ How frequently is (or for what proportion of families is) the middle child in a three-child family a boy?

■ How often can we expect the oldest child in a four-child family to be a girl?

■ What proportion of three-child families have all girls?

■ How frequently are there two girls in a row in a three-child family?

■ What would you do to simulate any of the above situations? What would a trial look like?

Undoubtedly, you and your students can think of other questions about families that can be answered using this simulation method.

Unit 7

Notes continued from page T491

1. f. In the frequency table above, there were 200 families with a total of $97(1) + 53(2) + 27(3) + 23(3)$ or 353 children; this is an average of 1.77 children per family. This means that total population will decrease.

Type of Family	Frequency	Number of Children
First Child is a Boy	97	97
Second Child is a Boy	53	106
Third Child is a Boy	27	81
Three Girls and no Boy	23	69
Total Number of Trials	200	353

The theoretical average is 1.75 children per family. This means that total population will decrease.

g. In the frequency table above, there were 177 boys out of the 354 children, or exactly 50%. (Most students won't get exactly 50%.) The number of boys and girls should be about equal since they are equally likely on each birth.

2. This situation is an example of a binomial distribution.

a. Responses may vary. Students may choose any random device that has two equally likely events such as two colored balls, even number vs. odd number on a six-sided die, or a coin. For example, for each question Jeffrey answers, flip a coin. If the coin is heads, he guessed the right answer. If the coin is tails, he guessed the wrong answer. Flip the coin 10 times and count the number of heads, which represents the number of answers Jeffrey got right.

b. A typical frequency table might look like this one:

Number of Correct Answers	Frequency
0	0
1	0
2	3
3	5
4	8
5	16
6	10
7	8
8	0
9	0
10	0
Total Number of Trials	50

Alert students may notice that the simulation model is the same as that for the "On Your Own" on page 490. Thus, all they need to do is add 30 additional trials to those results.

Teaching Notes *continued*

Notes continued
from page T494

3.

Class Size	Number of Classes
30	95
100	5

a. The average class size reported by the school would be $\frac{(30)(95) + (100)(5)}{100}$ or 33.5 students.

b. 2,850 students have a class size of 30 and 500 students have a class size of 100.

Class Size	Number of Students
30	2,850
100	500

The students would report an average class size of $\frac{(30)(2,850) + (100)(500)}{3,350}$ or approximately 40.45 students.

c. Part a is like Task 2, Part d. Each asks about size from the point of view of the class or family. Part b is like Task 2, Part f. Each asks about size from the point of view of an individual in the class or family.

4. a. Responses may vary. For example, the faces could be labeled 1–6 so that 1, 2, or 3 could represent a girl, and 4, 5, or 6 could represent a boy. Or, even numbers could represent girls, while odd numbers represent boys.

b. Yes. Label the faces with the numbers 1–4, then let half of the faces represent the birth of a boy and the other half represent the birth of a girl. The face that lands down will determine the gender.

c. Responses will vary. Any regular solid will do, including an octahedron, dedecahedron, or icosahedron

5. a. A reasonable estimate would be the ratio of area of the circle divided by the area of the square. The area of the circle is $\pi\,(6^2)$ or approximately 113.1 in.^{2} and the area of the square is 12×12 or 144 in.^{2}. So the probability the dart lands in the circle is $\frac{113}{144}$ or approximately 78.5%.

NOTE: This task connects probability to geometry and algebra.

Unit 7

Teaching Notes continued

Notes continued from page T496

4. **a.** The frequency table and histogram given below are based on the 50 World Series playoffs which took place between 1941 and 2000. (There was no series in 1994.)

Number of Games

Played in World Series	Frequency
4	9
5	12
6	13
7	25

World Series Playoffs

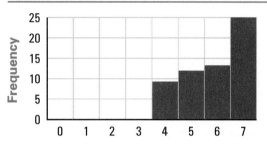

Number of Games Played in World Series

b. In both the real data and the simulation, a 4-game series is the least likely outcome. However, a 6-game and a 7-game series should be equally likely. So, there were fewer series that went six games than we would expect if the teams were equally matched.

c. Answers will vary. Students should realize that even if the teams are equally matched on each game, the results from the real World Series won't exactly match that of the simulation. The real data are not so different from the theoretical (when the teams are equally matched) that we cannot attribute the difference to chance.

Notes continued from page T498

c Responses will vary. You could revisit these predictions after students complete Activity 4 of Investigation 1 (page 500 in the student text).

d Put seven different colored balls in a bag. Draw out one and record its color. Replace it and mix up the balls. Repeat the process until all seven colors have been drawn.

Be sure students begin to think about the assumption they are making with this simulation: all prizes are equally likely on each trial. This may not be the case with prizes in cereal if, for example, one prize only is offered for a while, then another.

See Teaching Master 183 for a description of the steps in a simulation.

Teaching Notes *continued*

Notes continued from page T501

SHARE AND SUMMARIZE   full-class discussion

Checkpoint

See Teaching Master 185.

ⓐ A table of random digits is a list of the digits 0 through 9 inclusive. These numbers have two important features: the next digit in the array cannot be predicted with probability greater than $\frac{1}{10}$, and each digit occurs approximately $\frac{1}{10}$ of the time over the long run.

ⓑ It is much faster to use a table of random digits than to, say, flip a coin repeatedly. The random digits in a table generated by a calculator or computer really are rather random (actually, they are called pseudo-random as they are generated by an algorithm) while coin flipping or card drawing may not be; for example, the coin may be bent or top-heavy or the cards might not be shuffled thoroughly.

ⓒ In this case, you could associate the numbers 1 and 2 with the first figurine, 3 and 4 with the second, … , and 9 and 0 with the fifth. Begin at a random point in the table of random digits. If the first digit is a 6, for example, you have received the third figurine. Go to the next digit. If it is a 5 or 6, go to the next. Keep going this way until all five figurines have been received. Then go back and count every digit that was considered.

   For example, the string 8 0 9 5 7 3 5 6 5 0 2 would imply 11 boxes need to be purchased in order to get all five figurines.

JOURNAL ENTRY: You may wish to have students take the time to reflect on how they thought about the Cheerios® problem at the beginning of the lesson, and on any surprises they found in the results of the investigation.

NOTE: There are many new ideas here, and many of the answers students are getting may be counterintuitive. When you read the journal entries, do not be too disheartened to discover misconceptions still thriving. Research shows that these misconceptions tend to persist until students are confronted with their consequences.

Teaching Notes *continued*

Notes continued
from page T502

NOTE: As was mentioned in Part b of the last Checkpoint (page T501 of this guide), calculator- or computer-generated random numbers are really only pseudo-random as they are generated by an algorithm. Each random number generator uses a seed value. The initial seed value for all TI-82s and TI-83s is set to the same value. This means that each machine will generate the same sequence of random numbers unless the seeds are changed. To change the seeds, students will need to enter any integer into "rand." For example "453 → rand" will change the seed value for the random number generator to 453. You may wish to have students use the last four digits of their phone number as a seed number. This will reduce the likelihood of two students using the same seed number.

Responses to activities in this investigation will vary depending on the calculator or computer software that is used.

1. **a.** On the TI-82 and TI-83, the number can be set from 1 to 9 decimal places by changing the floating decimal under the MODE menu. Students may simply indicate 8 or 9 decimal places as a response. They do not need to be aware of the float option at this time. When a randomly generated number's decimal representation ends in 0, the 0 is simply not shown; hence some numbers will have fewer places.

    b. The numbers lie between 0 and 1.

    c. These numbers lie between 0 and 6.

    d. When "rand" is multiplied by 10, the random numbers lie between 0 and 10.
    When "rand" is multiplied by 36, the random numbers lie between 0 and 36.
    When "rand" is multiplied by 100, the random numbers lie between 0 and 100.

Notes continued
from page T511

2. **d.** The theoretical number of average matches, no matter how many people are in the gift exchange, is 1. The reasoning is easy to say but may be too deep for students to formulate at this stage: There are n opportunities for a match and the probability of a match each time is $\frac{1}{n}$, so the expected number of matches is $n\left(\frac{1}{n}\right)$ or 1.

3. Simulations will vary depending on the class size used. However, the amazing fact is that the answer to each question is about the same for all class sizes. Specifically, the probability is about 0.63 for all class sizes greater than 3, and the average number of students who will get their own names is always exactly 1. See Extending Task 2, Parts c and d, above.

4. Assign the digits 1, 2, 3, 4, and 5 to the five CDs. Begin at a random spot and observe the first ten digits that aren't 6, 7, 8, 9 or 0. For example, starting at the third line of the random digit table, 5 1 5 8 4   7 2 3 0 5   4 6 6 2 9   8 2 ..., we see that the ten songs are from CDs 5, 1, 5, 4, 2, 3, 5, 4, 2, and 2. There were songs from each of the CDs.

    Alternatively, use the instruction "int 5 rand + 1" on the calculator.

NOTE: Extending Task 4 is adapted from a problem from Sandy Smith, The Cate School, Carpinteria, California.

Teaching Notes *continued*

Notes continued from page T512

NOTE: Some students may wish to extend their knowledge by writing calculator or computer programs for simulations. The program below allows you to put 99 random digits into List 2. You may use this task for students who wish to learn about the programming capabilities of the TI-82. This program will work on the TI-83 as well, but the TI-83 can accept up to 999 entries in a list.

Placing Random Digits into a List
:ClrHome
:ClrList L2
:1 → I
:0 → A
:While I ≤ 99
:int 10rand → B
:B → L2(I)
:Disp B
:I+1 → I
:End

TI-82 Calculator TIP: Scrambling a List
PROGRAM: LSTSWTCH
:ClrHome
:ClrList L1,L2
:1 → I
:0 → A
:FOR (J,1,10,1)
:J − 1 → L1(J)
:L1(J) → L2(J)
:END
:While I ≤ 10
:int 10rand+1 → A
:L1(A) → B
:L1(I) → L1(A)
:B → L1(I)
:I + 1 → I
:END

The program at the right scrambles a list.

See Assessment Resources, pages 255–260.

Notes continued from page T514

4. c. A table with frequencies close to the theoretical ones follows.

Number of Games Won by the Cyclones in a Five-Game Series	Frequency	Theoretical Probability
0	13	0.064
1	23	0.1152
2	28	0.13824
3	136	0.68256
Total Number of Trials	200	

You need numbers up to 3 only because the series would be stopped when the Cyclones win 3 games.

Unit 7

Notes continued from page T515

6. a. As the number of games increases, the probability that the better team (Cyclones) will win increases, but at a decreasing rate. The Cyclones would have a better chance winning a best-of-nine series. A reasonable estimate for that probability is 0.73 or 0.74.

NOTE: If you happen to be doing this unit during the World Series, when the NBA play-offs are on television, or when a local junior league is in a play-off series, you can capitalize on this and extend activities like Activity 5 for students who finish group work early. In that activity, students find that the probability of the 60% favorite winning a seven-game series is about 71%. But suppose the 60% favorite has already lost the first two games (or whatever the topical situation is)? Is there still a 71% chance that they will win the series, or should we recalculate the probabilities for the remaining five games? Many students get interested in setting up simulations based on their own opinions about how good the teams are, and they will get more practice setting up and carrying out simulations as the situation changes.

b. The theoretical probability is 0.7334.

c. The better team is more likely to win a seven-game series than a five-game series.

7. Students' histograms will vary depending on the results of the simulations. Each histogram is skewed to the left, with each successive bar taller than the one to its left. The number of bars increases by one with each successive histogram. Although the right-most bar is the tallest in each case, it is proportionally taller with each successive histogram.

8. a. Start at a random place in the random digit table. If the first digit is even, Monica makes her first serve. If the first digit is odd, Monica misses and must try again. Look at the second digit. If it is 0, 1, 2, 3, 4, 5, 6, or 7, Monica makes her second serve. If the second digit is an 8 or 9, Monica misses her second serve. For example, using the fourth line of the random digit table, (3 0 ...), Monica misses the first serve and makes the second serve.

b. Use the command "int 10 rand" to generate the digits 0 through 9, inclusive, then proceed as outlined in Part a.

Notes continued from page T517

ⓑ When two outcomes are not equally likely, more of the randomly generated numbers can be assigned to represent the more likely outcome.

ⓒ One possibility is to use the "int 20 rand + 1" command to generate the integers from 1 to 20. Assign Sheila the numbers 1 through 11, and Bobby the numbers 12 through 20. Bobby should prefer a shorter series because the longer the series, the greater Sheila's chance of winning.

Teaching Notes *continued*

Notes continued
from page T521

4. d. Responses may vary. Our simulation gave the following result: 26, 27, 25, 26, and 24.

Number of People Who Show Up	Frequency
19 or fewer	0
20	1
21	2
22	3
23	5
24	9
25	10
26	11
27	8
28	4
29	2
30	0
Total Number of Trials	55

Notes continued
from page T528

| APPLY | individual task |

▶On Your Own

See Unit 7 Summary Masters.

Responses will vary. Above all, preparation of this unit summary should be something that is useful to the individual student. You may wish to have students use the unit summary masters for "Simulation Models" to help them organize the information.

See Assessment Resources, pages 267–282, for Unit 7 Assessments.

Unit 7

Capstone ▶ Looking Back at Course 1

CAPSTONE OVERVIEW This concluding unit is an important part of the course. It gives students a chance to review what they have learned in the context of one big project. In this way, they will finish the course with an emphasis on big ideas, connections, and an appreciation for their new mathematical power.

▶Approximate Timeline

- **1 day** Introduction and Investigation 1
- **6 days** 2 days for each of the three investigations that groups choose
- **3 days** Preparing and presenting reports, and discussing the final Checkpoint

▶Materials Needed

Investigation 3

- Centimeter grid paper
- Coffee stirrers and pipe cleaners for the ticket booth frame
- Rulers
- Protractors

As suggested in the student text (page 544), you may wish to have each group present one oral report and have each student write an individual report. Thus, this Capstone can provide a comprehensive assessment for Course 1. You may want to use the Capstone along with selected exam tasks from the bank of final assessment items on Assessment Masters 283–319 as an end-of-course assessment.

One way to assess group presentations and written reports is provided in Teaching Masters 197a–197c. You may wish to have each student evaluate the other groups' presentations.

Looking Back
at Course 1

529

Planning a Benefits Carnival

In this course, you have built useful mathematical models—including linear, exponential, geometric, simulation, and graph models. You have used these models to solve important problems in many different settings. You have investigated patterns in data, change, chance, and shape. And you have learned how to make sense of situations by representing them in differ-

ent ways using physical representations, words, graphs, tables, and symbols. In this Capstone, you will pull together many of the important concepts, techniques, and models that you have learned and use them to analyze one big project.

Think About This Situation

Many schools organize fund-raising events to raise money for improving their programs. The event might be a dance, a bike-a-thon, a book sale—anything that gets the community involved in raising money for the school. One event that is common for elementary schools is a benefits carnival. Suppose that a local elementary school is considering such a carnival. Your class has offered to plan the event and prepare a full report for the school's principal. (In return, your class will get part of the proceeds to use for yourselves!)

a Make a list of all the things that need to be done to plan, carry out, and clean up following such a carnival.

b Make a list of the kinds of booths or activities that might be good to have at the carnival. Think of as many as you can.

Capstone

Planning a Benefits Carnival

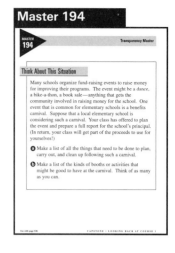
LAUNCH full-class discussion

Think About This Situation

See Teaching Master 194.

Responses will vary widely. Encourage students to brainstorm for plenty of ideas, then organize them. Some examples are given below.

a

Planning	Carry Out	Clean Up
Choosing Location	Selling Tickets	Disassembling Booths
Advertising	Serving Food	Taking Down Decorations
Recruiting Workers	Running Games	Sweeping Floors
Choosing Date	Holding a Raffle	Cleaning Food Area
Choosing Time		Counting Money
Selecting Games		
Figuring Financing		
Printing Tickets		
Getting Donations for Raffle Item(s)		
Planning Concessions		
Building Booths		

b Some ideas are:

Cakewalk	Pitching (How Fast Can You Throw?)
Penny Hunt	Batting Cage
Dunk the Teacher	Face Painting
Haunted House	Swirl Art
Duck Pond	Math Challenge
Miniature Golf	Graphing Calculator Games

Capstone

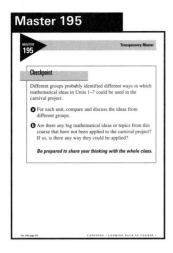

INVESTIGATION 1 ▸ Lots of Math

   This investigation is an opportunity for students to revisit systematically each unit of the course, to review briefly the big ideas, and to apply those ideas to the context of the carnival. You might want to ask each student to write at least one suggestion from each unit, before having students share their ideas. This might take 15 minutes. Then have small groups share their ideas and organize them by units, in preparation for presenting these to the whole class. The Checkpoint could be done as a large group, with a recorder for each group adding new ideas to the group list. You might want to copy these group lists and distribute them. What follows are some sample ideas.

1. *Patterns in Data*
   a. A list of possible games for the carnival could be distributed to the elementary students, having them circle their top two choices. This information could then be put into a *histogram* and analyzed.
   b. The idea of *mean* could be used in setting up a booth where a player has, say, three chances to win a prize by popping a balloon with a dart. Prior to the carnival, organizers could have ten children find the distance farthest from the dart board at which they are always successful in popping the balloon. The organizers could take the mean of these distances, then add two feet to this distance to make the game challenging yet possible.

2. *Patterns of Change*
   a. If a food such as caramel apples is to be sold in the concessions area, carnival organizers could figure the cost of making each caramel apple, decide on a selling price, *graph* both income and cost against the selling price, then use a *table* to find the break-even point in sales.
   b. An *equation* could be used to help determine what ticket price will maximize profit (since the number of students playing a game may be affected by the ticket price).

3. *Linear Models*
   Data could be collected that would be useful in planning a fair time period for a Penny Hunt. For example, an organizer could have a child search a sandbox for pennies for several time periods, say 5, 10, 15, 20, and 25 seconds. The number of pennies collected in each trial would be recorded. Using a *linear regression line* that is based on the five (*time*, *pennies*) ordered pairs, a time period could be found which is long enough to be fun, but short enough to ensure profit.

4. *Graph Models*
   A *project digraph* could be used as a way to plan how much time is needed for set-up. *Vertex coloring* could be used to schedule committee meetings, to find the minimum number of fish tanks needed for an aquarium display of predatory fish, or even to design a map-coloring game. *Euler paths* could be used to plan optimal routes through the carnival, or as the basis for some walk-through tracing games.

See additional Teaching Notes on page T545C.

INVESTIGATION 1 Lots of Math

Mathematics can be used in many different ways to help you organize the carnival. Think about the mathematics you have studied in each of the units in this course. The units are listed below. As a group, brainstorm and then write two ways the mathematics in each unit could be used in the carnival project.

1. *Patterns in Data*
2. *Patterns of Change*
3. *Linear Models*
4. *Graph Models*
5. *Patterns in Space and Visualization*
6. *Exponential Models*
7. *Simulation Models*

Checkpoint

Different groups probably identified different ways in which mathematical ideas in Units 1–7 could be used in the carnival project.

ⓐ For each unit, compare and discuss the ideas from different groups.

ⓑ Are there any big mathematical ideas or topics from this course that have not been applied to the carnival project? If so, is there any way they could be applied?

Be prepared to share your thinking with the whole class.

At the end of this Capstone, you will write an individual report for the principal of the elementary school. In this report, you need to explain how you used mathematics to help plan the carnival. To assist in the preparation of the reports, your group will complete three of the following investigations. Each group will present an oral report to the class on one of them. (Guidelines for the group report are given on page 544.)

As a group, examine Investigations 2 through 8 and choose three to complete. Confirm your choices with your teacher, and then start investigating!

Capstone

INVESTIGATION ▶ 2 Careful Planning

Careful planning is necessary to make the carnival a success. An important part of planning is identifying and scheduling all the tasks that need to be done.

1. Some of the tasks and task times for the carnival project might be building the booths (5 days), laying out the floor plan (2 days), designing a carnival logo (1 day), publicity (10 days), and finding a location (2 days). Write at least two more tasks that will need to be done. Estimate the times needed to complete these tasks.

2. Use the tasks from Activity 1 to do the following:

    a. Construct a prerequisite table showing the tasks, the task times, and the immediate prerequisites.

    b. Draw a project digraph.

    c. Find the critical tasks and the earliest finish time for the whole project.

    d. Set up a schedule for completing all the tasks. Your schedule should show earliest start times, earliest finish times, and slack times.

3. Committees must be formed to work on each of the tasks. Since some students will be on more than one committee, it is impossible for all the committees to meet at the same time. Assume there are five committees, each of which has a member in common with at least two other committees.

INVESTIGATION 2 Careful Planning

This is a popular choice with students. They realize that projects such as this require lots of planning, and will do a fine job of utilizing the techniques they learned in "Graph Models."

1. Responses will vary. Two more possible tasks are choosing the games that are to be played (3 days) and either hiring workers or recruiting volunteers (4 days).

2. **a.** Responses will vary. Student work will include parts of the table below, augmented by the tasks they suggest in Activity 1.

NOTE: You may need to remind students that they are concerned with *immediate prerequisites*. So, for example, in the sample table below, it would be incorrect to list Tasks A and B as immediate prerequisites of Task E, since Task A is an indirect prerequisite and not an immediate one.

Task	Task Time	Immediate Prerequisite
Finding a Location (*A*)	2 days	none
Choosing Games (*B*)	3 days	*A*
Designing a Carnival Logo (*C*)	1 day	*A*
Publicity (*D*)	10 days	*B, C*
Laying Out Floor Plan (*E*)	2 days	*B*
Recruiting Workers (*F*)	4 days	*B*
Building Booths (*G*)	5 days	*E, F*

b–d. Responses will vary and should reflect choices made in Activity 1. When setting up the schedule in Part d, students should make a table and/or a timeline showing earliest finish time, earliest start time, latest start time, and slack time for each task.

Capstone

3. Responses will vary depending upon which committees share members. Denote the committees by vertices *A*, *B*, *C*, *D*, and *E*. Connect two vertices if the committees they represent are in *conflict*; that is, if they share a member.

   a. One possible graph model is:

   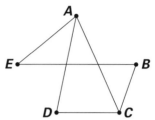

   b. For this graph you would need at least three meeting times. For example:
   From 3:00 – 3:30 P.M., committees *A* and *B* meet (color them red).
   From 3:30 – 4:00 P.M., committees *C* and *E* meet (color them blue).
   From 4:00 – 4:30 P.M., committee *D* meets (color it green).

   You can use the graph model from Part a to answer the question by letting colors be meeting times, and coloring the vertices in such a way that vertices that are adjacent (*i.e.*, committees that share a member) get different colors (*i.e.*, different meeting times). Since *A*, *D*, and *C* must all be different colors, then at least three colors are needed. In fact, since all the vertices can be colored using three colors, three is the minimum number of meeting times needed.

4. This is an important part of each investigation. It ensures that the groups do careful, neat work, and it gets different groups talking to one another about their ideas, attempts, and solutions.

EXPLORE small-group investigation

INVESTIGATION 3 Booths and Floor Plans

In this investigation, students will use two- and three-dimensional geometry, including measurement, similarity, and the Pythagorean Theorem. The activities comprising this investigation allow for plenty of exploration and creativity. You may wish to monitor groups doing this investigation, so that they make timely progress.

1. See student sketches. Different interpretations are possible. (For the ticket booth, note that 2.24 is approximately $\sqrt{5}$. Thus, students may draw a side of the hexagon with length 2.24 by drawing the hypotenuse of a right triangle whose legs have length 1 and 2.)

Capstone

a. Construct a vertex-edge graph model that shows the five committees and which committees share members. (You decide which committees share members.)

b. What is the fewest number of meeting times needed so that all committees can meet? Explain how you can use the graph model from Part a to answer this question.

4. Make a neat copy of your project digraph, showing the critical tasks and earliest finish time. Also make a copy of the graph model for the committee scheduling problem, showing the graph coloring.

a. File these two graphs at the location in the classroom designated by your teacher. Examine the graphs filed by other groups and compare their graphs to those from your group.

b. Write a question to at least one group asking them to explain something about their work that you found interesting or did not understand. Answer any questions your group receives.

INVESTIGATION 3 Booths and Floor Plans

In this investigation, you will sketch a floor plan for the carnival and build a scale model of a booth.

1. Assume that the carnival will be held in a rectangular-shaped gym with dimensions 40 meters by 30 meters. Using centimeter graph paper, with 1 centimeter corresponding to 1 meter, sketch a floor plan for the carnival. Your floor plan should show the placement of the following items:

- The ticket and information booth. This booth is hexagonal-shaped so that during peak times customers can line up at six windows to get information or tickets. Two sides of the booth have length 1 m and the other sides have length 2.24 m. The booth is to be placed in the center of the gym.

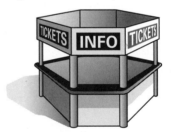

- The game booths. There are ten game booths to be arranged along the sides of the gym. Eight of them are U-shaped, 1.5 m × 2 m × 1.5 m. The 2 m side faces out. The other two are triangular-shaped—two sides are the same length and the third side, which faces out, is 2 m long.

Capstone

■ Concessions. Six tables, each of which has a 2 m × 1 m table top, are placed in a U-shape to serve as the area where food is sold.

■ Decide on one other feature of the floor plan. Describe it and add it to your plan.

2. Now consider the ticket booth in more detail.

   a. Build a model of the ticket booth frame using a scale of 10 cm to 1 m. The ticket booth has base dimensions as described in Activity 1. The walls of the booth are 2 m high.

   b. Design a tent-like canopy for the booth.

   c. Make a careful sketch of the ticket booth.

   d. How much canvas will be needed to cover the booth, including the canopy?

3. File your floor plan and your ticket booth model and sketch at the location in the classroom designated by your teacher. Study the floor plans, models, and sketches filed by other groups and compare these items to your group's work. Write a question to at least one group asking them to explain something about their work that you found interesting or did not understand. Answer any questions your group receives.

INVESTIGATION ▶ 4 Carnival T-Shirts

To help promote the carnival and raise more money, T-shirts will be designed and sold.

1. Design a logo for the carnival, to be used on the T-shirts as well as on other promotional materials. The logo might include the name of the school or a message of some sort. It could be an abstract design or a picture of something related to the carnival. It can be whimsical or serious. Be creative! The only requirement is that the logo must be symmetrical in some way.

   a. Describe the symmetry shown in your logo.

   b. Briefly explain why you chose your particular design and explain its meaning.

2. **a.** Students will need appropriate materials (for example, large sheets of grid paper, graph paper, paper, straws, pipe cleaners, glue, rulers, and compasses) for building the model ticket booth. There are several ways to construct the hexagon with 4 sides of 2.24 meters and 2 sides of 1 meter. One that is commonly chosen is shown here.

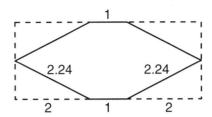

Students might use straws or pipe cleaners to build a scale model, or they might make scale drawings on graph paper and assemble them. Some students will want to paste their scale model in place on their plan. If they use straws, they will realize quickly that their scale model is not rigid. (This problem is taken care of later when they construct an appropriate roof.)

b. There probably will be many creative ideas for designing the tent-like canopy. Allow students to pursue all ideas, whether they are seat-of-the-pants designs or carefully-planned constructions. One option (which is by no means required) is to build a roof shaped like a pyramid with a hexagonal base. For your reference, and for possible use with students, instructions for this option are provided below.

- ■ Cut out the base of the roof.
- ■ Tape a short straw vertically onto the center of the base.
- ■ Tape a piece of paper onto one edge of the base.
- ■ Set the span of a compass to exactly the distance from the top of the straw to one of the vertices A of the roof base where the piece of paper is taped.
- ■ Put the center of the compass on A and draw an arc onto the attached piece of paper.
- ■ Repeat this process for the other vertex B of the edge on which the piece of paper is taped.
- ■ Draw segments from A and B to the intersection C of the two arcs.
- ■ Cut out this triangle. You now have a triangular face taped to one edge of the roof base. This will fold up into one side of the roof.
- ■ Repeat this process for each edge of the roof base.
- ■ Fold up all the triangular pieces to get the roof.

c. Students might sketch side views and/or a three-dimensional perspective.

d. Students will compute surface area to answer this question.

3. This is an important part of each investigation. It ensures that the groups do careful, neat work, and it gets different groups talking to one another about their ideas, attempts, and solutions.

EXPLORE **small-group investigation**

INVESTIGATION 4 Carnival T-Shirts

1. Responses will vary. Look for either rotational or reflection symmetry.

Capstone

2. **a.**   The set-up cost is $105.

Cost of Four-Color T-Shirts

Number of T-Shirts Purchased	Total Cost ($)
1	112.45
10	179.50
100	770.00
200	1,365.00
201	1,371.30
202	1,377.60

b. $NEXT = NOW + 6.30$

2. The price list for a T-shirt shop is shown below.

Midwest Athletic Supply and Screen Printing

Set-up

$17.50 for one color $12.50 for each additional color

Art

$25 per hour

T-Shirts

Prices for T-Shirts with one color:

1–15	$6.55 ea.	63–147	$5.75 ea.
16–31	$6.25 ea.	148 or more	$5.40 ea.
32–62	$5.95 ea.		

Add $0.30 per shirt for each additional color

---

a. Suppose you decide to go with a deluxe four-color design that requires two hours of artwork from the shop's designers. Complete a table like the one below.

Cost of Four-Color T-Shirts

Number of T-Shirts Purchased	Total Cost
1	
10	
100	
200	
201	
202	

b. Suppose that you buy more than 150 T-shirts. Using *NOW* for the cost to buy a given number of shirts and *NEXT* for the cost to buy one more, write an equation showing the relationship between *NOW* and *NEXT*.

Capstone

c. Using T for the number of T-shirts purchased and C for the total cost, write an equation showing the relationship between T and C for any number $T > 150$.

3. You plan to sell the T-shirts and make a profit. What price should you set for the shirts? Write a brief analysis justifying your choice of selling price. Your analysis should include the following:

- An equation and graph showing the relationship between profit P and number of T-shirts sold T, where $T > 150$

- An explanation of how to use the profit equation and graph to find the number of shirts you must sell to break even

- An estimate of the profit you expect to make

- A summary of why you chose your selling price

4. File a copy of your logo, an explanation of the symmetry it exhibits, and your profit analysis at the location in the classroom designated by your teacher. Examine the logos and solutions filed by other groups and compare these items to your group's work. Write a question to at least one group asking them to explain something about their work that you found interesting or did not understand. Answer any questions your group receives.

INVESTIGATION ▶ 5 Money Made and Money Spent

The main purpose of the carnival is to make money in a fun way. Both organizers and customers are concerned about the money aspect. The organizers want to know how much money the carnival will make. The customers want to know how much money they will spend.

1. Customers will buy tickets and then pay for the games using one or more tickets per game. Each ticket costs 25¢. This year, parents who buy tickets in advance can specify that the money paid goes to purchase equipment for their child's classroom. Parents are asking, "About how many tickets will I use at the carnival?"

2. c. $C = 6.30T + 105$, for $T > 150$

3. Students should decide on a selling price based on an analysis of potential profit. In order to use the cost equation that students developed in Activity 2, they need to assume that the number of shirts purchased is at least 148 (because of the different prices, depending on quantitites, from the T-shirt shop). Since the T-shirts are being sold at the carnival, they must decide beforehand how many they will purchase. Once this decision is made, the costs are fixed. If your students don't realize this, you may wish to ask them how many T-shirts they plan to have at the carnival. Students may go about this analysis symbolically, but their first efforts are more likely to be in a table, where they can examine the cost and income for several different selling prices.

Number of T-Shirts	Cost of Producing the T-Shirts	Income from Selling the T-Shirts	Profit
150			
160			
170			
etc.			

From this analysis they should be able to proceed to symbolic work.

One Possible Solution

For example, students may decide to purchase 300 T-shirts, and to sell the T-shirts for $10 each.

■ At this selling price, and using the cost equation from Activity 2, the profit equation is as follows:

$$P = 10T - [6.3(300) + 105] = 10T - 1,995$$

■ Students can figure out how many they must sell to break even by solving the equation with $P = 0$, by experimenting numerically, or by graphing the profit equation and finding where it crosses the T-axis. Under the conditions stated above, they would need to sell 200 T-shirts to break even.

■ They can estimate profit by estimating the number they expect to sell and then computing profit using their equation.

■ Students should summarize their rationale for the selling price they chose. They may include here a summary of their calculations above as well as a discussion of high price/low volume versus low price/high volume.

NOTE: Some students may analyze several cases by assuming purchases of 200, 250, or 325 T-shirts, and compare all combinations of price and likely number sold, to decide on the best choices.

4. Student work

Capstone

INVESTIGATION 5 Money Made and Money Spent

Mathematical ideas used in this investigation include measures of center and variability, box plots, and graphs, tables, and equations for exponential and linear patterns of change.

1. **a.** Below are box plots of the data. The top plot is three years ago, the bottom is last year.

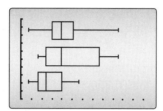

```
WINDOW
Xmin =0
Xmax =60
Xscl =5
Ymin =1
Ymax =11
Yscl =1
Xres =1
```

b. A variety of points could be included in the paragraph summaries, including:
■ Two years ago, Year 2, has the most variability judging from the IQR (although its range is smaller than three years ago, Year 3).
■ Years 2 and 3 have the same median, but Year 3 has more clustering about the median.
■ The median for Years 2 and 3 is the same as Q3 for last year, Year 1.
■ The median for Year 1 is the same as Q1 for Year 2.
■ Year 3 has the smallest IQR, so it is reasonable to assert that it has the least variability. However, Year 3 also has the largest range. So you might say that Year 3 has the least variability about the median, but it has a wide range in terms of some parents buying only a few tickets and others buying several.
■ In terms of numbers of tickets bought by each parent, last year seems least successful. However, there is not enough information to reliably conclude this since these data do not show total number of parents attending. Low ticket sales per parent could be offset by a large number of parents.

c–d. You could compute the mean and mode for each year; the mode would tell a customer the number of tickets the most people bought, which may be a good estimate for a given individual customer. You might look at histograms to get more information about the shape of the distributions and to better see the mode and mean. You could aggregate all the data and look at graphs and numerical statistics for the aggregate data; compiling over all three years together allows you to more succinctly base your advice on all three previous carnivals. For a parent who asks you how many tickets to buy, you might give a single answer (for example, the mode), and briefly explain what that means; or you might include information about measures of center and variability so the parent knows what the previous "average" has been and how much people varied from that average.

Capstone

At each of the last three carnivals, 25 parents were randomly chosen and asked how many tickets they used. These data are shown in the following table.

Number of Game Tickets Used by Sample of Parents at the Last Three Carnivals					
3 Years Ago		**2 Years Ago**		**Last Year**	
26	20	20	32	6	8
20	30	48	24	4	10
20	18	36	12	4	12
16	25	16	11	20	10
4	8	16	36	8	18
21	15	44	40	8	20
20	14	24	8	8	12
20	48	40	12	24	28
26	16	8	42	7	26
10	10	8	12	12	24
16	16	18	22	22	20
20	35	10	14	18	12
34	—	44	—	16	—

a. Make a box plot of each year's data. Divide the work among your group. Draw all three box plots one below the other on the same axis.

b. Write a brief summary of the information shown in each box plot. Describe how patterns of ticket usage vary from year to year.

c. What other graphs or statistics might be useful to help you inform parents about how many tickets they will need?

d. When a parent asks you, "How many tickets will I use?" what will you say? Explain the reasoning behind your response.

2. Someone suggests the carnival can do more than support the school for the current year. The class agrees to set up a fund that will grow and support the school in future years. Your goal is to put $800 of the carnival profits into a savings account for the school. The account pays 5% interest compounded annually.

  a. How much money will be in the account when you graduate, assuming no withdrawals?

  b. Write equations that will allow you to calculate the balance of this account:

  ■ for any year, given the balance for the year before.

  ■ after any number of years x.

  c. Use the equations from Part b to make a table and a graph showing the growth of this account.

  d. Describe the pattern of growth in the savings account over a 10-year period.

  e. Think about how fast the account grows:

  ■ Is the account growing faster in year 5 or year 10? How can you tell?

  ■ What would the graph look like if the account were growing at a constant rate of change?

  f. Suppose that the school wants to buy a new computer for the library. A local manufacturer has offered to give the school a great price. The computer is expected to cost about $1,000. How long will it be before there is enough in the account to buy the computer?

3. Make a neat copy of your work on this investigation, including graphs, plots, tables, equations, and explanations. File the copy at the location in the classroom designated by your teacher. Check the solutions filed by other groups and compare them to your group's work. Write a question to at least one group asking them to explain something about their work that you found interesting or did not understand. Answer any questions your group receives.

INVESTIGATION ▶6▶ Ring-Toss Game

The most important part of a carnival is, of course, the games. Suppose that you are setting up a ring-toss game. A number of two-liter bottles of soda are lined up. The goal of the game is to toss a ring around the top of one of them. If a

2. **a.** This depends on when a given student graduates. The balances for 1–5 years are as follows:

$840 after 1 year; $882 after 2 years; $926.10 after 3 years;
$972.41 after 4 years; $1,021.03 after 5 years.

b. $NEXT = 1.05 \times NOW$, where the initial deposit is $800.
Balance after x years: $B = 800 \times 1.05^x$

c.

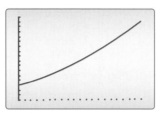

X	Y₁
0	800
1	840
2	882
3	926.1
4	972.41
5	1021
6	1072.1

X=0

WINDOW
Xmin =0
Xmax =20
Xscl =1
Ymin =500
Ymax =2200
Yscl =100
Xres =1

d. The savings account grows, first slowly, and then more rapidly.

e. ■ The account is growing faster in year 10 than in year 5. You can see this from the table by looking at successive year differences: from the graph by seeing that the slope is steeper at year 10; from the *NOW* and *NEXT* equation by noting that 1.05 is getting multiplied by bigger and bigger numbers; and from the exponential equation by noting that there is a greater successive change from 1.05^{10} to 1.05^{11} than there is from 1.05^5 to 1.05^6.

■ If the account was growing at a constant rate of change, then the graph would be a line.

f. By using some solution method like tracing the graph or using a small-step table, students might answer that after about 4.6 years there will be $1,000 in the account. However, this "exact" solution does not fit the conditions of the problem since interest is compounded yearly. Strictly speaking, then, if the interest is computed and added to the account at the end of each year, it would not be until the end of year 5, *i.e.*, $x = 5$, that the account would have enough money in it to buy the computer.

3. Student work

INVESTIGATION 6 ▶ Ring-Toss Game

Mathematical ideas used in this investigation include area of a circle, similarity, scatterplots, exponential and linear functions, and an intuitive treatment of expected value.

1. **a.**

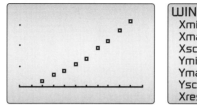 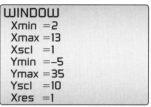

```
WINDOW
 Xmin =2
 Xmax =13
 Xscl =1
 Ymin =-5
 Ymax =35
 Yscl =10
 Xres =1
```

b. In general, the larger the diameter the larger the average number of ringers, which makes sense. The graph appears somewhat curved.

c. Consider a circle C_1 of diameter d and a circle C_2 of diameter $2d$. Consider their areas: $A(C_1) = \pi r^2 = \pi\left(\frac{1}{2}d\right)^2 = \frac{1}{4}\pi d^2$

$A(C_2) = \pi r^2 = \pi d^2$

Notice that $A(C_2) = 4 \times A(C_1)$.

A ring with twice the diameter has 4 times the area, and it seems reasonable that with 4 times the area you could get 4 times as many ringers.

Capstone

player hooks one of the bottles (which is called getting a "ringer"), then he or she gets to keep it. Your task is to design this game. You need to consider how large the rings should be, how far back the players should stand, and what the cost to play the game should be.

1. Examine the following data collected from a ring-tossing experiment. The data show the average number of ringers per 100 tosses at a distance of 1 meter from the bottles, for rings of varying diameters.

Sample Ring-Toss Data for 1-Meter Tosses	
Diameter of Ring (in centimeters)	Average Number of Ringers per 100 Tosses
4	3
5	6
6	8
7	11
8	14
9	19
10	22
11	27
12	32

   a. Make a scatterplot of the data.

   b. Describe and explain any patterns or unusual features of the data.

   c. Notice that when the ring diameter doubles, the number of ringers increases by a factor of about four. Can you suggest any explanation for this pattern in terms of the size of the circular rings?

2. Data collected from another ring-tossing experiment are shown in the following table. These data show the average number of ringers per 100 tosses with rings of diameter 12 cm, for players standing at varying distances from the bottles.

Sample Ring-Toss Data for 12-cm Diameter Rings

Distance from the Bottles (in meters)	Average Number of Ringers per 100 Tosses
1	32
2	15
3	8
4	4
5	1

a. Make a scatterplot of the data.

b. Describe any patterns you see in the data.

c. Suppose *NOW* is the average number of ringers at one of the distances in the table and *NEXT* is the average number of ringers for a distance 1 meter farther away. Write an equation that approximates the relationship between *NOW* and *NEXT*.

3. It is important to charge enough to play the game so that the income from ticket sales for the game is greater than the cost of the prizes given away. For this activity, assume that a ring with diameter 12 cm is used and players stand 2 meters away from the bottles.

a. Suppose that a local merchant offers to support the carnival by loaning you all the soda you need to set up your game. The merchant will charge you

2. a.

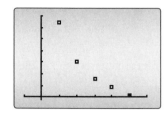

```
WINDOW
Xmin = -1
Xmax = 6
Xscl = 1
Ymin = -1
Ymax = 35
Yscl = 5
Xres = 1
```

b. The bigger the distance, the fewer ringers, which makes sense. The graph is nonlinear. The number of ringers decreases by about a factor of $\frac{1}{2}$ for every meter farther away. The data look as though they could be modeled by an equation of the form $y = ab^x$, where b is $\frac{1}{2}$.

c. $NEXT = \frac{1}{2} \times NOW$

Capstone

3. **a.** Students probably will find it challenging to go immediately to a symbolic representation, perhaps because the cost is figured for only 15% of the participants, while the income is from 100% of the participants.

Encourage students to organize the information in a table for the 2-meter toss.

Tosses	Ringers Expected	Cost of Soda (in dollars)	Income	Profit (in dollars)
100	15	$15(0.60) = 9$	$100(0.25) = 25$	$25 - 9 = 16$

By trying other prices per toss, they should see that the comparison they want to make is between the income from 100 tosses at x cents and the $9.00 cost of supplying the winners with soda. By working through the process for figuring the profit from different numbers of participants at different prices, students reach an understanding of the relationship.

Profit on 100 participants at 25 cents a toss $= 100(25) - 15(60)$

Profit on 200 participants at 25 cents a toss $= 200(25) - 30(60)$

Profit on T participants at 25 cents a toss $= T(25) - T\left(\frac{(15)(60)}{100}\right)$

Some students will see quickly that the cost per 1 participant is $\frac{(15)(60)}{100}$ or 9 cents. So the cost for T participants is $9T$ cents.

NOTE: The cost per toss is technically an "expected value" computation, which has not been covered in this course. In this context the reasoning is sensible enough that students should be able to think it through successfully.

---

b. The least that you can charge and still make a profit is 10¢ per toss, since the cost per toss is 9¢ (as calculated in Part a).

c. A reasonable price for a two-liter bottle of soda may be about $1.50. The number of ringers we expect from 100 tosses is 15. Thus to break even, we should charge $\frac{\$1.50 \times 15}{100} = 22.5$¢ per toss. Thus, 23¢ is the least that you can charge and still make a profit.

d. If players tossed rings at a distance of 3 meters instead of 2 meters, you would expect only 8% of the tosses to be ringers. So for 100 tosses, the cost of the soda given away is $8(\$0.60) = \$4.80$. Thus, the cost per toss is 4.8¢. Profit is then given by
$$P = 25T - 4.8T = 20.2T$$
assuming you charge 25¢ for a toss. The least you can charge and still make a profit is 5¢, since the cost is 4.8¢ per toss.

See additional Teaching Notes on page T545D.

Capstone

60¢ for every bottle you give away as a prize. You decide to charge 25¢ for a toss. Based on the data in the tables, you expect 15% of the tosses to be ringers. Use T for the number of tosses by customers and P for your profit from the game. Write an equation that shows the relationship between P and T.

b. Given the arrangement with the local merchant in Part a, what is the least you can charge for a toss and still make a profit?

c. Suppose you have no sponsor and must pay the usual retail price for the soda. For stores near where you live, what is a reasonable price for a two-liter bottle of soda? In this situation, what is the least you can charge for a toss at a distance of 2 meters and still make a profit?

d. Based on the data in Activity 2, how would your profit-modeling equation in Part a change if players tossed rings at a distance of 3 meters? In this situation, what is the least you can charge for a toss and still make a profit?

e. As designers of fun, profitable games, would your group recommend a 2-meter toss or a 3-meter toss? Explain your reasoning.

4. Make a neat copy of your work on this investigation, showing graphs, equations, and other answers. File this "solution sheet" at the location in the classroom designated by your teacher. Study the solutions filed by other groups and compare them to your solutions. Write a question to at least one group asking them to explain something about their work that you found interesting or did not understand. Answer any questions your group receives.

INVESTIGATION 7 Free-Throw Game: Beat the Pro

Games of skill, especially those involving sports, are always popular at carnivals. Suppose that you are in charge of setting up a basketball free-throw game where a challenger pits his or her skill against a pro. In this case, the pro is the top free-throw shooter from the girls' basketball team. The challenger and the pro each shoot ten free throws. If the challenger makes more baskets than the pro, then he or she wins a prize. Your job is to decide how much to charge to play the game and what prizes should be awarded to winners.

1. You know from the basketball season's statistics that the pro makes about 85% of her free throws. What about the challenger's percentage of successful free throws? You cannot know the shooting percentage of every challenger that might play the game. However, it would be helpful to get some information to help you decide on the price to charge and prizes to award. One of your friends, who likes basketball and is a pretty good shooter, agrees to help you gather some data by being a sample challenger. He completes 50 trials of 10 free throws and records the number of baskets for each trial. These data are shown in the following table.

Number of Free Throws Made (Out of 10) for 50 Trials by One Sample Challenger

8	8	9	6	7	8	7	6	8	7
8	8	10	9	8	7	7	8	5	5
7	5	6	10	6	8	9	8	9	10
8	7	8	9	8	5	8	6	8	7
7	6	9	4	9	6	8	10	7	6

a. Construct a histogram for these data. Describe and explain any patterns in the distribution.

b. Based on the data, about what percent of free throws does the sample challenger make? Explain using a statistical measure.

c. Does he appear to be a fairly consistent shooter? Justify your answer by using an appropriate plot and summary statistics.

2. To help make good decisions about the amount you should charge and the value of prizes, you can simulate a game between the sample challenger and the pro.

a. What is a reasonable estimate for the probability that the pro will make a particular free throw?

b. Explain why 0.75 is a reasonable estimate for the probability that the sample challenger will make a particular free throw.

c. Using the probabilities above, design a simulation to estimate the probability that the challenger wins the game.

Capstone

INVESTIGATION 7 Free-Throw Game: Beat the Pro

Mathematical ideas used in this investigation include simulation, measures of center and variability, statistical plots, shapes of distributions, probability, an intuitive introduction to expected value, and the Law of Large Numbers.

1. a.

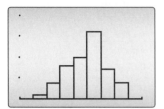 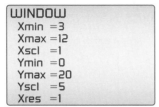

WINDOW
Xmin =3
Xmax =12
Xscl =1
Ymin =0
Ymax =20
Yscl =5
Xres =1

The distribution is approximately normal. The sample challenger shot some low scores and some high scores, but most were in the middle range of 6–9. The highest bar, *i.e.*, the mode, is 8; the challenger shot more 8s than anything else. The short bar at 4 shows a trial where the challenger was "off form."

b. The mean of the data is 7.46, and the median and the mode are 8. Student responses for the challenger's percentage of successful free-throws could be 74.6%, 75%, or 80%, depending on which measure of center they use and if they round. Any of these answers with a good explanation should be considered. The mean is technically the best choice when thinking about the long-run and designing a simulation, which is what they are asked to do later in the investigation.

c. Students may argue for either consistent or not consistent. Again, their explanation is critical. Arguments for consistency may refer to the large mound around 8 (clustering around 8), and the relatively small value of the MAD (1.18). Arguments for not-so-consistent may refer to the spread of the distribution, as shown by the histogram or a box plot, and the range of 6, which is quite large out of 10.

2. a. A reasonable estimate for the pro's probability is 0.85, based on her percentage of 85%.

b. 0.75 is a reasonable estimate for the challenger, since his mean was 7.46 baskets out of 10 shots.

c. Students could use their calculators to generate random numbers between 1 and 100. For the pro (who makes 85%), numbers between 1 and 85 count as baskets. For the challenger (who makes 75%), numbers between 1 and 75 count as baskets. Then simulate many trials of 10 shots each for the pro and the challenger and keep track of when the challenger gets more baskets than the pro.

Capstone

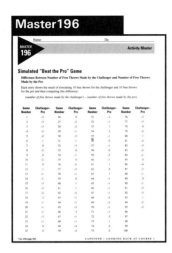

Master196

2. d. **See Teaching Master 196**.

To complete the table as it is set up in Teaching Master 196, students need to simulate 10 challenger shots and count the baskets, then 10 pro shots and count the baskets. Then they should subtract: (*challenger baskets*) – (*pro baskets*). Thus, entries in the table that are positive indicate games that the challenger won.

3. a. A sample histogram is shown below. Student histograms may vary slightly from this, as they will incorporate the outcomes of their trials.

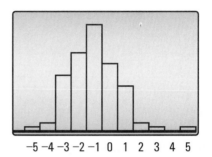

$$-5 \ -4 \ -3 \ -2 \ -1 \ \ 0 \ \ 1 \ \ 2 \ \ 3 \ \ 4 \ \ 5$$

The distribution is mound-shaped with a peak at -1. This makes sense since the difference between the challenger's percentage and the pro's percentage is -10% and the total number of shots is 10. There seems to be an outlier at 5. This makes sense as an outlier because you would not expect the challenger to get 5 more baskets than the pro. Positive numbers correspond to challenger wins, negative numbers correspond to pro wins, and 0s, which correspond to ties, also represent pro wins (according to the rules, the pro wins ties). So the challenger wins are represented by the bars to the right of 0. It is clear that the pro has many more wins.

b. Students' answers will depend on the outcomes of their trials. Their estimates should be based on the number of positive numbers (challenger wins) in the table. As partially completed, there are 15 challenger wins. Thus, their answers probably will be 0.15 or 0.16.

4. This activity is a bit beyond what they have specifically done in Unit 7, "Simulation Models," but students still should be able to reason through to some plausible answers.

a. Suppose there are 15 positive entries in the simulation table. Then the estimate of the probability of a challenger win is 0.15. In this case, with a prize that costs $8 and a 15% chance of giving away a prize, each game would cost on average (0.15)(8) or $1.20. (Again, this is technically an "expected value" computation, which has not been covered, but it is sensible enough that students often will think to do something like this.) So to make a profit you would reasonably need to charge at least $1.25 to play the game. Concerning the affordability issue raised in the question, students need to decide (and explain!) if this is a price, given the prize, that customers would be willing to pay. Students may go on to discuss the possibility of a higher price like $1.50, $2.00, or higher, since they are giving away such a nice prize and they want to be sure to make money on the game. They also could try to estimate the profit from the game by estimating the number of challengers they think will play the game.

See additional Teaching Notes on page T545E.

Capstone

d. Conduct 5 trials of your simulation. Add your results to the Simulated Beat The Pro Game table so there is a total of 100 trials. (The table can be obtained from your teacher.)

3. Now examine the simulation table you completed in Activity 2.

  a. Construct a histogram of the difference between the number of free throws made by the challenger and the number made by the pro. Describe the shape of the distribution. Interpret the shape in terms of outcomes of the "Beat The Pro" game.

  b. What is your estimate of the probability that the challenger wins? Remember that the challenger wins only if he or she makes *more* of the 10 free throws than the pro does.

4. A local sporting goods store will support the carnival by selling you top-quality basketballs at a discount for prizes. The balls will cost $8 each.

  a. Based on the simulation data and your analysis in Activity 3, determine how much you should charge the sample challenger to play the game. Remember, you want to keep the game affordable and yet ensure a profit over the course of many games.

  b. The actual game will be played with many different challengers, not just the one sample challenger. What do you think is a good price to charge for the actual game?

5. Would the pro be more likely to beat a 75% free-throw shooter in a game with 20 shots or one with 10 shots? Explain your reasoning.

6. Make a neat copy of your work on this investigation. File it at the location in the classroom designated by your teacher. Examine the work filed by other groups in the class and compare it to your work. Write a question to at least one group asking them to explain something about their work that you found interesting or did not understand. Answer any questions your group receives.

Capstone

INVESTIGATION ▶ 8 Further Analysis

In Investigations 2 through 7, you analyzed a variety of situations related to planning the carnival. Of course, there are other things to consider as well. Choose one of your ideas from Investigation 1 or from the "Think About This Situation" at the beginning of this Capstone. Carry out a brief mathematical analysis of the idea. Specifically, you should formulate and answer at least two questions related to your idea. For example, you might design and analyze another game, as is done in Investigations 6 and 7, or you might collect and analyze data on what kinds of games are most popular. File a copy of your analysis at the location designated by your teacher.

REPORTS: Putting It All Together

Finish this Capstone by preparing two reports, one oral group report and one individual written report as described below.

1. Your group should prepare a brief oral report on one of the investigations you have completed. You will present the report as if you are reporting to the principal of the elementary school that is planning to have the carnival. Your teacher will play the role of the principal. Your report should meet the following guidelines.

   ■ Choose one of the investigations you have completed. Confirm your choice with your teacher before beginning to prepare your report.

   ■ Examine the work that other groups have filed on your chosen investigation. Compare your work to theirs and discuss any differences with them. Modify your solutions, if you think you should.

   ■ Begin your presentation with a brief summary of your work on the investigation.

   ■ Convince the principal that your solutions are correct and should be adopted.

   ■ Be prepared to discuss alternative solutions, particularly those proposed by other groups that also worked on the same investigation.

   ■ Be prepared to answer any questions from the "principal" or your classmates.

2. On your own, write a two-page report summarizing how the mathematics you have learned in this course can be used to help plan a school carnival.

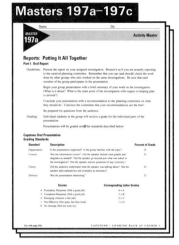

EXPLORE small-group investigation

INVESTIGATION 8 Further Analysis

Here is where groups can pursue their own ideas if they so choose, but they should do an analysis as detailed as was asked for in the other investigations in the lesson. Groups who choose this option should be encouraged but clearly forewarned about expectations.

SYNTHESIZE share and summarize

Reports: Putting It All Together

See Teaching Masters 197a–197c.

One possible way to organize the reports is provided as Teaching Masters 197a–197c. However, if you have been using a particular way to grade oral presentations, this is not the time to change.

This might be an excellent time to invite your principal, counselors, school board members, or parents of students to your classroom. Provide the observers with a copy of the investigation, and have student groups make their reports as if the observers really did have to give permission. Having a semi-stranger be the audience may make this final presentation more meaningful as a Capstone experience.

Capstone

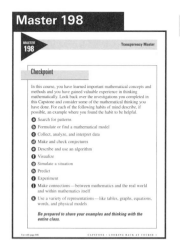

Assessments 283–319

NOTE: In addition to the Capstone, if you wish to administer a written, individual final exam, you may select items from the **Assessment Resources, pages 283–319**, which are appropriate for your students.

SHARE AND SUMMARIZE full-class discussion

Checkpoint

See Teaching Master 198.

In addition to learning concepts, techniques, and applications of mathematics, it is important for students to develop mathematical thinking skills. In this Checkpoint, students will have a chance to reflect on the mathematical thinking they have used in planning the carnival.

STORING MATH TOOLKITS: By this time, students will have accumulated extensive notes containing the important concepts from Course 1. You may wish to store the students' Math Toolkits in your classroom over the summer break to help prevent misplacement. Students should carry to Course 2 their Math Toolkits. This will allow them to access the mathematical tools they have learned this year.

Have students consider the investigations they have completed in this Capstone and look for examples of mathematical thinking in each.

It isn't necessary that students use precise definitions of the types of mathematical thinking. Look for examples that have the right "flavor."

Possible responses are:

ⓐ In the T-shirt investigation, students found the pattern between number of T-shirts purchased and total cost, and then expressed the pattern as an equation.

In the ring-toss investigation, the students found and described the pattern between number of ringers and distance from bottles, and also the pattern between number of ringers and diameter of ring.

In the free-throw game, they determined whether the shooter was consistent by looking for patterns in the free-throw data.

In the money-made-and-spent investigation, students searched for patterns of growth in the savings account.

ⓑ A vertex-edge graph model for committee scheduling or project planning was made. Sketches and models of booths and floor plans were created. Students formulated algebraic models for cost of T-shirts, profit, interest, and average number of ringers.

Graphs like histograms or box plots were constructed to represent (model) data.

ⓒ Data on the number of ringers, free-throws made, or number of game tickets used were collected, analyzed, and interpreted.

ⓓ In the T-shirt investigation, students made a conjecture about what price to set for T-shirts so that a profit would be made. They then justified the conjecture using graphs and equations.

In the free-throw game investigation, students made a conjecture about whether the pro is more likely to beat a 75% shooter in a 20-shot game or in a 10-shot game. They justified the conjecture by explaining their reasoning. They may have checked their conjecture by simulating a 20-shot game and comparing to the simulation in the investigation of a 10-shot game.

Investigation 8 was designed to be open-ended so students should have been making and checking conjectures in the process of the investigation.

See additional Teaching Notes on page T545F.

Checkpoint

In this course, you have learned important mathematical concepts and methods and you have gained valuable experience in thinking mathematically. Look back over the investigations you completed in this Capstone and consider some of the mathematical thinking you have done. For each of the following habits of mind, describe, if possible, an example where you found the habit to be helpful.

a Search for patterns

b Formulate or find a mathematical model

c Collect, analyze, and interpret data

d Make and check conjectures

e Describe and use an algorithm

f Visualize

g Simulate a situation

h Predict

i Experiment

j Make connections—between mathematics and the real world and within mathematics itself

k Use a variety of representations—like tables, graphs, equations, words, and physical models

Be prepared to share your examples and thinking with the entire class.

Looking Back, Looking Ahead

This Capstone has provided a review of Course 1 in the context of analyzing one big project. Throughout the investigations of the Capstone, students were able to pull together big ideas and specific skills from each of the Course 1 units. For example:

- From "Patterns in Data," graphical displays and summary statistics were used to analyze data for number of game tickets used in previous years, number of ringers made with different size rings in the ring-toss game, and number of free-throws made in the "Beat the Pro" game.
- From "Patterns of Change," graphs, tables, and algebraic rules were used to represent patterns in the ticket-use data and to predict profit from T-shirt sales.
- From "Linear Models," linear equations were used to determine the cost per toss and the profit in the ring-toss game, and linear growth was compared to exponential growth in the analysis of the school's savings account.
- From "Graph Models," vertex coloring and PERT charts were used to schedule committee meetings and to schedule all the tasks of the carnival project.
- From "Patterns in Space and Visualization," symmetry was used to design the T-shirts, surface area was a consideration in the design of the floor, surface area and the Pythagorean Theorem were used to design the information booth, and area was used in the analysis of the ring-toss game.
- From "Exponential Models," exponential functions were used to analyze data for number of ringers made from different distances and to predict how long it will take for a savings account to have enough money in it to purchase a school computer.
- From "Simulation Models," simulation methods were used to determine a good price to charge for the "Beat the Pro" game, and the Law of Large Numbers was used to help decide whether the pro is more likely to win a 10-shot game or a 20-shot game.

Thus, the Capstone has provided a conclusion to Course 1 that emphasizes big ideas as well as specific skills, connections within mathematics as well as connections to the real world, and the development of mathematical thinking. Important habits of mind that were cultivated in Course 1 and used in the Capstone were summarized in the final Checkpoint. Course 2 will continue the integrated development of the major strands of the curriculum. In particular:

- Algebraic models and methods will be extended to power functions (including direct and inverse variation) and the general quadratic function.
- The study of geometry will expand to include coordinate representations and methods and the analysis of triangles, quadrilaterals, and circles in the context of geometric form and its function. Trigonometry is introduced in the context of both right triangles and circular motion.
- In statistics, least squares linear models are revisited and *correlation* is investigated. New topics in probability will include the geometric (waiting-time) distribution, the multiplication rule for independent events, and expected value.
- In discrete mathematics, study of vertex-edge graphs will be extended to weighted graphs and problems involving network optimization; recursion will continue to be developed in the context of *NOW-NEXT* formulations; and matrices will be investigated as a means of modeling many real-world situations and connecting important mathematical ideas from all the strands.

Congratulations on finishing Course 1! In Course 2, your students will continue to investigate contemporary mathematics across a rich array of contexts.

Capstone

Teaching Notes continued

Notes continued from page T531

5. *Patterns in Space and Visualization*

   If T-shirts are to be designed, printed, and sold at the carnival, ideas of *rotational* and *reflection symmetry* could be used in designing the logo. Setting up the carnival may require a variety of measurements related to *perimeter*, *area*, *volume*, *surface area*, and the *Pythagorean Theorem*. Also, games could be designed based on symmetry—maybe players could be challenged to find foot-print versions of different strip symmetries.

6. *Exponential Models*

   Sometimes the best advertising for an event is word of mouth. Suppose someone knows about the carnival and proceeds to tell two friends. These two friends could each tell two friends, and so on. This relationship could be modeled by an *exponential model*.

7. *Simulation Models*

   In any game that involves chance (and most will!), a *simulation* could be performed to determine the approximate probability of winning. This information could be used to determine how prizes should be awarded to ensure profit.

SHARE AND SUMMARIZE   full-class discussion

Checkpoint

See Teaching Master 195.

This Checkpoint will provide students with a chance to see how versatile and widely applicable the mathematics is that they have learned. Encourage students to really listen to each other's ideas, and help them organize, see connections, and bring out ideas from all the strands of the course.

Completing at least 3 investigations from Investigations 2–8 is recommended. More may take too much time, and fewer will not give as valuable an experience. You may want to guide the groups in their choices so that all investigations are covered. You also may want to guide the choice of reports so that as many different investigations are reported on as possible.

Teaching Notes *continued*

Notes continued
from page T541

3. **e.** Encourage a thoughtful analysis here. There are many factors to consider. For a fixed price of 25¢ per toss, the profit equation of the 3-meter game looks better than that for the 2-meter game (20.2 versus 16 as the coefficient of T). Thus, the profit for a 3-meter game is 20.2¢ per toss, while the profit for a 2-meter game is only 16¢ per toss. However, since players are much less likely to win the 3-meter game, it may be less popular than a 2-meter game, and fewer people playing could mean less profit. So, for a fixed price of 25¢ per toss, students need to weigh the pros and cons. But the price per toss could be varied. For example, since the cost per toss is less for a 3-meter game, you could charge less to play the game. From this perspective, students might consider a fixed profit per toss, say 20¢, and then they can figure out what to charge to play each game. In this example, they could charge 25¢ for the 3-meter game and 29¢ for the 2-meter game. They might conclude that the lower price will attract more customers. In any case, encourage students to reason carefully and provide examples.

4. Student work

Capstone

Notes continued from page T543

4. b. This question is designed simply to elicit some initial thinking about the actual carnival setting where there are many different challengers. Their answers here should include an awareness that the simulation was based only on one sample challenger, who may not represent accurately the pool of challengers who actually play the game. Thus, they may argue for a higher price just to be safe or, alternatively, they may argue that their sample challenger was "much better than average" so they could safely lower the price to try to attract more players.

5. This question relates to the investigation of the Law of Large Numbers in Unit 7, "Simulation Models." One would expect that as the number of shots increases, the superiority of the pro will become more evident. That is, each player will make a number of baskets closer to the player's given percentage as the number of shots increases. Thus, the pro is expected to be more likely to win against a 75% challenger in a game of 20 shots than in a game of 10 shots. This is the answer that students should provide. Note, however, that the tie situation, where the pro wins all ties, complicates the problem so that the pro's winning probability does not go steadily up as the number of shots in the game increases. Nevertheless, it is definitely true that the pro's winning probability is higher for a 20-shot game than for a 10-shot game. For any students who notice this subtlety, you could have them explore, via simulation models, just how the probability changes for games with 1 shot, 2 shots, and so on, up to 20 shots. For your information, the table below shows the actual theoretical probability that the pro wins in games ranging from 1-shot games to 20-shot games. Of course, simulated probabilities will in all likelihood be somewhat different.

Number of Shots in a Game	Probability the Pro Wins	Number of Shots in a Game	Probability the Pro Wins
1	0.8875	11	0.808222
2	0.835469	12	0.812008
3	0.811105	13	0.815863
4	0.800006	14	0.819739
5	0.795599	15	0.823604
6	0.794753	16	0.827434
7	0.795894	17	0.831214
8	0.798190	18	0.834935
9	0.801175	19	0.838587
10	0.804575	20	0.842167

6. Student work

Teaching Notes *continued*

Notes continued
from page T545

ⓔ Students described and used an algorithm to find the critical path in the project digraph, or to color the committee-scheduling graph.

The simulation in the free-throw investigation must be carried out in a step-by-step manner; thus it is like using an algorithm.

Again, don't worry about precise definitions of the types of mathematical thinking. Just look for examples that have the right "flavor."

ⓕ Students needed to visualize the layout of the carnival in order to design the floor plan. In order to design the T-shirt logo, they needed to visualize designs and symmetry. They used visual displays to help them interpret data or relationships.

ⓖ They simulated the free-throw game.

ⓗ Based on data showing number of game tickets used in past years, students predicted how many will be used this year.

Using equations, they predicted the break-even point or profit for T-shirts, the number of ringers, and the associated profit.

Using simulation, they predicted the probability that the challenger would win the free-throw game.

ⓘ In the free-throw game investigation, doing the simulation is like carrying out an experiment to see what will happen.

Any investigation has components of an experiment in it. For example, in the T-shirt investigation students experimented with a four-color design T-shirt to see what it would cost and how much they should charge in order to make a profit. In the first investigation, they experimented with different tasks and committees.

ⓙ Many connections between mathematics and the real world have been made throughout the investigations in this Capstone.

The discussions within groups and between groups allowed students to see connections among a variety of ideas, strategies, and solutions.

  i. Connections within mathematics were made in several investigations; for example, representing data patterns with equations involved connections between statistics and algebra.

  ii. Connections between statistics and geometry were seen in the data analysis of diameters of circular rings.

  iii. Connections were made between equations in different forms that model a given situation, like the *NOW-NEXT* form and the "$y = \ldots$" form.

  iv. Connections were made between linear and exponential rates of change.

  v. Students made connections among different representations by answering questions using tables, graphs, and equations.

ⓚ Students used a variety of representations throughout the investigations, like physical models of a ticket booth, graphical representations of ticket-use data, verbal representations of the growth rate of money in a savings account, equations to represent cost or profit, and tables to represent prerequisite relationships between tasks.

Capstone

Index of Mathematical Topics

Index of Contexts

Photo Credits

We would like to thank the following for providing photographs of Core-Plus students in their schools. Many of these photographs appear throughout the text.

Janice Lee, Midland Valley High School, Langley, SC
Steve Matheos, Firestone High School, Akron, OH
Ann Post, Traverse City West Junior High School, Traverse City, MI
Alex Rachita, Ellet High School, Akron, OH
Judy Slezak, Prairie High School, Cedar Rapids, IA
The Core-Plus Mathematics Project